principles and applications of
BOOLEAN ALGEBRA

Hayden Series In Applied Mathematics

principles and applications of

BOOLEAN ALGEBRA

SALVATORE A. ADELFIO Jr.

Senior Instructor
Electronic Technology
RCA Institutes, Inc.

and

CHRISTINE F. NOLAN

HAYDEN BOOK COMPANY, INC., NEW YORK
a division of HAYDEN PUBLISHING COMPANY, INC.

To Mom and Dad, Anita and Bill

Copyright © 1964

HAYDEN BOOK COMPANY, INC.

Library of Congress Catalog Card Number 64-25296

Printed in the United States of America

Preface

There are many textbooks that explain the concepts of Boolean algebra and electronic circuits. However, these books, in trying to cover a wide scope, can only cover these topics superficially. Since this is the case, the authors have endeavored to write a book explaining the basic concepts of Boolean algebra and its basic electronic applications without attempting to bring in the applications of Boolean algebra to computers and related areas. Many excellent textbooks deal with the more complex concepts of Boolean algebra, but we have tried to simplify these concepts so that they will be readily understood by the student. In summary, this book has been written for two purposes:

1. To describe, in simple terms, the basic mathematical concepts involved in the development of logic systems.
2. To apply these concepts to basic electronic circuits.

One of the primary applications of Boolean algebra and logic circuits is in digital-type computers. There are many different types of digital computers, but they are all designed using the basic concepts of Boolean algebra and electronic circuits. Since these computers are essentially electronic devices, an understanding of the application of Boolean algebra to electronic circuits is necessary to comprehend how a digital-type computer functions.

The first six chapters are devoted primarily to Boolean algebra. Chapter 1 deals with the basic concepts of number systems and codes, including counting, the development of different number systems, numerical and positional value, and codes. These are fundamental ideas of which the reader must be aware to fully understand the following chapters. In Chapter 2, arithmetic operations such as addition, subtraction, multiplication, and division are explained; and the mechanics of each operation are applied to different number systems. The fundamentals of Boolean algebra are then discussed in Chapter 3. In addition to the basic definitions and the basic postulates, Boolean statements are represented by logic blocks, and the laws of combination are discussed and compared to the laws of combination in conventional algebra. Chapter 4 covers visual aids such as the Venn and Veitch diagrams which are extremely helpful in understanding and proving Boolean concepts and identities. In Chapter 5, the fundamentals of truth tables and designation numbers are introduced. The reader learns how to develop Boolean statements using truth tables and designation numbers. Chapter 6 is unique in that it is devoted entirely to solving illustrative problems. Nine problems are presented: three are solved by Veitch diagrams, three are solved by Boolean algebra, and three are solved by designation numbers. The use of truth tables to verify solutions is also demonstrated.

Chapters 7 and 8 offer a review of electronic principles, and serve as background for the chapters that follow. Chapter 7 discusses basic d-c principles, including some important network theorems. In Chapter 8, some of the important topics are: types of diodes, semiconductor physics, basic transistor physics, and basic transistor circuits.

Finally, in the remaining three chapters, the ideas and principles set forth in Chapters 1 through 8 are applied. Chapters 9 and 10 deal with diode logic circuits and transistor logic circuits, respectively. In these chapters, the reader learns about circuits such as AND gates, OR gates, diode and transistor half adders, diode and transistor full adders, a Binary-Coded-Decimal-Adder (BCDA), and matrix circuits. The solution of Boolean statements using diodes and transistors is also shown. In the last chapter, Chapter 11, the basic diode and transistor logic circuits are used to develop electronic counting circuits. The counters discussed include feedback-type counters and pulse advancing counters; in addition, counters are designed to operate in various codes. The design of lighting systems for use with the counters is also shown.

Some of the approaches and techniques that have been employed in this textbook have been successfully used by the authors in courses at RCA Institutes, Inc. We are grateful to the student body at the Institutes for their comments and suggestions.

S. A. ADELFIO JR.

and

C. F. NOLAN

New York, New York
September 1964

Contents

1

Number Systems and Codes

The need to express quantities became apparent thousands of years ago when man began to acquire possessions, and to communicate with other men. If a man had two cows when everyone else had only one cow, he wanted to let everyone know it. But, although man could distinguish between different amounts, there was no way for him to express them. So he set out to invent something that would help him to measure his possessions; and the concept of numbers and counting was the result. The first step was to assign a word or a symbol to each quantity, as shown in Table 1-1. Each symbol or *number* represented a *specific* quantity, and the value of each quantity was "one" greater than the preceding quanttity.

The total number of items, or cows, in a group was determined by *counting*. In order to count, man took the smallest quantity, or fundamental unit, increased it by the same amount, and obtained a new quantity. In other words, he took $\triangle$ cow, added $\triangle$ cow, and obtained $\triangle\triangle$ cows. The symbol he assigned for $\triangle\triangle$ was $\odot$. To count further, another fundamental unit or $\triangle$ cow was added to the existing number, $\odot$, and a new quantity, $\odot\triangle$ cows, was obtained. The symbol for $\odot\triangle$ was $\square$. You can see by referring to Table 1-1 that:

$\odot$ is $\triangle$ more than $\triangle$,
$\square$ is $\triangle$ more than $\odot$, and
$\square$ is $\odot$ more than $\triangle$.

Using Arabic symbols, this is the same as saying:

2 is 1 more than 1,
3 is 1 more than 2, and
3 is 2 more than 1.

As long as there was no need to identify large quantities, the number of symbols was limited. Early civilizations usually had a set of numbers that accounted for individual quantities up to fifteen, for instance, and had one extra symbol that represented any number greater than fifteen. Systems such as this were adequate as long as there weren't too many symbols. But

1

TABLE 1-1. SYMBOLS

QUANTITY	ARABIC SYMBOLS	OTHER SYMBOLS		
	1	△	|	I
	2	⊙	||	II
	3	□	|||	III
	4	◠	||||	IV
	5	⌣	卌	V

as time went on, the number of symbols increased until it became impractical to invent more. At that point, the development of number systems was retarded until the Arabic system was introduced in the 11th Century. The Arabic system, which is now universally used, consists of an *ordered* set of symbols or *digits*. An ordered set of digits is one in which the first digit is zero, and the value of each succeeding digit increases by 1; for example, 0, 1, 2, 3, etc. The number of digits in a set is arbitrary, and many forms of the Arabic system of numbers are based on this fact. The decimal form of the Arabic system is one with which we are all familiar. In the decimal system, ten digits are used, and these are 0, 1, 2, 3, 4, 5, 6, 7, 8, and 9. The number of digits used in a system is called the *base* or the *radix* of the system. For example, the binary system has a radix of 2. This means that there are two digits, 0 and 1, in the binary system. The octal system, which has a radix of 8, uses the digits 0, 1, 2, 3, 4, 5, 6, and 7. Here again, the number of digits in the set corresponds to the radix of the system. Systems such as those discussed earlier, which have symbols for different quantities, but which have no specific number of symbols in a set, are called baseless systems.

1-1. Counting

In order to obtain or write large numbers in any form of the Arabic system, digits are given *positional* as well as *numerical* values. All numbers are composed of digits, and the value of any number depends on the numerical value and the position of the digits. For example, the digits 1 and 2 are both contained in the numbers 12 and 21. The values of these numbers are not the same, however, because of the difference in the position of the digits. Positional value is the characteristic of the Arabic system that makes counting and calculating relatively simple.

The rules for counting are completely general, and can be applied to sets containing any number of digits. Using a set of five digits, we begin a count at 0 and proceed through each digit until all the digits in the set have been used. As shown in Table 1-2, a *1* is placed in column 2 to indicate that one cycle has been completed. Beginning with *0* again in the first column, we count through the set a second time until the second cycle has been completed. Now a *2* is recorded in the second column. This process continues until a *4* appears in column 1 and in column 2. At this point, column 2 has used up all the digits in the set and must begin again at *0*. To indicate that one cycle has been completed in column 2, a *1* is placed in column 3; columns 1 and 2 then begin a new cycle at *0*.

TABLE 1-2. COUNTING WITH A SET OF FIVE DIGITS

COLUMN 4	COLUMN 3	COLUMN 2	COLUMN 1	
			0	
			1	
			2	
			3	
			4	1 CYCLE
		1	0	
		1	1	
		1	2	
		1	3	
		1	4	2 CYCLES
		2	0	
		2	1	
		2	2	
		2	3	
		2	4	3 CYCLES
		3	0	
		3	1	
		3	2	
		3	3	
		3	4	4 CYCLES
		4	0	
		4	1	
		4	2	
		4	3	
		4	4	10 CYCLES
	1	0	0	

To show that the rules for counting are completely general, we can apply them to an ordered set of geometrical digits such as ○, △, ⊙, and □. The count is shown in Table 1-3. Notice that the counting of geometrical digits proceeds in exactly the same way as the counting of Arabic digits. This method of counting can be applied to number systems of any radix, and there are several number systems of different radix that are frequently used in various applications. Among the most popular number systems are the decimal, binary, and the octal systems.

1-2. The Decimal System

An important part of every number system is the way in which numbers are represented, for if we know this, it is very easy to change a number

TABLE 1-3. COUNTING WITH AN ORDERED SET OF GEOMETRICAL DIGITS

COLUMN 4	COLUMN 3	COLUMN 2	COLUMN 1	
			O	
			△	
			⊙	
			□	△ CYCLE
		△	O	
		△	△	
		△	⊙	
		△	□	⊙ CYCLES
		⊙	O	
		⊙	△	
		⊙	⊙	
		⊙	□	□ CYCLES
		□	O	
		□	△	
		□	⊙	
		□	□	△O CYCLES
	△	O	O	
	△	O	△	
	△	O	⊙	
	△	O	□	⊙△ CYCLES
	△	△	O	
	△	△	△	
	△	△	⊙	
	△	△	□	

in one system to an equivalent number in any other system. The decimal system, which has a radix of 10, uses the digits from 0 through 9. When these digits appear in column 1, they represent different quantities of *units*. Column 1 is therefore called the *units position*. The completion of one cycle in the units position means that one group of ten units has been counted. The digits appearing in column 2, the *tens position*, indicate how many groups of ten units have been counted. When one full cycle has been completed in the tens position, ten groups of ten units each, or one group of 100 units has been counted. Digits appearing in column 3, the *hundreds position*, represent how many groups of 100 units each have been counted; digits appearing in column 4, the *thousands position*, indicate how many groups of 1000 units each have been counted; etc. This can be illustrated by using a number such as 2345, which can be broken up into separate parts: 2 groups of 1000, 3 groups of 100, 4 groups of 10, and 5 units. The number, 2345, can also be represented by the equation:

$$2345 = 2 \times 1000 + 3 \times 100 + 4 \times 10 + 5 \times 1 \qquad (1\text{-}1)$$

Still another and very significant way of writing 2345 involves the use of the powers-of-ten notation. This notation is easily demonstrated with the number 1000: 1000 is the same as 2×500, 4×250, 1×1000, 1000×1, and $10 \times 10 \times 10$. Notice that $10 \times 10 \times 10$ also means 10 cubed or 10^3. The notation, 10^3, or ten to the third power, is a shorthand way of writing

1000 called the powers-of-ten notation. Similarly, 100 is also 10×10, or 10 squared, 10^2, in powers of ten; and the number 10 is 10^1.

It is interesting to note that the number, 1, can also be represented in several ways, for instance:

$$1 = 1 \times 1 = 1/1 = 2/2 = (1 \times 10^1)/(1 \times 10^1)$$

Another way of expressing the fraction $(1 \times 10^1)/(1 \times 10^1)$ is $1 \times (10^1/10^1)$. In mathematics, *when a number is brought from the denominator of a fraction to the numerator, the sign of the exponent or power of the number changes:*

$$1/2^2 = 2^{-2}; \quad 1/10^2 = 10^{-2}; \quad 10^3/10^2 = 10^3 \times 10^{-2}$$

Using this rule, we can write:

$$1 \times (10^1/10^1) = 1 \times 10^1 \times 10^{-1} \tag{1-2}$$

Another mathematical rule states that *when multiplying two numbers that have the same base but different exponents, the base number remains the same and the exponents are added.* This is clearly illustrated by the following examples:

$$2^1 \times 2^1 = 2^{1+1} = 2^2 = 4$$
$$2^2 \times 2^1 = 2^{2+1} = 2^3 = 8$$
$$10^3 \times 10^2 = 10^{3+2} = 10^5 = 100,000$$
$$10^3 \times 10^{-2} = 10^{3-2} = 10^1 = 10$$
$$10^1 \times 10^{-1} = 10^{1-1} = 10^0 = 1$$

It might seem that 10^0 should be 0 and not 1; but it is quickly proven that this is not so. We know from Eq. (1-2) that:

$$10^1/10^1 = 10^1 \times 10^{-1} = 10^0$$

We have also established that:

$$10^1/10^1 = 1$$

Therefore, $10^0 = 1$.

Thus far in our discussion, most of the numbers considered have had positive exponents, and lie to the left of the decimal point; e.g., 1000.0, 100.0, 10.0, and 1.0. However, the powers-of-ten notation also applies to numbers that lie to the right of the decimal point. These numbers are all less than 1; e.g., 0.1, 0.01, 0.001, etc. They are converted to the powers-of-ten notation in this manner:

$$0.1 = 1/10^1 = 10^{-1}$$
$$0.01 = 1/10^2 = 10^{-2}$$
$$0.001 = 1/10^3 = 10^{-3}$$

Table 1-4 shows a set of numbers and their equivalents in powers of ten. To change a number into its powers-of-ten equivalent, always start from the decimal point, and count the number of digits from the decimal point to the last unit or units. For example, in moving the decimal point from 1,000,000.0 to 1.000,000, the number of *digits* counted is six. Therefore, the equivalent of 1,000,000.0 is 10^6. The exponent is positive because the decimal was moved to the left. The number of digits counted in moving the decimal point from 0.000,001 to 1.0 is also six; however, since the decimal point is moved toward the right, the exponent is negative. Therefore, the equivalent of 0.000,001 is 10^{-6}.

TABLE 1-4. POWERS-OF-TEN NOTATION FOR DECIMAL NUMBERS

NUMBER	POWERS-OF-TEN NOTATION
1,000,000.0	10^6
100,000.0	10^5
10,000.0	10^4
1000.0	10^3
100.0	10^2
10.0	10^1
1.0	10^0
0.0	0
0.1	10^{-1}
0.01	10^{-2}
0.001	10^{-3}
0.0001	10^{-4}
0.00001	10^{-5}
0.000001	10^{-6}

It is possible to write any number in the decimal system using powers of ten by simply moving the decimal point to the left or to the right, and counting the number of places that the decimal point is moved. This is illustrated in the following examples:

$$975.0 = 9.75 \times 10^2$$
$$1077.0 = 1.077 \times 10^3$$
$$0.023 = 2.3 \times 10^{-2}$$
$$0.009 = 9.0 \times 10^{-3}$$

Now that the powers-of-ten notation has been examined, we can further develop Eq. (1-1). Equation (1-1) is: $2345 = 2 \times 1000 + 3 \times 100 + 4 \times 10 + 5 \times 1$. Using powers of ten,

$$2345 = 2 \times 10^3 + 3 \times 10^2 + 4 \times 10^1 + 5 \times 10^0 \qquad (1\text{-}3)$$

If you multiply and add the terms on the right side of the equation, you will find that they equal 2345. This representation of a number has a very significant form as you will now see. Notice that each digit is multiplied by the radix, 10, to some power. We can represent the radix by R and the digits by d, and write a general statement:

$$N_R \rightarrow d_3R^3 + d_2R^2 + d_1R^1 + d_0R^0 \tag{1-4}$$

The numerical subscripts are used to differentiate between the different values of d; and each subscript is the same as the corresponding power of ten. The arrow denotes representation rather than equality. N_R is a number in the radix, R. For example, $(2345)_{10}$ means that 2345 is written in the radix 10, $(1101)_2$ is written in the radix 2, and $(365)_8$ is written in the radix 8. In using this general representation, it is no longer correct to refer to a decimal point. Instead, we refer to the *radix point*. In the binary system, the radix point is called the binary point; in the octal system, it is the octal point; in the decimal system, it is the decimal point; etc. Statement (1-4) limits a number to four digits; to represent numbers containing more than four digits, a more general statement is used:

$$N_R \rightarrow d_nR^n + d_{n-1}R^{n-1} + d_{n-2}R^{n-2} + \ldots + d_2R^2 + d_1R^1 + d_0R^0 \tag{1-5}$$

Each term in this statement tells us the numerical value and position of each digit. In everyday usage, we are accustomed to seeing N_R written as $d_3d_2d_1d_0$; in this form, it is understood that d_0 is in the units position, R^0; d_1 is in the R^1 position; d_2 is in the R^2 position; and d_3 is in the R^3 position. The reason for writing N_R this way is that it is easier to write 2126 than it is to write $2 \times 10^3 + 1 \times 10^2 + 2 \times 10^1 + 6 \times 10^0$. In both cases, $d_3 = 2$, $d_2 = 1$, $d_1 = 2$, and $d_0 = 6$.

So far, we have considered only numbers that are larger than one, or numbers that are on the left side of the radix point. Numbers that are less than one or that are on the right side of the radix point are represented in the same way by a general statement:

$$N_R \rightarrow d_{-1}R^{-1} + d_{-2}R^{-2} + d_{-3}R^{-3} + \ldots + d_{n-1}R^{n-1} + d_{-n}R^{-n} \tag{1-6}$$

To illustrate the statement's use, we can use a number such as $(0.519)_{10}$, which is represented as $5 \times 10^{-1} + 1 \times 10^{-2} + 9 \times 10^{-3}$. In this illustration, d_{-1} is 5, d_{-2} is 1, and d_{-3} is 9; you can see that the statement fully describes the number $(0.519)_{10}$. As in the case where N_R is greater than one, there is an easier way to write N_R when it is less than one: $d_{-1}d_{-2}$ $d_{-3}d_{-4} \cdots$. Here, it is understood that d_{-1} is in the R^{-1} position, d_{-2} is in the R^{-2} position, d_{-3} is in the R^{-3} position, and d_{-4} is in the R^{-4} position, etc. Representing numbers as in Sts. (1-5) and (1-6) is very important because it enables us to convert numbers in any radix to equivalent numbers in the radix ten. You will see how this is done, and why it is important later in this chapter.

1-3. The Binary System

The binary system has a radix of 2, and uses the digits 0 and 1. Binary digits are called *bits,* which is a combination of the first two letters of *bi*nary and the last two letters of dig*its*. The simplicity of the binary system is by no means an indication of its utility. Since many electronic systems, such as tubes, diodes and transistors are binary by nature, the binary number system is particularly suited in such applications. In fact, computers are designed to operate in binary or binary-coded systems. The term *binary* is used to indicate that there are two possible states: in the binary number system, there are two digits, 0 and 1; a tube, diode or transistor can be made to conduct or not conduct; as you will see later, in Boolean algebra, something either exists or does not exist. Another reason for being especially interested in the binary system of numbers is that Boolean algebra is essentially a binary system and a knowledge of the binary number system will help you to understand Boolean algebra.

The fact that only two digits are used does not mean that the rules for counting cannot be applied. Table 1-5 illustrates binary counting, and if you refer to Table 1-3, you can see that the general rules for counting are applied. In Table 1-5, the columns are headed by R^0, R^1, R^2, R^3, etc. The radix of the binary system is two, therefore, $R^0 = 2^0$, $R^1 = 2^1$, $R^2 = 2^2$, $R^3 = 2^3$, etc. Any number in the binary system can be represented by

TABLE 1-5.   COUNTING IN THE BINARY NUMBER SYSTEM

DECIMAL NUMBER	BINARY NUMBERS				
	$R^4 = 2^4$	$R^3 = 2^3$	$R^2 = 2^2$	$R^1 = 2^1$	$R^0 = 2^0$
0					0
1					1
2				1	0
3				1	1
4			1	0	0
5			1	0	1
6			1	1	0
7			1	1	1
8		1	0	0	0
9		1	0	0	1
10		1	0	1	0
11		1	0	1	1
12		1	1	0	0
13		1	1	0	1
14		1	1	1	0
15		1	1	1	1
16	1	0	0	0	0
17	1	0	0	0	1
18	1	0	0	1	0
19	1	0	0	1	1
20	1	0	1	0	0
21	1	0	1	0	1
22	1	0	1	1	0
23	1	0	1	1	1
24	1	1	0	0	0
25	1	1	0	0	1

Statements (1-5) and (1-6). For example, the binary number corresponding to the decimal number 9 is 1001; 1001 is written in the form $d_3d_2d_1d_0$. The number $(1001)_2$, or any other binary number, can be written in the form of Statement (1-5):

$$(1001)_2 \rightarrow 1(2)^3 + 0(2)^2 + 0(2)^1 + 1(2)^0$$

In the decimal system, this method of writing a number is said to use the powers-of-ten notation, but in the binary system, it is called the *powers-of-two notation*. Furthermore, a *binary* point is used rather than a decimal point.

1-4. The Octal System

The octal system, which has a radix of eight and uses the digits 0, 1, 2, 3, 4, 5, 6, and 7, is used mainly in coding and converting decimal numbers into binary numbers. This is of special interest in computer applications, where the octal number system facilitates computer operations. Counting in the octal system is shown in Table 1-6. Since $R = 8$, the column headings in this table are 8^3, 8^2, 8^1, and 8^0. Octal numbers such as $(737)_8$, for example, can be written using the *powers-of-eight* notation:

$$(737)_8 \rightarrow 7(8)^2 + 3(8)^1 + 7(8)^0$$

In this system, the radix point is referred to as the *octal* point.

1-5. Changing Radixes

Although N_R is represented by the expression $d_nR^n + d_{n-1}R^{n-1} + \ldots + d_2R^2 + d_1R^1 + d_0R^0$, N_R is not necessarily equal to this expression. Whether or not N_R is equal to or represented by this expression depends on the number substituted for R. By substituting a decimal number for R, as we have been doing, and performing the indicated mathematical operations, we obtain a decimal quantity. This decimal quantity is the exact equivalent of N_R in the decimal system, however, it is not equal to N_R numerically. This expression provides a method of changing numbers in any radix to the radix ten, and the proof of this method can be shown by working out some sample conversions. We know from Table 1-5 that $(1010)_2$ is equivalent to $(10)_{10}$; hence, we can use this to check the results of the conversion.

Example 1-1. Convert $(1010)_2$ to N_{10}.

$$N_{10} = 1(2)^3 + 0(2)^2 + 1(2)^1 + 0(2)^0$$
$$= 1(8) + 0(4) + 1(2) + 0(1)$$
$$= 8 + 2$$
$$= (10)_{10}$$

Example 1-2. Convert $(11001)_2$ to N_{10}.

$$N_{10} = 1(2)^4 + 1(2)^3 + 0(2)^2 + 0(2)^1 + 1(2)^0$$
$$= 1(16) + 1(8) + 0(4) + 0(2) + 1(1)$$

$$= 16 + 8 + 1$$
$$= (25)_{10}$$

In the binary system, the same results can be obtained by renaming the columns $(16)_{10}$ instead of 2^4, $(8)_{10}$ instead of 2^3, $(4)_{10}$ instead of 2^2, $(2)_{10}$ instead of 2^1, and $(1)_{10}$ instead of 2^0. By doing this, we perform

TABLE 1-6. COUNTING IN THE OCTAL NUMBER SYSTEM

DECIMAL NUMBER	OCTAL NUMBERS			
	8^3	8^2	8^1	8^0
0				0
1				1
2				2
3				3
4				4
5				5
6				6
7				7
8			1	0
9			1	1
10			1	2
11			1	3
12			1	4
13			1	5
14			1	6
15			1	7
16			2	0
17			2	1
⋮			⋮	⋮
63			7	7
64		1	0	0
65		1	0	1
66		1	0	2
67		1	0	3
68		1	0	4
69		1	0	5
70		1	0	6
71		1	0	7
⋮		⋮	⋮	⋮
511		7	7	7
512	1	0	0	0
513	1	0	0	1
514	1	0	0	2

half of the conversion automatically, and the decimal equivalent of a binary number is found simply by adding the column headings wherever a *1* appears in the binary number. For example, add the column headings wherever a *1* appears in each number in the following tabulation, and check with Table 1-5 to verify the results.

16	8	4	2	1	*Decimal Number*
0	1	0	1	0	10
1	0	1	0	1	21
1	0	0	0	1	17
0	1	1	1	0	14

Now, when you see a number such as $(1111)_2$, you can immediately convert it to $(15)_{10}$ by adding $8 + 4 + 2 + 1$. This short-cut holds true for the binary system only because the highest digit is 1. Numbers in any other system must be converted to N_{10} by the method used in **Examples 1-1** and **1-2**.

Example 1-3. Convert $(107)_8$ to N_{10}.

$$N_{10} = 1(8)^2 + 0(8)^1 + 7(8)^0$$
$$= 1(64) + 0(8) + 7(1)$$
$$= 64 + 7$$
$$= 71$$

Example 1-4. Convert $(777)_8$ to N_{10}.

$$N_{10} = 7(8)^2 + 7(8)^1 + 7(8)^0$$
$$= 7(64) + 7(8) + 7(1)$$
$$= 448 + 56 + 7$$
$$= 511$$

Numbers less than 1 in any radix are converted to the decimal system in the same manner as numbers greater than 1. The conversion is accomplished by performing the indicated mathematical operations for each term, and then adding the terms. Remember that a number with a negative exponent such as 8^{-2} is really $1/8^2$ as you learned in a previous discussion. Therefore, each time a quantity such as $2(8)^{-2}$ appears, it must be rewritten as $2/8^2$ before you can perform the indicated mathematical operations.

Example 1-5. Convert $(0.65)_8$ to N_{10}.

$$N_{10} = 6(8)^{-1} + 5(8)^{-2}$$
$$= 6/(8)^1 + 5/(8)^2$$
$$= 6/8 + 5/64$$
$$= 0.75 + 0.078$$
$$= 0.828$$

Example 1-6. Convert $(0.0101)_2$ to N_{10}.

$$N_{10} = 0(2)^{-1} + 1(2)^{-2} + 0(2)^{-3} + 1(2)^{-4}$$
$$= 0/(2)^1 + 1/(2)^2 + 0/(2)^3 + 1/(2)^4$$
$$= 1/4 + 1/16$$
$$= 0.25 + 0.0625$$
$$= 0.3125$$

Just as numbers of different radixes can be changed to the radix 10, numbers in the radix 10 can be converted to equivalent numbers in other radixes. The process of converting N_{10} into the radix, R, involves successive divisions by R and a tabulation of the remainders obtained from each division. To illustrate the procedure, we will convert the number $(502)_{10}$ to a number, N_8, in the octal system. The following arrangement is convenient for the successive divisions:

	R	N_{10}	Remainder	
Step 1:	8	/502	6	
Step 2:	8	/ 62	6	Read Up
Step 3:	8	/ 7	7	
Step 4:	8	/ 0	0	

In *Step 1*, 502 is divided by 8 with a result of 62 and a remainder of 6. The number 62 is written directly below the 502, and the remainder 6 is written to the right of 502. In *Step 2*, 62 is divided by 8 with a result of 7 and a remainder of 6. The number 7 is placed below the 62, and the remainder of 6 is placed to the right of the 62. In *Step 3*, the result of dividing 7 by 8 is 0 with a remainder of 7. The 0 is placed beneath the 7 in the N_{10} column, and the 7 is placed to the right of 7 in the *Remainder* column. As soon as a zero appears in the N_{10} column, the conversion is completed because further divisions by 8 will result in only additional zeros. The number in the octal system is obtained by reading the digits in the remainder column from bottom to top as indicated by the arrow. In this example, the digits read 766; therefore, $(502)_{10} = (766)_8$.

Example 1-7. Convert $(20)_{10}$ to N_2.

	R	N_{10}	Remainder	
Step 1:	2	/20	0	
Step 2:	2	/10	0	
Step 3:	2	/ 5	1	
Step 4:	2	/ 2	0	
Step 5:	2	/ 1	1	
Step 6:	2	/ 0	0	

Ans: $(20)_{10} = (10100)_2$

This result can be easily checked by using the method of adding the column headings wherever a 1 appears in the binary number. The number $(10100)_2$ contains a 1 in the 16 column and in the 4 column; therefore, $(10100)_2$ is equal to $16 + 4 = (20)_{10}$. You can use this method to check the results of all decimal-to-binary conversions.

Example 1-8. Convert $(28)_{10}$ to N_2.

	R	N_{10}	Remainder	
Step 1:	2	/28	0	
Step 2:	2	/14	0	
Step 3:	2	/ 7	1	
Step 4:	2	/ 3	1	
Step 5:	2	/ 1	1	
Step 6:	2	/ 0	0	

Ans: $\qquad\qquad (28)_{10} = (11100)_2$

Check:

$$1 \quad 1 \quad 1 \quad 0 \quad 0$$
$$\downarrow \quad \downarrow \quad \downarrow \quad \downarrow \quad \downarrow$$
$$16 + 8 + 4 + 0 + 0 = (28)_{10}$$

Example 1-9. Convert $(345)_{10}$ to N_8.

	R	N_{10}	Remainder
Step 1:	8	/345	1
Step 2:	8	/ 43	3
Step 3:	8	/ 5	5
Step 4:	8	/ 0	0

Ans: $\qquad\qquad (345)_{10} = (531)_8$

Check: $\quad N_{10} = 5(8)^2 + 3(8)^1 + 1(8)^0$
$$= 320 + 24 + 1$$
$$= 345$$

Decimal numbers that are *less than 1* are converted to equivalent numbers in other radixes by a method similar to that used for converting numbers *greater than 1* to other radixes. In this method, successive multiplications by R are performed. Each time a multiplication is performed, the result is a product that consists of a whole part and a fractional part. The whole part of the product, which is to the left of the decimal point, is recorded in the W column. The fractional part, which is to the right of the decimal point, is placed in the N_{10} column and is multiplied by R. Converting the number $(0.635)_{10}$ to N_8 will illustrate the procedure:

	R	N_{10}	W
Step 1:	8 × 0.635		5
Step 2:	8 × 0.080		0
Step 3:	8 × 0.640		5
Step 4:	8 × 0.120		0
Step 5:	8 × 0.960		7
Step 6:	8 × 0.680		

Ans: $\qquad (0.635)_{10} \cong (0.50507)_8 \cong (0.5051)_8$

Check: $\quad N_{10} = 5(8)^{-1} + 0(8)^{-2} + 5(8)^{-3} + 1(8)^{-4}$
$$= 5/8 + 0 + 5/512 + 1/4096$$
$$= 0.625 + 0.0098 + 0.0002$$
$$= 0.635$$

In *Step 1*, 0.635 is multiplied by 8, and the product is 5.080. The whole part, 5, is recorded in the W column, and the fractional part, 0.080, is placed beneath the 0.635 in the N_{10} column. In *Step 2*, 0.080 is multiplied by 8 and the product is 0.64. The whole part, 0, is placed in the W column, and the fractional part, 0.64, is placed in the N_{10} column. Theoretically, this procedure continues until only zeros occur in the N_{10} column. Usually, however, accuracy greater than 3 or 4 places is not required. In this example, five successive multiplications yield the octal number $(0.50507)_8$. As indicated, the numbers are read *downward*. If, for example, only four-place accuracy is needed, $(0.50507)_8$ can be rounded off to $(0.5051)_8$. The accuracy of this conversion is demonstrated by checking the solution as shown to three places, which gives $(0.635)_{10}$. As you can see, this is the number originally converted.

Example 1-10. Convert $(0.78)_{10}$ to N_2.

	R	N_{10}	W
Step 1:		2×0.78	1
Step 2:		2×0.56	1
Step 3:		2×0.12	0
Step 4:		2×0.24	0
Step 5:		2×0.48	0
Step 6:		2×0.96	1
Step 7:		2×0.92	1
Step 8:		2×0.84	1
Step 9:		2×0.68	1
Step 10:		2×0.36	

Ans: $(0.78)_{10} = (0.110001111)_2$

Check: $N_{10} = 1(2)^{-1} + 1(2)^{-2} + 0(2)^{-3} + 0(2)^{-4}$
$$+ 0(2)^{-5} + 1(2)^{-6} + 1(2)^{-7} + 1(2)^{-8} + 1(2)^{-9}$$
$$= 1/2 + 1/4 + 0 + 0 + 0 + 1/64 + 1/128 + 1/256 + 1/512$$
$$= 0.5 + 0.25 + 0.0156 + 0.0078 + 0.0039 + 0.0020$$
$$= 0.7793, \text{ or rounded off to two places, } N_{10} = 0.78$$

1-6. Codes

Pretend, for a moment, that you do not know how an electrical switch operates; all you know is that when a certain button is pressed, a signal is sent to the switch. Imagine that the switch is connected in such a way that it can control a lamp. How the switch turns the lamp ON and OFF is of no concern; rather, we are interested in how to *tell* the switch to turn the lamp ON and OFF. Experimenting with this simple electrical machine, we discover that, by pressing the button once, we can make the switch turn the lamp ON. We also discover that, by pressing the button twice, we can make the switch turn the lamp ON and OFF. Having discovered these two pieces of information, we have found a way to communicate with an electrical device in a language it understands and responds to. We have effectively set up a *code* in which human-language ideas are represented by a language that the electrical machine understands:

ON—1 signal
ON—OFF—2 signals

Electronic circuits and combinations of circuits (systems) have been designed to function in many remarkable and complex applications. For instance, one can buy an electronic machine that controls the proportion of ingredients in a can of soup. If any machine suddenly begins to add too much of a certain ingredient, the special machine immediately detects this error and produces a correction. The operation of some machines is so un- believably complex that it almost seems as if the machine can think for itself. In designing and operating electronic machines such as these, it is usually necessary to communicate with the machine so that it can be given instructions, just as our simple electrical switch was given instruc- tions. This necessity to communicate has initiated the development of many practical codes which machines can understand and to which they respond.

Most electrical machines or devices are binary by nature, or at least, their operation is more clearly defined or observable when they are em- ployed in a binary fashion. To illustrate this concept, let us use the electric lamp again, in a binary fashion. This means that the lamp can receive only two signals, for instance, 0 volts and 110 volts. When 0 volts is applied to the lamp, the lamp does not light. When 110 volts is applied, the lamp lights brightly. There can be no mistake about the two conditions or states of the lamp; it either *lights*, or it *does not light*. Since there are only two states in which the lamp can be, it is being operated in a binary fashion.

If the lamp is operated in a fashion other than binary, it has more than two states. For example, to operate the lamp in decimal fashion, ten different voltage levels must be provided, say, 0, 10, 20, 30, 40, 50, 60, 70, 80, 90, and 100 volts. At each of these voltage levels, the lamp would light with a different intensity, beginning with no light at 0 volts, and burning brightest at 100 volts. Unlike binary operation, however, there is no clear distinction between the states of the lamp in decimal operation. One could look at the lamp with 60 volts applied, and then, with 50 volts applied, and hardly be able to detect the difference between the two states. In binary operation, therefore, more than in any other type of operation, the response of an electronic machine is clearly defined.

So far in this discussion of codes, two significant facts have been estab- lished:

1. An operator can "communicate" with an electronic machine by using a code in which human-language ideas are represented by a language that the machine understands.
2. The response or operation of an electronic machine is more clearly defined or is more exact when the machine is operated in a binary fashion rather than in any other fashion.

These characteristics of electronic machines indicate that the simplest way to communicate with a machine is to use a code that is binary by nature. The specific types of machines whose operations depend upon this unique concept will be discussed in more detail in later chapters. For now, we are only concerned with knowing that such machines exist, and we will proceed to examine the language or codes to which they can be made to respond.

The communications carried on between humans and machines are gen- erally in the form of numbers and letters. These numbers and letters are translated into, or represented by, a binary code. One very obvious method of representing numbers in code is provided by the binary number system, with which you are already familiar. By using the binary number system, decimal digits could easily be represented by their exact binary equivalents in the binary number system. Although this arrangement would greatly facilitate arithmetic operations performed by electronic machines, there are certain reasons why the binary system is not practical as such. One reason is that in the binary system, there exists a *number-to-number* relationship rather than a more desirable *digit-to-digit* relationship. For example, the decimal number 35 has an exact binary equivalent, $(100011)_2$. In order to convert from $(35)_{10}$ to $(100011)_2$ or vice versa, the use of conversion techniques is required. In a digit-to-digit relationship, each digit is always represented by a specific group of binary digits (bits) such as: 3 is represented by 011, or 5 is represented by 101. Using these relationships, the number $(35)_{10}$ can be written, 011 101. These bits are *not equivalent* to $(35)_{10}$; they simply *represent* the 3 and the 5 in a digit-to-digit relationship. To change from $(35)_{10}$ to 011 101 and vice versa, it is only necessary to arrange the bits in groups of three (in this example), and to replace each group of three by the decimal digit it represents. One of the reasons this ease of translation is desirable is that the human operators who use the electronic machines may not be familiar with the binary number system, or with the conversion techniques discussed earlier.

Another reason that the binary number system is not practical as a code is that, in addition to representing numbers in a binary manner, it is often necessary to represent alphabetical symbols in a binary manner. There are no equivalents for these symbols in the binary number system; hence, the system is inadequate.

The minimum number of bits needed to represent a decimal symbol depends on the number of decimal symbols that have to be coded. For example, if only four decimal symbols are to be represented by binary digits, a minimum of two bits is needed for each decimal symbol. This is true because the two binary digits can be arranged into four different two-bit combinations as shown:

00

01

10

11

No other two-bit combinations exist. If the decimal symbols to be coded are 0, 1, 2, and 3, then 00 always represents 0, 01 always represents 1, 10 always represents 2, and 11 always represents 3.

If the number of decimal symbols to be coded is 8 or less, the minimum of bits needed for each decimal symbol is three. This is true because the two binary digits can be arranged into only eight possible three-bit combinations:

000

001

010
011
100
101
110
111

No other three-bit combination exists. The decimal digits from 0 through 7 would always be represented by the binary combinations from 000 to 111, respectively, when coded. The number of combinations it is possible to obtain by arranging the binary digits in groups of different size can be calculated by using this simple equation:

$$C = 2^n$$

In this equation, C is the number of combinations, 2 is the radix of the binary system, and n is the number of bits in each group. If a minimum of two bits is used to represent the decimal symbols, the number of possible combinations is 2^2 or 4. Similarly, we can prove that eight different combinations are possible if the bits are arranged in groups of three:

$$C = 2^3 = 8$$

One of the most popular codes is the *Natural Binary Coded Decimal (NBCD)* system shown in Table 1-7. Each four-bit combination represents the decimal digit listed in the adjacent column. Notice that there are six combinations of bits that do not represent a decimal digit. Although these four-bit combinations exist, they are not used as a part of the code and are known as *forbidden combinations*. In Table 1-7, you see that the NBCD system only accounts for the coding of decimal digits. Because of the digit-

TABLE 1-7. THE NATURAL BINARY CODED DECIMAL (NBCD) SYSTEM

DECIMAL DIGIT	NBCD CODE			
	8	4	2	1
0	0	0	0	0
1	0	0	0	1
2	0	0	1	0
3	0	0	1	1
4	0	1	0	0
5	0	1	0	1
6	0	1	1	0
7	0	1	1	1
8	1	0	0	0
9	1	0	0	1
FORBIDDEN COMBINATIONS	1	0	1	0
	1	0	1	1
	1	1	0	0
	1	1	0	1
	1	1	1	0
	1	1	1	1

to-digit relationship in this system of coding (and in other systems you will learn about), the code can also be adapted to represent alphabetical characters. This is usually accomplished by using more bits per character (symbol), and the number of bits necessary depends on the total number of numerical and alphabetical symbols that have to be represented.

The NBCD system is often referred to as the 8-4-2-1 code because, in addition to representing decimal digits, it also gives the true binary translation (equivalents) of the decimal digits. The 8, 4, 2, and 1 are the weights given to the four binary digit positions, where 8 is 2^3, 4 is 2^2, 2 is 2^1, and 1 is 2^0. Any system that possesses this characteristic is called a *weighted* code; coding systems that do not have this characteristic are called *nonweighted* codes. One of the most important advantages of weighted codes is that calculations are usually more easily performed than they are in nonweighted codes.

An example of a nonweighted code is the *Excess Three Binary Decimal Code*, or XS3. This code is shown in Table 1-8 along with the decimal digit each four-bit combination represents. You can see that the XS3 code is non-

TABLE 1-8.   THE EXCESS THREE BINARY CODE

DECIMAL NUMBER	XS3 CODE			
0	0	0	1	1
1	0	1	0	0
2	0	1	0	1
3	0	1	1	0
4	0	1	1	1
5	1	0	0	0
6	1	0	0	1
7	1	0	1	0
8	1	0	1	1
9	1	1	0	0

weighted by observing that the binary digits representing the decimal numbers are not exact equivalents of the decimal numbers. The XS3 code is formed by adding the binary equivalent of the decimal digit, 3, to each of the natural binary coded decimal combinations representing the decimal digits. For example, the natural binary coded decimal combination representing $(0)_{10}$ is 0000. To form the XS3 representation of $(0)_{10}$, 0011 is added to 0000; hence, $(0)_{10}$ in the XS3 code is 0011 as shown in Table 1-8. Although the XS3 code is nonweighted, arithmetic operations may be performed in the code with relative ease. Another advantage of this code is that it is easy to translate the coded digits back to the decimal system.

Another system of coding which is quite different from the first two we discussed is called the *Biquinary Code*. In the two representative codes discussed, one was a nonweighted system, the other was a weighted system, and both used four bits to represent the decimal digits. The biquinary code is a weighted system; however, it uses seven bits to represent each decimal digits as shown in Table 1-9. The weights of each column are shown in the table. To the left of the slash, the column weights are 5 and 0; to the right of the slash, the weights are 4, 3, 2, 1, and 0. Out of the seven bits in each combination, two of the bits always exist. One of these bits, known

TABLE 1-9. THE BIQUINARY CODE

DECIMAL NUMBER	BIQUINARY CODE						
	5	0 /	4	3	2	1	0
0	0	1	0	0	0	0	1
1	0	1	0	0	0	1	0
2	0	1	0	0	1	0	0
3	0	1	0	1	0	0	0
4	0	1	1	0	0	0	0
5	1	0	0	0	0	0	1
6	1	0	0	0	0	1	0
7	1	0	0	0	1	0	0
8	1	0	0	1	0	0	0
9	1	0	1	0	0	0	0

as the binary bit, is to the left of the slash, and the other bit, known as the quinary bit, is to the right of the slash. Because there are always two bits present in every combination, the biquinary code is also known as the two-out-of-seven-bit code. Notice also that no combination consists entirely of zeros. Because there are a constant number of 1's in the biquinary code, it is self checking. In spite of the apparent complexity of this code, arithmetic operations are not very difficult.

The variety of codes that have been developed for use in different applications are too numerous to detail here. However, as long as you are aware of the function of codes in general, and are familiar with the particular characteristics of the commonly used codes, it will be easy for you to understand practically any code you encounter. In Table 1-10, some other common four-bit weighted codes are listed for reference.

TABLE 1-10. COMMON FOUR-BIT WEIGHTED CODES

DECIMAL NUMBER	CODES															
	2'	4	2	1	5	4	2	1	6	3	1	1	5	2	1	1
0	0	0	0	0	0	0	0	0	0	0	0	0	0	0	0	0
1	0	0	0	1	0	0	0	1	0	0	0	1	0	0	0	1
2	0	0	1	0	0	0	1	0	0	0	1	1	0	1	0	0
3	0	0	1	1	0	0	1	1	0	1	0	0	0	1	1	0
4	0	1	0	0	0	1	0	0	0	1	0	1	0	1	1	1
5	1	0	1	1	1	0	0	0	0	1	1	1	1	0	0	0
6	1	1	0	0	1	0	0	1	1	0	0	0	1	0	0	1
7	1	1	0	1	1	0	1	0	1	0	0	1	1	0	1	1
8	1	1	1	0	1	0	1	1	1	0	1	1	1	1	1	0
9	1	1	1	1	1	1	0	0	1	1	0	0	1	1	1	1

Table 1-11 shows how a code is used in feeding information to an RCA 501 computer. In 501 operation, the decimal digits, 0 through 9, are first changed to the octal number system. As you can see from the table, the exact octal equivalents are not used; instead, the octal numbers shown are *defined* to represent the decimal digits. The octal number system is used

TABLE 1-11. THE OCTONARY CODE

DECIMAL NUMBER	OCTAL NUMBER	OCTONARY CODED OCTAL NUMBER	
0	$(23)_8$	01|0	011
1	$(24)_8$	01|0	100
2	$(25)_8$	01|0	101
3	$(26)_8$	01|0	110
4	$(27)_8$	01|0	111
5	$(30)_8$	01|1	000
6	$(31)_8$	01|1	001
7	$(32)_8$	01|1	010
8	$(33)_8$	01|1	011
9	$(34)_8$	01|1	100
			XS3 CODE

as an intermediary between the decimal system and the code because it simplifies the conversion from decimal system to code and vice versa. The octal numbers are then changed to code, and are fed into the computer. The code shown in Table 1-11 uses three-bit combinations in a digit-to-digit relationship. Although it is sometimes called the octonary code, it is essentially the same as the NBCD code.

By defining the octal numbers in Table 1-11 to represent the decimal digits, a useful property is given to the coded numbers. In column 3, a dash line has been drawn between the two leftmost bits and the four rightmost bits. To the right of this dash line, you should recognize the XS3 code. The computer receiving the coded numbers is capable of recognizing the XS3 code inherent in each number, and performing arithmetic operations in the XS3 code. The advantage in having the XS3 code inherent in the octonary code used in the RCA computer lies in the fact that arithmetic operations are easily performed in this code.

1-7. Problems

1. Using symbols similar to those in Table 1-3, develop a table showing the count in a system containing ten geometrical digits. Show the count through two columns.

2. Rewrite the following numbers using the powers-of-ten notation:
   (a) 256.43   (b) 16,002
   (c) 0.0307   (d) 10.090
3. Represent the following numbers by using the general equation for N_R:
   (a) $(735)_8$ (b) $(952)_{10}$
   (c) $(10010)_2$ (d) $(0.080)_{10}$
   (e) $(2301)_4$ (f) $(0.01101)_2$
4. Convert the following numbers to the radix 10:
   (a) $(537)_8$ (b) $(52.74)_8$
   (c) $(1011.001)_2$ (d) $(6348)_9$
5. Perform the conversions indicated.
   (a) $(54)_{10} = (?)_8$ (b) $(72)_8 = (?)_2$
   (c) $(37)_{10} = (?)_2$ (d) $(323)_4 = (?)_3$
6. What characteristic of the Arabic system of numbers differentiates it from the number systems of early civilizations? Why is this important?
7. What is another way of writing *twelve groups of ten units each?*
8. Why is the binary number system very useful? List several examples of binary devices.
9. What does a negative exponent indicate? Solve the following problem in two ways: $2(10)^{-2} \times 3.5(10)^4$.
10. What is the equivalent of $(364)_{10}$ in the radix 2? In the radixes 4, 8, 12, and 16?
11. Which of the following numbers does not exist in the octal number system? Why?
    (a) 1101   (b) 2468
    (c) 10,567   (d) 249
    (e) 7777   (f) 10
12. In your own words, explain what a code is. Can a number system be considered a code? Why?
13. If 43 symbols are to be coded, what is the minimum number of bits that can be used in each combination? How many symbols could be coded if we use five-bit combinations?
14. What is a weighted code? Is the NBCD system a weighted code?
15. What is the similarity between the NBCD system and a straight binary count? What are forbidden combinations?
16. Explain why the biquinary code is also called the two-out-of-seven-bit code. How is the XS3 code formed?

2

Arithmetic Operations In Any Radix

Addition, subtraction, multiplication, and division are arithmetic operations that can be performed in number systems of any radix. Each operation is governed by a specific set of rules that are applicable to any number system (except baseless systems) whether or not the digits are geometrical, Roman, Arabic, etc. Anyone who can add, subtract, multiply and divide in the decimal system should be capable of performing these operations in systems of any other radix. Nevertheless, one would find that most people are not able to solve such problems as $(71)_8 \times (6)_8$, $(11011)_2 - (1111)_2$, or $(\triangle\bigcirc)_\square + (\triangle\triangle)_\square$. The reason for this is that arithmetic operations are performed so frequently in the course of everyday living that they become purely mechanical actions; after a time, one never thinks about the rules or reasons because the desired results are easily obtained mechanically, without thinking. In order to obtain a thorough understanding of Boolean algebra, and more so, its applications in electronics, it is necessary to review the principles of arithmetic and to apply them to systems of different radixes.

2-1. Decimal Addition

Addition is one of the simplest arithmetic operations, and it depends only on a previous knowledge of counting. In fact, when a child first learns how to add, his initial efforts are actually counting—on his fingers, or with the aid of pictures such as shown in Fig. 2-1. Given a problem such as $2 + 3$, the beginner first counts to 2 and then *continues to count* until he has counted three more digits. Upon counting three more digits, he arrives at the digit, 5, which is the sum of 2 and 3. A person who is experienced in decimal addition has no need to count in this manner because he has memorized the results of adding all the possible combinations of digits. An addition table that contains the results of the simple additions of every combination of digits in the decimal system is shown in Table 2-1. (A simple addition is the result of adding *two digits*.) From experience, you know the results of the simple additions in the decimal system; however, tables such as this are very convenient for performing additions in other radixes with which you may not be familiar.

QUESTION: 3 APPLES AND 2 APPLES ARE_____APPLES?

ANSWER:

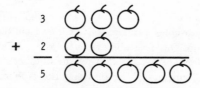

Fig. 2-1. Addition with the aid of pictures.

In the example, $2 + 3$, the 2 is generally considered to be the *given* number, and the 3 is the number that is *added to* to the given number. In formal mathematics, these two parts of an addition are given names: the given number is called the *augend,* and the number that is added to the augend is called the *addend.* These two terms are used to identify the operands of additions in any number system.

TABLE 2-1. THE DECIMAL ADDITION TABLE

AUGENDS	ADDENDS									
	0	1	2	3	4	5	6	7	8	9
0	0	1	2	3	4	5	6	7	8	9
1	1	2	3	4	5	6	7	8	9	10
2	2	3	4	5	6	7	8	9	10	11
3	3	4	5	6	7	8	9	10	11	12
4	4	5	6	7	8	9	10	11	12	13
5	5	6	7	8	9	10	11	12	13	14
6	6	7	8	9	10	11	12	13	14	15
7	7	8	9	10	11	12	13	14	15	16
8	8	9	10	11	12	13	14	15	16	17
9	9	10	11	12	13	14	15	16	17	18

The addition of two digits in any number system always results in a number composed of two parts: a *sum* and a *carry.* Some examples willl illustrate this concept:

	Augend		*Addend*		*Carry*	*Sum*
Example 2-1.	9	+	8	=	1	7
Example 2-2.	7	+	3	=	1	0
Example 2-3.	2	+	6	=	0	8

In **Example 2-1**, the result of adding 9 and 8 is the number 17. Digit 7 is the sum, and it is placed in the units position; digit 1 is the carry, and it is placed in the tens position. In **Example 2-2**, the result of adding 7 and 3 is a sum of 0 and a carry of 1. The sum is placed in the units position, and the carry is placed in the tens position. In **Example 2-3**, the sum is 8 and the carry is 0. These digits are placed in their proper positions as explained for **Examples 2-1** and **2-2**. Notice that the value of the carry may be zero or finite. Differentiating between the sum and carry parts of the result of an addition applies to additions in number systems of any radix. The significance of distinguishing between the sum and carry in addition will become more apparent in later chapters when the laws of Boolean algebra are applied to special electronic circuits.

The addition of more than two digits and of numbers containing more than one digit is accomplished by performing a series of simple additions. Consider, for instance, the addition of $2 + 3 + 6$. Although this problem can be readily done mentally, there are several steps involved in obtaining the solution. First, the digit 2 is considered to be the augend, and the 3, the addend. Adding these two digits yields a sum of 5 and a carry of 0. Now, the result of the first simple addition becomes the augend and the 6 is the addend. This second simple addition yields a sum of 1 and a carry of 1. The result of the last simple addition is the solution to the problem: $2 + 3 + 6 = 5 + 6 = 11$.

An addition such as $76 + 54$ follows a definite procedure:

Hundreds	Tens	Units	
	7	6	*Augend*
	5	4	*Addend*
	1	0	*Augend*
1	2		*Addend*
1	3	0	*Result*

Adding 6 and 4 (in the units position) gives a sum of 0 and 1 to carry. The 0 is placed in the units position and the carry, 1, is placed in the tens position. Next, the 7 and 5, which are in the tens position, are added; their sum is 2, and their carry is 1. Because the 7 and 5 are in the tens position, their sum is placed in the tens position, beneath the 1 from the previous simple addition. The carry of 1 is then placed in the next higher position or the hundreds position. Now, the results of the first two simple additions are added, and the final solution to the problem is 130. At first glance, this method of addition seems to be more complicated than the conventional method used by most people. The only difference, however, is that here each step is methodically written down instead of being done mentally. By writing down each step, it is easier to understand exactly what is happening and, if you thoroughly understand decimal addition, you will have no trouble adding numbers in other radixes.

2-2. Binary Addition

The binary addition table, shown in Table 2-2, is extremely simple because the binary number system contains only two digits. Because of this simplicity, the results of all the simple binary additions can be memorized almost instantly and binary addition can, as a result, be performed without

TABLE 2-2. THE BINARY ADDITION TABLE

AUGENDS	ADDENDS	
	0	1
0	0	1
1	1	10

constant reference to the table. As demonstrated in the following examples, the procedure used for adding binary numbers is the same as that used in the decimal system. At first, it will be necessary for you to write each step as you perform each addition. When you become more adept at binary addition, much of the work will be done mentally. Along with each of the following binary additions, the equivalent decimal addition is given. If you convert the binary result into the decimal system and compare it with the decimal result, you will find that they are the same quantity.

Example 2-4.

	Binary	*Decimal*
	1101	13
	+ 1001	+ 9
	10	12
	00	01
	01	22
	10	
	10110	

Example 2-5.

	1010	10
	+ 0100	+ 4
	1110	14

Example 2-6.

	110110	54
	+ 101010	+ 42
	1100000	96

2-3. Octal Addition

The octal addition table in Table 2-3 looks similar to the decimal addition table; however, if you look carefully, you will see that digits 8 and 9 appear nowhere in this table. In the octal system, the addition of 1 and 7, 2 and 6, 3 and 5, 4 and 4, etc., is equal to $(10)_8$. Similarly, $2 + 7$, $3 + 6$, $4 + 5$, etc.,

TABLE 2-3.   THE OCTAL ADDITION TABLE

AUGENDS	ADDENDS							
	0	1	2	3	4	5	6	7
0	0	1	2	3	4	5	6	7
1	1	2	3	4	5	6	7	10
2	2	3	4	5	6	7	10	11
3	3	4	5	6	7	10	11	12
4	4	5	6	7	10	11	12	13
5	5	6	7	10	11	12	13	14
6	6	7	10	11	12	13	14	15
7	7	10	11	12	13	14	15	16

are all equal to $(11)_8$. If an octal addition results in a number greater than 7, you can check the number by referring to Table 1-6. Suppose you want to verify that $(6)_8 + (3)_8 = (11)_8$. Count to $(6)_8$ in Table 1-6, and then count three more digits; you'll find that the result is $(11)_8$. Using the addition table to get the results of the simple octal additions saves considerable time in working out problems in octal addition. In the first two problems in octal addition to follow, each simple addition is shown so that you can see the steps involved in obtaining the answer. In the third problem, the simple additions are done mentally and the answer is written directly. The equivalent problems in the decimal system are shown for each octal addition. If you convert the octal results into the decimal system and compare them with the results in the decimal system, you will find that they are the same quantities.

Example 2-7.

	Octal	*Decimal*
	77	63
	+ 23	+ 19
	12	12
	11	7
	122	82

Example 2-8.

	755	493
	+ 63	+ 51
	10	04
	13	14
	7	4
	1040	544

Example 2-9.

	52	42
	+ 76	+ 62
	150	104

2-4. Decimal Subtraction

Subtraction is essentially the opposite of addition: instead of increasing or "adding to" a given number, as in addition, subtraction involves decreasing or "taking away" from the given number. The basic operation of subtraction is to count backwards from a given number instead of counting beyond a given number. For example, the problem 3 − 2 is solved by counting back two digits from 3 to obtain the solution of 1. In contrast, 3 + 2 is solved by counting two digits beyond 3 to obtain the solution of 5. By counting backwards, the operator is actually taking away or subtracting.

In the example, 3 − 2, the digit 3 is generally considered to be the given number and the 2 is the number that is taken away from the given number. In formal mathematics, these two parts of a subtraction are given names: the given number, 3, is called the *minuend,* and the number, 2, that is taken away from the minuend is called the *subtrahend.* The result of a subtraction is called the *difference.* These terms are used to identify the operands of a subtraction in any number system.

Unlike the operands of an addition, the operands of a subtraction cannot be interchanged. The minuend is usually the *larger* of the two quantities, and the subtrahend is usually the *smaller* of the two quantities. With the exception of certain applications (e.g., negative numbers), this rule is always observed. In addition, however, either number could be the augend or the addend without affecting the solution.

As shown in the following two cases, there are two standard ways to indicate subtraction:

$$Minuend - Subtrahend = Difference$$
$$3 \quad - \quad 2 \quad = \quad 1$$

$$
\begin{array}{ll}
3 & Minuend \\
\underline{- \ 2} & Subtrahend \\
1 & Difference
\end{array}
$$

In the first case, the operands of the subtraction are written horizontally in a straight line, with the subtrahend placed at the right of the minuend and the difference to the right of the subtrahend. In the second case, the operands are written vertically, with the subtrahend placed beneath the minuend and the difference beneath the subtrahend. Both of these methods are standard and are used interchangeably.

There is no special table for subtraction as there is for addition. However, by using a certain procedure, an addition table may be used, if necessary, to find the difference of two digits. An example will illustrate this procedure. Suppose you want to subtract 6 from 8. Locate the 6 (subtrahend) in the augend column in Table 2-1. Then, look across the row of digits until you find the digit 8 (minuend). The digit at the head of the addend column in which the 8 appears is the difference of 8 and 6, or 2. Since you are familiar with subtraction in the decimal system, this use of the decimal addition table is of little value to you. Nevertheless, the use

of addition tables may be very useful for performing subtractions in unfamiliar number systems.

The subtraction of numbers containing more than one digit frequently
involves a technique called *borrowing*. In a problem such as 50 − 39, the
complete minuend is 50, and the complete subtrahend is 39. Although the
minuend in this problem is a larger quantity than the subtrahend, as you
would expect, this problem shows that the individual digits of the minuend
are not necessarily larger than the corresponding digits of the subtrahend.
For instance, the 0 in the units position of the minuend is a smaller quantity than the 9 in the units position of the subtrahend. The technique of
borrowing, which depends upon the positional value of numbers, provides a
way of subtracting two quantities when a digit in the minuend is smaller
than the corresponding digit in the subtrahend. To demonstrate the mechanics of borrowing, it is necessary to identify the positional value of each
digit as in the following example:

Tens	*Units*	
4	$10 + 0 = 10$	
5̸	0̸	*Minuend*
− 3	9	*Subtrahend*
1	1	*Difference*

From the point of view of positional value, the minuend, 50, actually means
five groups of ten units each plus 0 units; the subtrahend, 39, actually means
three groups of ten units each plus 9 units. Suppose we borrow one group
of ten units from the five groups in the minuend. That leaves four groups of
ten units in the tens column. To indicate that a group of ten has been borrowed, we cross out the 5, as shown in the example, and record a 4 above
it. To show that we have *added* a group of ten units to the units column, we
simply add the ten units to the number of units already in the units column.
By borrowing from the tens column and adding to the units column, we
do not change the value of the number quantitatively: Isn't five groups of
10 units each plus 0 units the same amount as four groups of ten units each
plus 10 units?

Now that there are ten units in the units column of the minuend, it is
quite simple to subtract 9 from 10 to get 1. Because there are only four
groups of ten in the tens column of the minuend, we subtract 3 from 4 to get
1. The difference then is 11, or one group of ten units plus 1 unit. In this
example, it is only necessary to borrow once; in some problems, however, it
is necessary to borrow several times before the subtraction is completed.
The following problem illustrates multiple borrowing: Subtract 99 from 202.

Step 1:	*Hundreds*	*Tens*	*Units*	
	1	$10 + 0 = 10$		*First Borrow*
	2̸	0̸	2	*Minuend*
	− 0	9	9	*Subtrahend*

In order to subtract in the units column, we have to borrow a group of ten units from the tens column; but, there are no groups of ten in the tens column. We, therefore, go to the hundreds column and borrow one group of one hundred units, which is the same as ten groups of ten units. There are no longer two groups of one hundred units in the hundreds column so we cross out the 2 and record a 1 above it. Now, there are ten groups of ten units in the tens column as a result of the first borrow.

Step 2:	*Hundreds*	*Tens*	*Units*	
		9	$10 + 2 = 12$	*Second Borrow*
	1	1̸0̸		
	2̸	0̸	2̸	*Minuend*
	− 0	9	9	*Subtrahend*
	1	0	3	*Difference*

We can now borrow a group of ten units from the tens column and add it to the units column. In doing this, we cross out the 10 in the tens column and record a 9 above it as shown in *Step 2*. We then add 10 units to the number of units, 2, already in the units column. As a result of the second borrow, there are 12 units in the units column of the minuend; 9 units subtracted from 12 units gives a difference of 3 units. Subtracting 9 from 9 in the tens column yields 0; and 0 from 1 in the hundreds column is 1. The answer to the problem, or the difference, is 103.

2-5. Binary Subtraction

As was the case with addition, the mechanics of binary subtraction are the same as those used for decimal subtraction. In fact, the rules for any arithmetic operation are the same in all number systems, providing that the number system contains an ordered set of symbols having positional as well as numerical value. There is no special subtraction table in the binary system; however, the addition table can be used as explained earlier to obtain differences.

Because there are so few digits in the binary number system, borrowing occurs more frequently in a problem of binary subtraction than it does in decimal subtraction. This is apparent in the illustrative examples at the end of this section. Another dissimilarity between subtraction in the two systems is that the positional notation is in terms of groups of ten in the decimal system and groups of two in the binary system. The following problem demonstrates binary subtraction: Subtract $(0101)_2$ from $(1100)_2$.

Step 1:	2^3	2^2	2^1	2^0	
		0	$10 + 0 = 10$		*First Borrow*
	1	1̸	0̸	0	*Minuend*
	− 0	1	0	1	*Subtrahend*

Before we can subtract in the units column, we have to borrow a group of 2^1 or two units from the 2^1 column. In the binary system, two units is the same as $(10)_2$; you can verify this by looking at the binary addition table for the sum of 1 and 1 which is 10, or two units. Since there is a 0 in the 2^1 column of the problem, we have to go to the 2^2 column for the first borrow. This column contains groups of 2^2 units, or $(10)_2$ groups of $(10)_2$ units each. To indicate that we are borrowing from the 2^2 column, we cross out the 1 and record a 0 above it as shown in *Step 1*. $(10)_2$ groups of $(10)_2$ units are then added to the 2^1 column; hence, the first borrow is completed.

Step 2:	2^3	2^2	2^1	2^0	
			1	$10 + 0 = 10$	*Second Borrow*
		0	1̸0̸		
	1	1̸	0̸	0̸	*Minuend*
	− 0	1	0	1	*Subtrahend*
			1	1	*Difference*

Now that there are $(10)_2$ groups of $(10)_2$ units in the 2^1 column, we can borrow one of these groups and add it to the units column. As shown in *Step 2*, we cross out the $(10)_2$ in the 2^1 column, record a 1 above it, and add a group of $(10)_2$ units to the units column. Now it is possible to subtract in the units column: $(10)_2 − (1)_2$ is $(1)_2$. In the 2^1 column, $1 − 0$ is 1. Proceeding to the 2^2 column, we find that there is a 0 in the minuend and a 1 in the subtrahend. Before we can subtract, we have to borrow from the 2^3 column which contains groups of 2^3 units or eight units.

Step 3:	2^3	2^2	2^1	2^0	
	0	$10 + 0 = 10$			*Third Borrow*
		0̸	1	10	
	1̸	1̸	0̸	0̸	*Minuend*
	− 0	1	0	1	*Subtrahend*
	0	1	1	1	*Difference*

As shown in *Step 3*, the third borrow is indicated by crossing out the 1 in the 2^3 column and recording a 0 above it. Since one group of $(2)^3$ units is the same as $(10)_2$ groups of 2^2 units, we add $(10)_2$ groups of 2^2 units to the 2^2 column. Now it is possible to subtract: $(10)_2 − (1)_2$ is $(1)_2$. In the 2^3 column, $0 − 0$ is 0, and the complete difference is $(0111)_2$. To see if the solution is correct, it is only necessary to convert all the binary quantities into decimal quantities and perform the subtraction in the decimal system. $(1100)_2 = (12)_{10}$; $(0101)_2 = (5)_{10}$; $(0111)_2 = (7)_{10}$. In the decimal system, $12 − 5 = 7$; you can see that the solution is correct.

The following examples further illustrate binary subtraction. By working them out, you will gain a better understanding of how to perform subtraction in this number system. At first, you will probably have to write out each step as you proceed, but when you have more practice with binary subtraction, you will be able to do most of the steps mentally. The equivalent decimal subtractions are given with each binary problems for comparison.

Example 2-10.

	Binary	*Decimal*
	1101	13
	− 1001	− 9
	0100	4

Example 2-11.

	0	10	0	10	
	¢	ø	¢	ø	10
−	0	1	0	1	− 5
	0	1	0	1	5

Example 2-12.

				10			
	0	10	0	ø	10		
1	¢	ø	¢	¢	ø		54
− 1	0	1	0	1	1		− 43
0	0	1	0	1	1		11

2-6. Octal Subtraction

Although the radix of the octal system is different from the radixes of the decimal and binary systems, the mechanics of subtraction are the same in each system Having already investigated the general mechanics of subtraction and applied them to the decimal and binary systems, the discussion of octal subtraction can be confined to an illustrative problem and a few reference examples. The octal addition table may be used as explained for other systems to obtain unfamiliar differences between octal numbers. You may want to refer to the octal addition table in Table 2-3 to verify the differences obtained in the following problem. For simplicity, we will not indicate the radix 8 of each number by using parentheses; each number is, however, an octal quantity. Subtract $(053)_8$ from $(247)_8$.

8^2	8^1	8^0	
1	$10 + 4 = 14$		
$\not{2}$	$\not{4}$	7	*Minuend*
− 0	5	3	*Subtrahend*
1	7	4	*Difference*

In the units, or 8^0, column, there is a 7 in the minuend and a 3 in the subtrahend. The difference of these two digits is 4. In the 8^1 column, there are four groups of 8 units each in the minuend, and five groups of 8 units each in the subtrahend. Since the digit in the minuend is smaller than the digit in the subtrahend, we must borrow from the 8^2 column before we can subtract. The 8^2 column contains two groups of 8^2 units each. This quantity is the same as:

      1 group of 8^2 units + 8^2 units, or

      1 group of 8^2 units + 8^1 groups of 8^1 units.

Realize that the column headings 8^0, 8^1, 8^2, etc., are in decimal notation and that 8^1 in decimal notation is the same quantity as 10^1 in octal notation. We can, therefore, change one group of 8^2 units $+ 8^1$ groups of 8^1 units to one group of 8^2 units $+ (10)_8$ groups of 8^1 units. By writing the quantity in the 8^2 column this way, it is easier to see what happens when we borrow from this column. Let's backtrack for a moment to clarify the steps: In the 8^2 column, there are two groups of 8^2 which can be written as one group of 8^2 units $+ (10)_8$ groups of 8^1 units; remember that $(10)_8$ groups of 8^1 units is equal to one group of 8^2 units.

To borrow one group of 8^2 units from the 8^2 column, we cross out the 2 in the 8^2 column and record a 1 above it, as shown in the problem. Then, we add $(10)_8$ groups of 8^1 units to the quantity already in the 8^1 column. The result in the 8^1 column is $10 + 4 = 14$. Now we can subtract 5 from 14. If you refer to the octal addition table, you will see that $14 - 5 = 7$. In the 8^2 column, $1 - 0 = 1$; and the complete difference of the problem is 174.

Once you understand what happens when you borrow, it is not necessary to go through this detailed procedure. If you are borrowing from the 8^2 column, for instance, you simply decrease the quantity in that column by 1 and add $(10)_8$ to the quantity in the 8^1 column. Similarly, if you borrow 1 from the 8^1 column, you add $(10)_8$ to the 8^0 column. Along with the following examples of octal subtraction, the equivalent decimal problems are given. Convert your octal differences to the decimal system, and verify the results of each problem.

Example 2-13.

	Octal			Decimal
	4	11		
	$\cancel{5}$	$\cancel{1}$	6	334
$-$	0	2	6	$-$ 022
	4	7	0	312

Example 2-14.

		12		
	1	$\cancel{16}$	12	
	$\cancel{2}$	$\cancel{3}$	$\cancel{2}$	154
$-$	1	6	7	$-$ 119
	0	4	3	035

Example 2-15.

	1	10		
	$\cancel{2}$	$\cancel{0}$	3	131
$-$	1	7	3	$-$ 123
	0	1	0	008

2-7. Subtraction by Complementation

Complementing is a method by which the difference of two numbers can be found by adding them in a certain manner. One of the advantages of being able to subtract by complementing is greatly simplified computer circuitry. Since the arithmetic operation involved in complementing is addition, the computer's adding circuits may be used to obtain differences;

hence, the need for separate subtracting circuits is eliminated.

To introduce complementing very simply, we can liken the process to a selection switch that can *only* be moved in a clockwise direction. As shown in Fig. 2-2, the switch points to 5. Suppose we want to subtract 3 from 5. This can be done by counting back 3 digits from the 5 to obtain a difference of 2. But this switch cannot be moved in a counterclockwise direction; thus

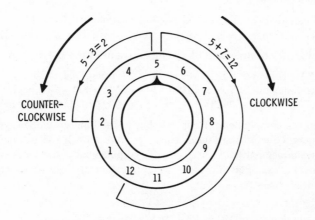

Fig. 2-2. The process of complementation may be compared to a selection switch that can only be turned in the clockwise direction.

it is impossible for us to count back. The difference can still be found, however, by determining the "complemented form" of the subtrahend and adding this number to the minuend. The complemented form of 3 is 7. To add 7 to 5, we count forward 7 places, beginning at 5. This is done on the selector switch by moving the pointer 7 places in a clockwise direction, beginning from 5. As indicated in the figure, the switch selects the number 12. By adding 7 to 5, we made the answer one cycle too large; thus, we can ignore the digit 1, which represents 1 group of 10 units, and merely consider the 2 as $(12 - 10 = 2)$. By using the selector switch, we have demonstrated that subtraction can be performed by adding the complement of the subtrahend to the minuend. Let us now see how complements are formed, and how they are used in different number systems.

There are two common types of complements for each number system. These are known as the *true complement* (R's complement), and the radix-minus-one, (R-1)'s complement. In general terms,

$$R\text{'s complement of } N_R = R^{\text{mod}} - N_R \qquad (2\text{-}1)$$

and

$$(R - 1)\text{'s complement of } N_R = (R^{\text{mod}} - 1) - N_R \qquad (2\text{-}2)$$

In both equations, N_R is the subtrahend whose complement is being determined, R is the radix of the number system, and "mod" is the modulus of N_R, or the number of places to which N_R is written in the problem. For example, the modulus of 102 is 3, the modulus of 32 is 2, the modulus of 076 is 3; etc. In the decimal system, the R's complement is called the 10's complement, and the $(R\text{-}1)$'s complement is called the 9's complement. By substituting into Eq. (2-1), let us find the 10's complement of 64. We are given that N_R is 64, R is 10, and the modulus of 64 is 2. Therefore,

$$10\text{'s complement of } 64 = 10^2 - 64 = 100 - 64 = 36$$

In the same manner,

$$10\text{'s complement of } 752 = 10^3 - 752 = 1000 - 752 = 248$$
$$10\text{'s complement of } 3921 = 10^4 - 3921 = 10000 - 3921 = 6079$$

To find the 9's complement of a number, we use Eq. (2-2):

$$9\text{'s complement of } 64 = (10^2 - 1) - 64 = 99 - 64 = 35$$
$$9\text{'s complement of } 752 = (10^3 - 1) - 752 = 999 - 752 = 247$$
$$9\text{'s complement of } 3921 = (10^4 - 1) - 3921 = 9999 - 3921 = 6078$$

To find the complement of any number in the binary number system, the same general equations are used. However, R is now 2; the R's complement is the 2's complement, and the $(R - 1)$'s complement is the 1's complement. The following examples illustrate the application of Eqs. (2-1) and (2-2) to the binary system.

Example 2-16.

$$2\text{'s complement of } 101 = 2^3 - 101 = 1000 - 101 = 011$$

Example 2-17.

$$2\text{'s complement of } 110111 = 2^6 - 110111 = 1000000 - 110111$$
$$= 001001$$

Example 2-18.

$$1\text{'s complement of } 101 = (2^3 - 1) - 101 = 0111 - 101 = 010$$

Example 2-19.

$$1\text{'s complement of } 110111 = (2^6 - 1) - 110111 = 0111111$$
$$- 110111 = 001000$$

Having seen how to determine complements in the decimal and binary number systems, you should be able to find complements in the octal and other number systems using Eqs. (2-1) and (2-2).

Except for the disposition of the carry digit, obtaining differences is the same using the R's complement and the $(R\text{-}1)$'s complement. In the decimal system, $78 - 32$ is 46. To obtain the difference, 46, using the 10's complement, determine the 10's complement of the subtrahend, 32, and *add* this number to the minuend, 78. The 10's complement of 32 is:

$$10^2 - 32 = 100 - 32 = 68$$

Adding 68 to the minuend,

$$
\begin{array}{r|r}
  & 78 \\
+ & 68 \\
\hline
1 & 46 \\
\end{array}
$$

The modulus of the numbers in this problem is 2, and we are not concerned with the carry that appears in the third position. We simply disregard the 1, and our difference, obtained by using the 10's complement, is 46. This is the same number obtained by ordinary subtraction. In a problem such as 1726 − 0054, the difference by ordinary subtraction is 1672. Although the subtrahend is 54, the modulus of the problem is 4. By 10's complements,

10's complement of $0054 = 10^4 - 0054 = 10000 - 0054 = 9946$

Adding the complement of 0054 to the minuend,

$$
\begin{array}{r|l}
 & 1726 \\
+ & 9946 \\
\hline
1 & 1672
\end{array}
$$

Ignoring the carry in the fifth position, the difference is 1672.

Differences are similarly obtained by R's complement in the binary and other number systems. In the following examples, binary differences are obtained using the 2's complement and by ordinary subtraction for comparison. Remember that the carry is disregarded when the R's complement is used.

Example 2-20. Using the 2's complement, find $11011 - 01101$.

2's complement of $01101 = 2^5 - 01101 = 100000 - 01101 = 10011$

$$
\begin{array}{r|l}
 & 11011 \\
+ & 10011 \\
\hline
1 & 01110
\end{array}
$$

By ordinary binary subtraction,

$$
\begin{array}{r}
11011 \\
- \ 01101 \\
\hline
01110
\end{array}
$$

Example 2-21. Using the 2's complement, find $101 - 010$.

2's complement of $010 = 2^3 - 010 = 1000 - 010 = 110$

$$
\begin{array}{r|l}
 & 101 \\
+ & 110 \\
\hline
1 & 011
\end{array}
$$

By ordinary binary subtraction,

$$
\begin{array}{r}
101 \\
- \ 010 \\
\hline
011
\end{array}
$$

To perform subtraction using the $(R\text{-}1)$'s complement, the procedure is the same with one exception. Instead of disregarding the carry, we must add it to the rightmost digits of the result. When we add the $(R\text{-}1)$'s complement of the subtrahend to the minuend in the decimal system, for example, the result is $R^{\text{mod}} - 1$ too large, where $R^{\text{mod}} - 1$ may be 9, 99, 999, etc. By adding 1 to the result, we make the result R^{mod} too large, where R^{mod} may be 10, 100, 1000, etc. Having done this, we then disregard the carry as in the R's complement. The following examples of subtraction using the $(R-1)$'s complement in the decimal and binary systems clearly illustrate the procedure.

Example 2-22. Using the 9's complement, find $78 - 32$.

9's complement of $32 = (10^2 - 1) - 32 = 99 - 32 = 67$

$$
\begin{array}{r}
78 \\
+ \ 67 \\
\hline
{}^{\frown}1 \ 45 \\
{}_{\longrightarrow}1 \\
\hline
46
\end{array}
$$

Example 2-23. Using the 9's complement, find $1726 - 0054$.

9's complement of $0054 = (10^4 - 1) - 0054 = 9999 - 54 = 9945$

$$
\begin{array}{r}
1726 \\
+ \ 9945 \\
\hline
{}^{\frown}1 \ 1671 \\
{}_{\longrightarrow}1 \\
\hline
1672
\end{array}
$$

Example 2-24. Using the 1's complement, find $101 - 010$.

1's complement of $010 = (2^3 - 1) - 010 = 111 - 010 = 101$

$$
\begin{array}{r}
101 \\
+ \ 101 \\
\hline
{}^{\frown}1 \ 010 \\
{}_{\longrightarrow}1 \\
\hline
011
\end{array}
$$

Example 2-25. Using the 1's complement, find $11011 - 01101$.

1's complement of $01101 = (2^5 - 1) - 01101 = 11111 - 01101$
$= 10010$

$$
\begin{array}{r}
11011 \\
+ \ 10010 \\
\hline
{}^{\frown}1 \ 01101 \\
{}_{\longrightarrow}1 \\
\hline
01110
\end{array}
$$

2-8. Decimal Multiplication

Multiplication is an arithmetic operation that is closely associated with addition because it is basically a series of additions. For example, to multiply or increase two times a number such as 3, we merely add another 3:

$3 + 3 = 6$. It is obvious that 6 is twice as much as 3. Suppose we want to make the 3 three times larger than it is. We could add two more 3's to the given 3 and obtain $3 + 3 + 3 = 9$. The number 9 certainly is three times larger than 3. This procedure becomes quite cumbersome when it is applied to larger quantities. Imagine trying to make the number 9, eight times larger. This would involve a problem in addition that extends across the page and takes a considerable amount of time to perform. To avoid the long additions required to solve problems such as these, multiplication was developed. Multiplication is essentially a shorthand procedure based on addition, rather than a unique concept.

In multiplication, the *result* of adding a number to zero as many times as indicated by a certain number is called the *product*. The *given* number is called the *multiplicand,* and the number that indicates how many times to add the given number to zero is called the *multiplier.* One of the most common ways to write a multiplication is:

$$\begin{array}{r} 3 \quad Multiplicand \\ \times\ 2 \quad Multiplier \\ \hline 6 \quad Product \end{array}$$

Other frequently used arrangements are:

$$2 \times 3 = 6$$
$$(2)(3) = 6$$
$$2 \cdot 3 = 6$$

As in addition, the position of the operands of a multiplication can be changed without affecting the result of the multiplication; that is, either the 3 or the 2 may be the multiplicand or the multiplier, and the product will be the same in both cases.

It was mentioned before that multiplication is a shorthand technique based on addition. This property of multiplication arises from the fact that a multiplication table is used, and this table lists the products obtained by adding each digit in the system to zero, according to each of the simple multipliers in the system. The number of simple multipliers in a number system is equal to the radix of the system, or the number of digits. In the decimal system, for instance, the simple multipliers are 0, 1, 2, 3, 4, 5, 6, 7, 8, and 9. To compile the simple products for the multiplication table, each digit, 0 through 9, is added to zero according to each multiplier: first 0 times, then 1 time, then 2, 3, 4, 5, 6, 7, 8 and 9 times. Each product is then listed or tabulated as shown in Table 2-4. This table shows that no matter how many times 0 is added to 0 the result is 0. In multiplication, any number, N, times 0, is still 0: $N \times 0 = 0$. Look at the multiplicand 5 in the table. When the multiplier is 0, it is like saying, add 5 to 0 zero times; hence, $5 \times 0 = 0$. When the multiplier is 1, 5 is added to 0 only once: $5 + 0 = 5$, or, $1 \times 5 = 5$. Similarly, when the multiplier is 5, we really add 5 to 0 five times: $5 + 5 + 5 + 5 + 5 + 0 = 25$, or $5 \times 5 = 25$. Once the multiplication table has been compiled in this manner, it is no longer necessary to work out any additions to obtain the simple products because all the simple products in the number system are listed in the table. When each simple product in the table is memorized, multiplication of any numbers can be performed quite rapidly and easily. Hence, the multiplication table makes it possible for memory to substitute for addition.

TABLE 2-4.   THE DECIMAL MULTIPLICATION TABLE

MULTIPLIER	MULTIPLICAND									
	0	1	2	3	4	5	6	7	8	9
0	0	0	0	0	0	0	0	0	0	0
1	0	1	2	3	4	5	6	7	8	9
2	0	2	4	6	8	10	12	14	16	18
3	0	3	6	9	12	15	18	21	24	27
4	0	4	8	12	16	20	24	28	32	36
5	0	5	10	15	20	25	30	35	40	45
6	0	6	12	18	24	30	36	42	48	54
7	0	7	14	21	28	35	42	49	56	63
8	0	8	16	24	32	40	48	56	64	72
9	0	9	18	27	36	45	54	63	72	81

The multiplication table, which contains the simple products of single digits, is used to solve more complex problems in multiplication. A more complex problem is one that involves numbers containing more than one digit. In this type of problem, the positional value of numbers is a very important consideration, as shown in this simple problem: 3 times 32.

Tens	Units	
3	2	*Multiplicand*
×	3	*Multiplier*
	6	
9	0	
9	6	*Product*

The multiplicand, 32, is basically the same as 2 units plus 3 groups of 10 units. When the multiplicand is multiplied by 3, the quantity in the units column and the quantity in the tens column are both multiplied by 3. The first simple product is $3 \times 2 = 6$ units. This product is recorded in the units column beneath the problem, as shown. When we multiply 3 groups of ten units by 3 units, we obtain 9 groups of ten units plus 0 units. The 9 is recorded in the tens column beneath the first simple product, and the 0 is recorded in the units column. Because the addition of 0 to any number does not change the value of the number, it is customary to ignore this 0; it is usually not recorded in the units column. When all the simple products have been found, they are added together as shown and the complete product is 96. If you add 32 to 0 three times, you will obtain the same result.

The general practice in a problem such as this is to record the second simple product, 9 groups of ten units, directly in the tens column next to the first simple product, instead of tabulating the products and adding them. This procedure may be used satisfactorily in number systems with which you are familiar, such as the decimal system. However, the practice of tabulating the simple products is an extremely useful technique in number systems that are not familiar.

Now let us solve a more complex problem in decimal multiplication: 64 times 78.

Step 1:

Hundreds	Tens	Units	
	7	8	*Multiplicand*
	× 6	4	*Multiplier*
	3	2	
2	8	0	

The multiplicand is multiplied by the 4 in *Step 1*, and the simple products, 32 and 280, are tabulated as shown. After the multiplication by 4 has been completed, the multiplicand is then multiplied by the 6 in the tens column of the multiplier as shown in *Step 2*.

Step 2:

Thousands	Hundreds	Tens	Units	
		7	8	*Multiplicand*
		× 6	4	*Multiplier*
		3	2	
	2	8	0	
	4	8		
4	2			
4	9	9	2	*Product*

Multiplying 8 units by 6 groups of ten units gives us a simple product of 48 groups of ten units, or 4 groups of 100 units and 8 groups of ten units. The 4 is recorded in the hundreds column, and the 8 is recorded in the tens column. The 0 that may be placed in the units column is disregarded in this problem. Now we multiply the 7 groups of ten in the multiplicand by the 6 groups of ten in the multiplier and obtain 42 groups of 100 units. This is the same as 4 groups of 1000 and 2 groups of 100. The 4 is recorded in the thousands column, and the 2 in the hundreds column as shown. All the simple products are then added and the complete product is found to be 4992.

It is often convenient to perform some of the addition mentally because it saves time and space, and minimizes the tabulation necessary in problems where the operands contain two or more digits. Keep in mind, though, that it may not be easy to perform the additions mentally when you are working in unfamiliar systems; furthermore, tabulation may improve your accuracy and efficiency in unfamiliar number systems.

2-9. Binary Multiplication

The binary multiplication table, shown in Table 2-5, is extremely simple because there are only two digits, 0 and 1, in the system. The inherent simplicity of the binary number system is reflected in binary multiplication. The simple products in any multiplication problem can be written at sight; and obtaining the complete products is only a matter of binary addition.

TABLE 2-5. THE BINARY MULTIPLICATION TABLE

MULTIPLIER	MULTIPLICAND	
	0	1
0	0	0
1	0	1

Since zero occurs so frequently in binary numbers, many of the simple products are zero. Instead of tabulating all the zero simple products, a single zero is simply placed in the proper column beneath the problem. The proper column is the column in which the digit of the multiplier is 0. This is illustrated in the following example: $(100)_2$ times $(111)_2$.

$$
\begin{array}{llllll}
\text{(a)} & 2^4 & 2^3 & 2^2 & 2^1 & 2^0 \\
           &   &   & 1 & 1 & 1 \\
           &   & \times & 1 & 0 & 0 \\ \hline
           &   &   & 0 & 0 & 0 \\
           &   & 0 & 0 & 0 & \\
           & 1 & 1 & 1 & & \\ \hline
           & 1 & 1 & 1 & 0 & 0
\end{array}
\qquad
\begin{array}{llllll}
\text{(b)} & 2^4 & 2^3 & 2^2 & 2^1 & 2^0 \\
           &   &   & 1 & 1 & 1 \\
           &   & \times & 1 & 0 & 0 \\ \hline
           & 1 & 1 & 1 & 0 & 0
\end{array}
$$

In (a), the conventional method of tabulating the simple sums is used. See how unnecessarily long the solution is and how many zeros are written needlessly. In (b), since a zero appears in the 2^0 and 2^1 columns of the multiplier, zeros are placed in the corresponding columns of the product. The remainder of the problem is solved as in the conventional procedure.

Binary multiplication is further illustrated in the following examples. The equivalent decimal problems are again given with each binary problem for comparison.

Example 2-26.

$$
\begin{array}{ccccc}
 & 1 & 1 & 0 & 1 \\
\times & 1 & 0 & 0 & 1 \\ \hline
 & 1 & 1 & 0 & 1 \\
1\;1 & 0 & 1 & 0 & 0 \\ \hline
1\;1\;1 & 0 & 1 & 0 & 1
\end{array}
\qquad
\begin{array}{r}
\textit{Decimal} \\
13 \\
\times\;9 \\ \hline
117
\end{array}
$$

Example 2-27.

	Binary								Decimal
			1	1	1	1			15
		×	1	0	1	0			× 10
			1	1	1	1	0		150
	1	1	1	1	0				
1	0	0	1	0	1	1	0		

Example 2-28.

			1	0	0	0	1	1	35
		×	1	1	0	1	0		× 26
		1	0	0	0	1	1	0	210
	1	0	0	0	1	1	0		70
1	0	0	0	1	1				910
1	1	1	0	0	0	1	1	1	0

2-10. Octal Multiplication

The octal multiplication table is shown in Table 2-6. You can see that it looks very similar to the decimal multiplication table; but since there is no 8 or 9 in the octal system, most of the simple products in the octal table are different from those in the decimal table. For instance, 2×4 in the

TABLE 2-6. THE OCTAL MULTIPLICATION TABLE

MULTIPLIER	MULTIPLICAND							
	0	1	2	3	4	5	6	7
0	0	0	0	0	0	0	0	0
1	0	1	2	3	4	5	6	7
2	0	2	4	6	10	12	14	16
3	0	3	6	11	14	17	22	25
4	0	4	10	14	20	24	30	34
5	0	5	12	17	24	31	36	43
6	0	6	14	22	30	36	44	52
7	0	7	16	25	34	43	52	61

decimal table shows a product of 8, whereas the same problem in the octal table shows a product of 10. You can verify each simple product in the octal multiplication table by adding octal digits to zero the amount of times indicated by the multipliers, and comparing the results of the additions with the products given in the table. When you solve problems in octal multiplication, the table will save a considerable time in finding the simple products. When all the simple products have been found, be sure to add them in the octal system, using the octal addition table if necessary. A common error frequently made by beginners is to find the octal simple products, and then forgetting and adding the simple products in the decimal system.

In the first illustrative example to follow, all of the simple octal products are tabulated and then added so that you can check each step with the octal multiplication table. In the second and third examples, mental addition is used, and the carried digits are indicated for reference. The equivalent problems in the decimal system are given for each of the octal problems for comparison.

Example 2-29.

		Octal			*Decimal*
		5	6		46
	×	2	3		× 19
		2	2		54
	1	7			36
	1	4			46
1	2				874
1	5	5	2		

Example 2-30.

		1	3			2
		𝚡				𝚡
	3	1	5			205
	×	5	2			× 42
		6	3	2		410
2	0	0	1			820
2	0	6	4	2		8610

Example 2-31.

		1				22
		𝚡				𝚡𝚡
	7	5	0			488
	×	2	0	7		× 135
		6	5	3	0	2440
1	7	2	0	0		1464
2	0	0	5	3	0	488
						65880

2-11. Decimal Division

Division is an arithmetic operation that is essentially the opposite of multiplication: whereas multiplication is a series of additions, division is a series of subtractions. More specifically, division is the process of determining how many times a number is contained in another number, and this is accomplished by a series of subtractions. For example, suppose we are given the number 49 and asked to find out how many 7's are contained in it. If we subtract a number of 7's from 49, we would find out how many 7's there are:

$$49 - 7 = 42 \qquad \text{one}$$
$$42 - 7 = 35 \qquad \text{two}$$
$$35 - 7 = 28 \qquad \text{three}$$
$$28 - 7 = 21 \qquad \text{four}$$
$$21 - 7 = 14 \qquad \text{five}$$
$$14 - 7 = \;\;7 \qquad \text{six}$$
$$7 - 7 = \;\;0 \qquad \text{seven}$$

This series of subtractions indicates that there are seven 7's in 49. Division, which makes use of subtraction and multiplication, eliminates the need for such a long procedure as the series of subtractions shown above.

In division, the result of dividing a given number by another is called the *quotient*. The given number is called the *dividend*, and the number that is divided into the dividend is called the *divisor*. There are a number of ways in which a division is commonly indicated:

$3 \div 2$ *is read* three divided by two.

$3/2$ *is read* three divided by two.

$2\,)\overline{3}$ *is read* three divided by two.

In each instance, the 3 is the dividend, and the 2 is the divisor.

There is no special table for division as there is for multiplication; however, the multiplication table can be used to obtain quotients by using a certain procedure. For example, suppose you want to divide 56 by 7. In the decimal multiplication table in Table 2-4, locate the dividend, 56, in the multiplicand column, beneath the 7. Then, look across the row of digits to the left of the 56, and read the quotient, 8, in the multiplier column. If you subtract 7 from 56 a number of times, you will also find that there are eight 7's in 56; this is the same result as that obtained from the multiplication table.

It does not always happen that the quotient is a whole number. By this we mean that sometimes a divisor does not go into the dividend an integral number of times and, therefore, there is a *remainder*. For instance, there is a remainder when we try to divide 20 by 3. Looking in the multiplication table in the column under 3, we find that the numbers go from 18 to 21, and there is no 20. From this we can conclude that 3 is not contained in 20 an integral number of times. To solve the problem, we use the next smaller number than 20 in the column under the 3. This we find is 18. Looking across the row to the left of the 18, we find the number 6 in the multiplier column. Now we know that if we subtract a series of 3's from 20, the number of 3's subtracted will be 6. However, six 3's are 18 and there are 2 digits left over. These two digits are the remainder. The quotient, therefore, is 6 and a remainder of 2, or 6-2/3. By writing the remainder as 2/3, it is shown that the divisor, 3, does not go into the remainder, 2, evenly.

The multiplication table can be used to obtain quotients directly provided that the divisor is a single-digit number, and as long as the dividend is not larger than the square of the largest digit in the number system. In the decimal system, the largest digit is 9; hence, the largest dividend that can be located directly on the table is 81. This, however, does not limit the usefulness of division or the range of quantities that can be divided. You will now see how multiplication and subtraction are used in division.

Consider first, the case where the dividend is a larger number than the square of the largest digit in the number system, and the divisor is a single-digit quantity:

$$9 \overline{)1\ 6\ 2}$$

Since the dividend, 162, does not appear in the multiplication table, we cannot find the quotient directly. But the problem can be approached by considering the positional value of the digits, and by dividing the dividend one part at a time. We cannot divide 9 into 1 a whole number of times; but it is possible to divide 16 by 9. By interpreting the dividend as 16 groups of 10 units plus 2 units, we can divide the dividend one column at a time. Referring to the multiplication table, we see that 9 goes into 16 only once, and that there is a remainder. To show that the simple quotient of 16/9 is 1, we record a 1 over the 16 as shown:

$$
\begin{array}{r}
1 \\
9 \overline{)1\ 6\ 2} \\
9 \\
\hline
7\ 2
\end{array}
$$

Then, to find the remainder, we multiply the 9 by 1 and place the product beneath the 16, as shown, and subtract. The difference is 7. Because we have actually divided 16 groups of 10 units by 9 units, the remainder is 7 groups of 10 units; and you can see that this 7 is properly recorded in the tens column. Now we can consider the quantity in the units column of the dividend. After the first division, we are left with 7 groups of 10 units, and 2 units. To show this, we bring down the 2 as shown by the arrow and record it next to the remainder of 7. Then we find how many times the divisor, 9, is contained in the remainder, 72. Looking again at the multiplication table, we locate 72 under the 9 in the multiplicand column. Across the row to the left of the 72, we locate a simple quotient of 8 in the multiplier column. To show that the simple quotient of 72/9 is 8, we record the 8 above the 2 as shown:

$$
\begin{array}{r}
18 \\
9 \overline{)162} \\
9 \\
\hline
72 \\
72 \\
\hline
0
\end{array}
$$

To find if there is a remainder, we multiply the divisor by the second simple quotient, 8, and place the product under the 72. Since 9×8 is 72 and $72 - 72$ is 0, there is no remainder in this example. The complete quotient is 18; and if you multiply the quotient by the divisor, you will find that their product is the dividend, 162. Of course, if you wish to prove that this is the correct solution in a more rigorous manner, see how many times you can subtract 9 from 162. You will find that it is 18 times.

Now consider the case where the divisor is a number that is composed of more than one digit:

$$25 \overline{)825}$$

The procedure for solving a problem such as this is the same as the procedure used to solve the previous problem. Although the dividend may be considered one part at a time, the divisor must always be treated in its entirety; that is, we cannot first divide by 2 and then by 5. Rather, the whole divisor, 25, must be used. The first step in the solution is to determine how many times 25 goes into the first two digits of the dividend. Since 25 does not go into 8 a whole number of times, we divide instead into 82. The number 82 does not appear in the multiplication table, but we can estimate the first simple quotient. A good rule of thumb for estimating the quotient is to see how many times the 2 in the divisor will go into the 8 in the dividend. In this case, we will estimate 4. This estimated quotient is placed above the 2 in the dividend as shown:

$$\begin{array}{r} 4 \\ 25 \overline{)825} \end{array}$$

When we multiply the estimated quotient and the divisor to see if there is a remainder, we find that 25×4 is 100. This product is larger than the 82 in the dividend, and this means that the simple quotient that was estimated is too large. Let us then estimate a smaller simple quotient of 3:

$$\begin{array}{r} 3 \\ 25 \overline{)825} \\ 75 \\ \overline{75} \end{array}$$

The product of 3 and 25 is 75. Subtracting 75 from 82 gives us a remainder of 7 groups of 10 units. Now we can bring down the 5 units we have not considered in the dividend to give us a total of 75 in the remainder. The next step is to divide the 75 by 25. Again the quotient is estimated. The second simple quotient is also 3, and this is recorded above the 5 as shown:

$$\begin{array}{r} 33 \\ 25 \overline{)825} \\ 75 \\ \overline{75} \\ 75 \\ \overline{0} \end{array}$$

Multiplying the 25 by the second simple quotient, we find that the remainder of the problem is 0 and the complete quotient is 33. If in any problem, there is a remainder that is less than the divisor, this remainder is recorded as a part of the complete quotient. For example, if the remainder is 2, the divisor is 6, and the quotient is 55, the complete quotient is written as 55 and 2/6, showing that the divisor cannot go into the remainder an integral number of times.

2-12.   Binary Division

Binary division is performed exactly the same way as decimal division. The only difference is that the binary multiplication table is used instead of the decimal table. To illustrate the use of the binary multiplication in division, we will solve the following problem:

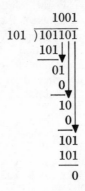

The divisor, 101, does not go into 1, or 10, but it does go into 101, which is the first three digits of the dividend. Dividing the 101 by the divisor, we obtain a simple quotient of 1. To see if there is a remainder, we multiply the divisor by the first simple quotient, and obtain a 101 which is written below the 101 of the dividend as shown. The remainder is 0, but we now have to consider the rest of the dividend. We bring down the 1 as shown by the arrow and divide it by 101. Since 101 will not go into 1 a whole number of times, we record a 0 in the quotient as shown. Next, we multiply the simple quotient, 0, and the divisor and obtain a product of 0. Subtracting 0 from 01, we obtain 1. The next digit in the dividend is then brought down to give us 10. Again, the divisor will not go into 10 a whole number of times; hence, another 0 is recorded in the quotient. Multiplying the divisor by the third simple quotient, 0, yields a product of 0. This product is subtracted from 10, and the difference is 10. Finally, we bring down the last digit in the dividend and obtain 101. The divisor goes into 101 one time. A 1 is, therefore, recorded as the fourth simple quotient in the quotient. Multiplying the divisor by the fourth simple quotient gives 101, which is subtracted from the remainder 101. The difference is the remainder of the problem and is 0. Since the dividend has now been completely accounted for, the complete quotient of the problem is 1001. You can check this result by multiplying the quotient by the divisor. The product should be the same quantity as the original dividend.

The following examples further illustrate binary division; the equivalent examples in the decimal system are given for comparison.

Example 2-32.

	Binary		*Decimal*

$$\begin{array}{r} 111 \\ 101 \overline{)100011} \\ 101 \\ \hline 111 \\ 101 \\ \hline 101 \\ 101 \\ \hline 0 \end{array} \qquad\qquad \begin{array}{r} 7 \\ 5 \overline{)35} \\ 35 \\ \hline 0 \end{array}$$

Example 2-33.

$$\begin{array}{r} 111 + 1/111 \\ 111 \overline{)110010} \\ 111 \\ \hline 1011 \\ 111 \\ \hline 1000 \\ 111 \\ \hline 1 \end{array} \qquad\qquad \begin{array}{r} 7 + 1/7 \\ 7 \overline{)50} \\ 49 \\ \hline 1 \end{array}$$

Example 2-34.

$$\begin{array}{r} 101 \\ 1010 \overline{)110010} \\ 1010 \\ \hline 101 \\ 0 \\ \hline 1010 \\ 1010 \\ \hline 0 \end{array} \qquad\qquad \begin{array}{r} 5 \\ 10 \overline{)50} \\ 50 \\ \hline 0 \end{array}$$

2-13. Octal Division

Octal division is performed in the same way as decimal and binary division. The simple octal quotients are found in the octal multiplication table in Table 2-6. In doing octal division, each arithmetic operation involved, multiplication and subtraction, must also be done in the octal system. As mentioned earlier, because of the similarity between the decimal and octal systems, there is a tendency to slip back into the decimal system. The result is an incorrect solution to the octal problem. The following examples illustrate octal division. Study the step-by-step solution to each problem carefully, and verify the simple quotients by referring to the octal multiplication table. The equivalent problems in the decimal system are given for comparison.

Example 2-35.

Octal	*Decimal*

$$
\begin{array}{r}
213 \\
76\ \overline{)20652} \\
174 \\
\overline{125} \\
76 \\
\overline{272} \\
272 \\
\overline{0}
\end{array}
\qquad
\begin{array}{r}
139 \\
62\ \overline{)8618} \\
62 \\
\overline{241} \\
186 \\
\overline{558} \\
558 \\
\overline{0}
\end{array}
$$

Example 2-36.

$$
\begin{array}{r}
756 \\
35\ \overline{)33766} \\
313 \\
\overline{246} \\
221 \\
\overline{256} \\
256 \\
\overline{0}
\end{array}
\qquad
\begin{array}{r}
494 \\
29\ \overline{)14326} \\
116 \\
\overline{272} \\
261 \\
\overline{116} \\
116 \\
\overline{0}
\end{array}
$$

Example 2-37.

$$
\begin{array}{r}
513 + 5/13 \\
13\ \overline{)7076} \\
67 \\
\overline{17} \\
13 \\
\overline{46} \\
41 \\
\overline{5}
\end{array}
\qquad
\begin{array}{r}
331 + 5/11 \\
11\ \overline{)3646} \\
33 \\
\overline{34} \\
33 \\
\overline{16} \\
11 \\
\overline{5}
\end{array}
$$

2-14. Problems

1. The problem, $5 + 16 + 39 = 60$ is given in the decimal system. Perform the equivalent addition in the binary and octal number systems.
2. Solve the following:
   (a) $(742)_8 - (247)_8$ (b) $(11100)_2 - (10001)_2$
   (c) $(6324)_{10} - (928)_{10}$ (d) $(056)_8 - (003)_8$
   (e) $(10101)_2 - (1111)_2$ (f) $(212)_3 - (121)_3$
3. Using the $R's$ complement, solve the following:
   (a) $(83)_{10} - (71)_{10}$ (b) $(995)_{10} - (463)_{10}$
   (c) $(1110)_2 - (1001)_2$ (d) $(1001)_2 - (0011)_2$
4. Using the $(R\text{-}1)'s$ complement, subtract the quantities in **Problem 3**.
5. Perform the following problems in multiplication:
   (a) $(22)_{10} \times (73)_{10}$ (b) $(22)_8 \times (73)_8$
   (c) $(1011)_2 \times (101)_2$ (d) $(111)_{10} \times (10)_{10}$
   (e) $(111)_8 \times (10)_8$ (f) $(111)_2 \times (10)_2$

6. Solve the following:
   (a) $(673)_8/(7)_8$ (b) $(3452)_8 \div (42)_8$
   (c) $(724)_8/(522)_8$ (d) $(1110)_2/(10)_2$
   (e) $(1010)_2/(110)_2$ (f) $(101)_2 \div (100)_2$

7. Does the addition of two quantities always result in a sum and a carry? Explain.

8. Construct an addition table for a number system that contains three digits: 0, 1, and 2. Construct a multiplication table for this system.

9. Upon what characteristic of the Arabic number system does the technique of borrowing depend? If a group of ten units is borrowed from the tens column, what is added to the units column?

10. Identify the operands associated with problems in addition, subtraction, multiplication, and division.

11. In your own words, explain the concept of complementation. What is the difference between the true complement and the radix-minus-one complement of a number.

12. What is the difference between finding the difference of two numbers using the R's complement and the $(R\text{-}1)$'s complement? Why does this dissimilarity exist?

13. When a number is raised to a given power, what arithmetic operation is employed?

14. The quotient of a certain problem in division is $5 \div 7/10$. What is the remainder? What is the divisor? The dividend?

15. Describe a good rule of thumb for estimating how many times the divisor will go into the dividend.

3

Fundamentals of Boolean Algebra

Boolean algebra, which is similar to conventional algebra in many respects, is a unique, self-contained mathematical system. Conventional algebra is a deductive mathematical system that deals almost exclusively with *quantitative* relationships whereas Boolean algebra is a similar system primarily concerned with *logical* relationships. In conventional algebra, symbolic quantities such as A, B, X, and Y are used to represent or express numerical problems written in common language. The symbolic representation of a problem is known as an algebraic expression, and, by manipulating such expressions in accordance with the rules of conventional algebra, it is possible to obtain a numerical solution to a problem. To illustrate the representation of numerical problems by conventional algebra, we can use this common-language problem: If the sum of two numbers is 30 and the difference of these numbers is 6, what are the two numbers? If we let X equal the larger number, and Y equal the smaller number, we can rewrite the common-language problem in its symbolic form:

$$X + Y = 30 \quad \text{and} \quad X - Y = 6$$

These algebraic expressions can now be operated on according to the rules of conventional algebra to determine the numerical values of X and Y. In Boolean algebra, which is an extremely simple algebra, symbolic representation is also used. As you will see in this chapter, the symbols in Boolean algebra represent logic quantities rather than numerical quantities; after a logic problem is represented by a Boolean expression, it is then manipulated according to the rules of Boolean algebra to obtain a logical solution.

3-1. Definitions and Postulates

Before any mathematical system can be developed, certain definitions and postulates must be established; upon this foundation, complex mathematical systems are derived. Since Boolean algebra is a mathematical system, it too has a set of basic definitions and postulates:

D-1. The objects, classes, or elements considered in Boolean algebra are called *variables,* and these variables are generally represented by alphabetical symbols. For example, if the objects under consideration are apples and bananas, an *A* could be used to designate the apples, and a *B* could be used to designate the bananas. Similarly, if a class of tall people and a class of rich people were under consideration, a *T* could represent all the tall people, and an *R* could represent all the rich people.

D-2. The entire collection or group of all the variables under consideration is defined as the *universe*, which, in general, is known as the universe *K*. A typical universe might contain only books and pencils; or you may have a universe of dogs, or a universe of cats.

D-3. To aid in solving problems in Boolean algebra, two ways of combining variables are defined: the first is addition, and the second is multiplication. Addition is indicated by the symbol "+", which in common language *is read* OR; and multiplication is indicated by the symbol "·" which *is read* AND in common language. The symbol "=" means that the variables or groups of variables it separates are identical quantities; that is, they can be substituted for each other without changing the value of the Boolean expression in which the substitution is made.

D-4. It is further defined that, in Boolean algebra, a variable can have only two possible values; these values are 1 and 0. Since we are not concerned with *quantitative* relationships, the 1 and the 0 must have some logical interpretation: a 1 means that a variable (or combination of variables) *exists* or *is present;* the 0 means that a variable (or group of variables) *does not exist* or *is absent*. In addition to having these logic meanings, 1 and 0 are also interpreted to mean *true* and *not true* (false), respectively.

D-5. A fundamental and unique concept in Boolean algebra is *negation* or the NOT function. The negation of a variable results in the opposite or the negative of the variable. For example, the negation of *A* is NOT *A*. Or in common language, the negation of *cold* is *not cold*. Negation is indicated in several ways, and two ways often found in literature are the prime (′) and the bar (−); e.g., $\bar{A}$ is NOT *A* and *A*′ is also NOT *A*. In this text, we will use the bar placed over the variable to indicate negation. Carrying the concept of negation a step further, we can see the effect of negation on the specific values of a variable. If a variable, *A*, has a value of 1, the negation of the variable, $\bar{A}$, has the value of 0. If another variable, *B*, has the value 0, the negation, $\bar{B}$, has a value 1. This is equivalent to saying that NOT 0 is equal to 1.

D-6. It was previously defined that a variable is an element under consideration that can have only two possible values or conditions, 0 or 1. In addition to this type of element, or variable, two other types of elements are defined. These are the *null* and *all* elements. The *null* element represents all the classes that *do not exist* in the universe *K;* hence, it always has the value of 0. The *all* element represents all the classes that *do exist* in the universe *K;* hence, this element always has the value 1. Because these special elements have only one value, they may be considered *constants* in the same respect as the constants in conventional algebra. The fact that the null and all elements have constant values of 0 and 1, respectively, induces many authors to use these values as symbols representing the null and all elements. This practice tends to be misleading so, to avoid confusion, the symbol I will be used here to represent the all elements whose value is 1, and the symbol ϕ will represent the null element whose value is 0.

Having established a set of definitions, we can now proceed to the postulates of Boolean algebra. (A postulate is a proposition or statement whose truth is taken for granted; that is, the truth of the proposition is intuitively accepted as being self-evident.)

P-1a. If a variable A is a member of the universe K and another variable B is also a member of K, then the combination $(A + B)$ is also a member of K.

P-1b. If a variable A is a member of the universe K, and another variable, B, is also a member of K, then the combination $(A \cdot B)$ is also a member of K.

P-2a. The combination by addition of any variable in the universe K with the null element is equivalent to the variable itself:

$$A + \phi = A$$

P-2b. The combination by multiplication of any variable in K with the *all* element is equivalent to the variable itself:

$$A \cdot I = A$$

P-3. The operations $(+)$ and $(\cdot)$ are distributive over each other. The Distributive Law of Combination is discussed later in this chapter.

P-4. The operations $(+)$ and $(\cdot)$ are commutative. The Commutative Law of Combination is discussed later in this chapter.

P-5. For every variable such as A in the universe K, there is a variable $\bar{A}$ in K such that $A + \bar{A} = I$ and $A \cdot \bar{A} = \phi$. Sometimes the truth of a Boolean statement is more obvious in the common-language form of the statement. The first statement, for instance, means it is always true that either A or $\bar{A}$ exists. Since either A or $\bar{A}$ always exists, $(A + \bar{A})$ is the same as the *all* element. The second statement means that both A and $\bar{A}$ can never exist at the same time. Since both A and $\bar{A}$ cannot both exist at the same time, $(A \cdot \bar{A})$ is the same as the *null* element.

3-2. Boolean Statements and Logic Blocks

There are three general types of Boolean statements. The first type is the OR statement, and it is formed by combining variables by logic addition. For example, $A + B$ and $A + B + C$ are OR statements. $A + B$ *is read* either A or B. (More correctly, the statement *is read* either A or B *or both.*) Usually, however, it is more convenient to simply read the statement: A or B. There is a special type of OR statement which is known as an *exclusive* OR statement and *is read* A or B *but not both.* There are several ways to indicate an exclusive OR, the most common being a circle around the OR sign as: $A \oplus B$.

The second type of Boolean statement is the AND statement which is formed by combining variables by logic multiplication. For example, $A \cdot B$ and $A \cdot B \cdot C$ are AND statements. An AND statement such as $A \cdot B$ means both A and B. For convenience, though, the word *both* is usually omitted and the statement *is simply read A and B*. In addition to omitting the word *both*, it is customary to eliminate the symbol of multiplication and to indicate the multiplication as AB, ABC, etc.

The third type of Boolean statement is the *mixed* statement which contains both AND and OR statements. An example of a mixed statement is: $AB + \bar{A}B + A\bar{B}$; and it *is read A and B, or not A and B, or A and not B*. In mixed statements, parentheses are frequently used to indicate logic multiplication. The need for parentheses is illustrated in this example: If we multiply A times $B + C$ without using parenthesis, the result *reads AB + C*, which means A and B, or C. The correct statement, $A(B + C)$, *reads A, and B or C*. By using parenthesis then, we have eliminated the possibility of misinterpreting the multiplication.

Boolean variables (A, B, C, etc.) are general symbols that can represent many different objects or quantities. For instance, A can represent a certain switch; when the switch is open, A has the value of 0, and when the switch is closed, A has the value, 1. A can also represent a voltage level; if a voltage is not present at a certain terminal, we can say that A has the value of 0. When a voltage is present at that terminal, A has the value, 1. We are primarily concerned with the use of Boolean variables to represent voltage levels, and with the application of Boolean statements to electronic circuits. However, before we can effectively examine specific circuits and arrange them so that they function *logically*, it is best to approach the application of Boolean algebra to electronic circuits by the use of *logic blocks*. A logic block is similar to the electronic *black box* which is defined to perform a specific function. In electronics, for instance, if a black box is defined as an amplifier, we know that the output signal will be larger than the input signal to the box. The function of a logic block is similar, except that the block takes its inputs of separate variables (or combinations of variables) and combines them in some defined manner so that the output is a Boolean statement. Suppose we have the logic block shown in Fig. 3-1. Then, suppose that, although we do not know what is inside the logic block, we do know that it combines the inputs by Boolean

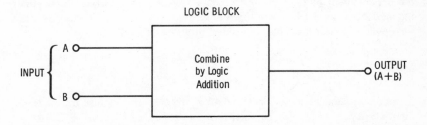

Fig. 3-1. A block diagram showing combination by logic addition.

addition. Hence, if the inputs are the variables A and B as shown in the figure, the output of the logic block is $A + B$. As you will see in a later chapter, this logic OR block is the symbol for an OR *gate*.

In the same way that a logic block is defined to combine inputs by Boolean addition, a block is also defined to combine inputs by Boolean multiplication. Such a block is shown in Fig. 3-2. In this figure, the inputs are the variables C and D, and the output of the logic block is CD. This logic AND block, as you will see, is the symbol for an AND *gate*.

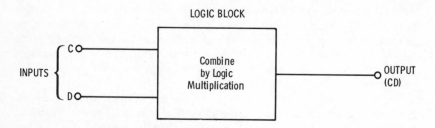

Fig. 3-2. A block diagram showing combination by logic multiplication.

If you examine the literature available on Boolean algebra, you would note that the shape of logic blocks differs from text to text. Some of the more common shapes are illustrated in Fig. 3-3. In this text, we will use the symbols shown in Fig. 3-3A as logic AND and OR blocks, respectively.

A logic block may have any number of inputs, depending, of course, on the number of variables in the universe K. Each block, however, has only one output. To illustrate the use of logic blocks, we will use the symbols in Fig. 3-3A to combine Boolean variables and produce the three general types of Boolean statements: AND, OR, and mixed AND and OR. The inputs to the logic AND block in Fig. 3-4A are the variables, A, B, and C. These variables (in electronic applications) usually represent voltage levels. The logic block combines them by multiplication and the output is the Boolean statement, ABC. In Fig. 3-4B, the logic block combines the same three variables by addition, and the output is the Boolean statement, $A + B + C$. A mixed statement may be generated in many different ways, depending on the arrangement of the AND and OR logic blocks. To illustrate three possible arrangements, let us write three different mixed statements and examine the combination of logic blocks needed to generate each statement.

Statement 1: $A(B + C) + BC$
Statement 2: $A(BC + A) + C$
Statement 3: $A + B + C(A + B)$

The combination of logic blocks needed to generate the first mixed statement is shown in Fig. 3-5. The first term of *Statement 1* is $A(B + C)$. Logic block 1 in the figure combines variables B and C and has an output of $(B + C)$. Block 2 has as its inputs, the output of block 1 and the variable

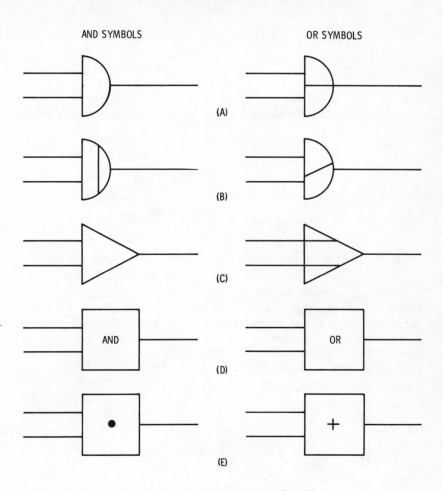

AND SYMBOLS   OR SYMBOLS

(A)

(B)

(C)

(D)

(E)

Fig. 3-3. Some commonly used logic block symbols.

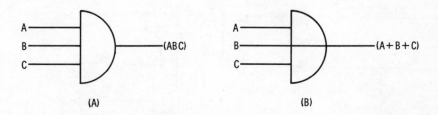

(A)   (B)

Fig. 3-4. (A) A logic block showing the combination of three variables by logic multiplication; and (B) a logic block showing the combination of three variables by logic addition.

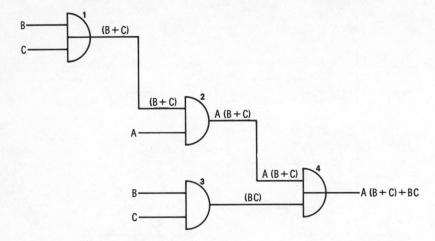

Fig. 3-5. Using logic blocks to generate a mixed Boolean statement: A(B + C) + BC.

A. This block combines its inputs by logic multiplication, and its output is $A(B + C)$. At this point, one term of the statement has been generated. The second term, BC, is generated by block **3**, which combines variables B and C by logic multiplication and has an output of BC. Now, the two terms of the statement have to be combined by logic addition; this is the function of block **4**. As shown in the figure, the inputs to block **4** are $A(B + C)$ and BC, and the output is *Statement 1:* $A(B + C) + BC$.

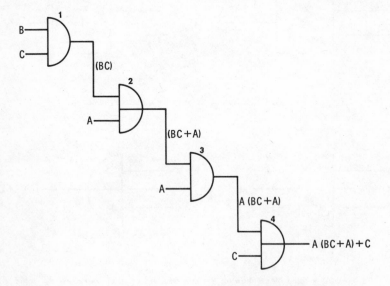

Fig. 3-6. Using logic blocks to generate the Boolean statement: A(BC + A) + C.

Figure 3-6 shows the combination of logic blocks needed to generate Boolean *Statement 2*. Again, the three variables are A, B, and C. Block **1** combines its inputs, B and C, by logic multiplication and has an output of BC. This output and the variable A are fed into block **2** which combines its inputs by logic addition. The output of block **2** is $(BC + A)$. The first term of Boolean *Statement 2* is generated by combining the output of block **2** and variable A by logic multiplication. This is done in block **3**, whose output is $A(BC + A)$. The second term of the statement is merely the variable C. This is fed into block **4** along with the output of block **3**, and the two inputs are combined by logic addition. The result is *Statement 2*: $A(BC + A) + C$.

Statement 3 is generated by the combination of logic blocks shown in Fig. 3-7. If you understood the explanation of the logic circuits in Figs. 3-5 and 3-6, you should be able to trace through this circuit quite easily

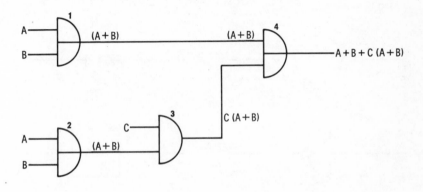

Fig. 3-7. Using logic blocks to generate the Boolean statement: $A + B + C(A + B)$.

to see how *Statement 3* is generated. Using Fig. 3-7, though, let us now see how a logic-block circuit operates from the viewpoint of the 0 and 1 values of the input variables. For the purpose of this discussion, let us assume that 0 means no voltage exists, and that 1 means a voltage exists. Further, let us say that A is 1, B is 1, and C is 0. With these assumptions in mind, we can examine Fig. 3-7. Blocks **1** and **2** generate an output voltage whenever A or B or both exist. Since we have assumed that A and B are 1, the outputs of blocks **1** and **2** are 1; and one of the inputs to blocks **3** and **4** is 1. Block **3** performs logic multiplication, and only produces an output voltage when both of its inputs exist, that is, the value of $(A + B)$ is 1 and the value of C is 1. We know that $(A + B)$ is 1, but we have previously assumed that C is 0. Therefore, the output voltage of block **3** does not exist: $C(A + B) = 0$. The inputs to block **4** are the outputs of blocks **1** and **3**. We have shown that $(A + B)$ is 1 and that $C(A + B)$ is 0; hence, only one input voltage is present at block **4**. But block **4** performs logic addition and will generate an output when either one of its inputs is present. The output of block **4**, hence of the entire circuit, exists: the value of $A + B + C(A + B)$ is 1.

For contrast, let us assume that A and B are 0, and that C is 1. We can tell by looking at the Boolean statement that the output of the logic-block circuit will not exist under these conditions because each term contains an A or a B or both of these variables: A is 0; B is 0; $C(A + B)$ is 0 because A and B are 0. But let us examine the circuit. Neither of the inputs to block **1** exist; therefore, this block has no output voltage. The same input and output conditions apply to block **2**. The $(A + B)$ input to block **3** does not exist, but the input, C, is present. Block **3**, however, performs logic multiplication, and only generates an output when all of its input voltages exist simultaneously. Since $(A + B)$ is 0, block **3** has no output voltage. The inputs to block **4** are the outputs of blocks **1** and **3**. These voltages do not exist, therefore, the output of block **4**, hence of the entire circuit, is 0.

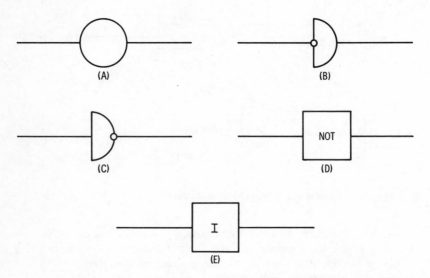

(A)

(B)

(C)

(D)

NOT

I

(E)

Fig. 3-8. Commonly used inverter or inhibitor symbols.

Earlier in this chapter, the concept of negation was introduced and defined. Since it is possible for the negation of a variable (or combination of variables) to exist in the universe K, it is necessary to have some device to generate negation. There are two ways in which negation is accomplished symbolically: one way is to have separate logic blocks that perform negation exclusively; another way is to modify an AND or OR block so that it can negate any of the variables at the input and then combine the negation(s) with the other inputs in the prescribed manner. Actually, both methods are frequently used. Figure 3-8 shows some of the logic blocks, which perform negation, that are found in the literature. We shall use the symbol shown in Fig. 3-8A. Logic blocks that perform negation are usually called *inhibitors* or *inverters*, and they have only one input and one output. The input to an inverter may be a single variable, a combination of variables, or a complete Boolean statement. The various methods of showing a modified AND or OR block found in the literature are shown in Fig. 3-9. The symbol shown in Fig. 3-9A and B will be used in this text. In these

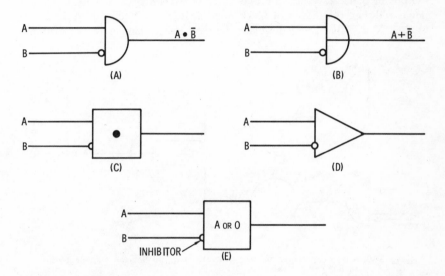

Fig. 3-9. Methods of modifying logic blocks to perform negation.

symbols, a small circle is drawn at the input of the block to show that the input variable is negated before it is combined with the other inputs. For example, suppose that there are two input variables to the block in Fig. 3-9B. If the input, B, is inhibited and then the two variables are combined by logic addition, the output of the OR block is $(A + \bar{B})$. Similarly, the block of Fig. 3-9A performs logic multiplication. Its output will be $A\bar{B}$.

Let us examine some logic circuits that can generate Boolean statements containing negation. We shall examine the circuits that can generate the following three statements:

Statement 1: $\bar{A}(B + \bar{C}) + \overline{BC}$
Statement 2: $\overline{(A + B)} + \bar{C}(A + B)$
Statement 3: $A(\bar{B}C + A) + \bar{C}$

Statement 1 contains the negation of two Boolean variables and one combination of variables; and it is generated by the combination of logic blocks shown in Fig. 3-10. Variables B and C are the inputs to block **1** which is modified to negate the variable C. The output of block **1** is $(B + \bar{C})$. This output is then combined with the variable A in block **2**;

this block is modified to negate the A before combining it with $(B + \bar{C})$. The output of block **2** is the first term of *Statement 1*, $\bar{A}(B + \bar{C})$. The second term of the statement is $\overline{BC}$. To generate this term, variables B and C are fed into block **3** and are combined by logic multiplication. The output of block **3** is BC and this combination of variables must be negated. The negation is accomplished by block **4** which is an inverter; the output of block **4** is $\overline{BC}$, and this output is then fed to block **5** along with the output of block **2**. When the two terms of *Statement 1* are combined by logic addition, the output of block **5** is the Boolean statement: $\bar{A}(B + \bar{C})$ $+ \overline{BC}$. Notice that this logic block diagram is very similar to the diagram

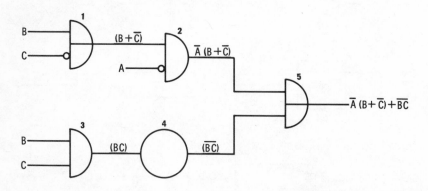

Fig. 3-10. A logic block diagram that generates a mixed Boolean statement containing negated variables.

in Fig. 3-5. Actually, *Statement 1,* and the statement generated by the circuit in Fig. 3-5 are identical except for the negation of some variables. It is reasonable, then, that the two logic block diagrams be similar, except for the addition of inverters and modification of some of the AND and OR logic blocks.

Boolean *Statement 2* is generated by the combination of logic blocks shown in Fig. 3-11. Combining variables A and B by logic addition in block **1** results in $(A + B)$. To produce the first term of the statement which is the negation of $(A + B)$, the output of block **1** is fed into the inverter, block **2**. In block **3**, variables A and B are again combined by logic addition to produce $(A + B)$. This time, however, it is not necessary to feed this OR statement into an inverter to produce a negation. The output of block **3** is fed into block **4** along with the variable C. The small circle indicates that C is negated before it is combined by logic multiplication with the other input to block **4**. The output of block **4** is the second term of *Statement 2;* and the complete statement is produced at the output of block **5** which combines the two terms by logic addition. As shown in the figure, the statement generated is: $\overline{(A + B)} + \bar{C}(A + B)$. Again, notice the similarity between the logic block diagrams of Figs. 3-7

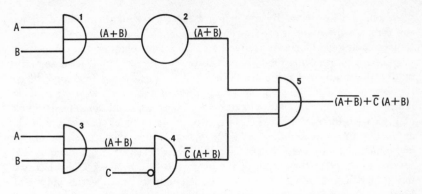

Fig. 3-11. The block diagram that generates the Boolean statement:
$(\overline{A + B}) + \overline{C}(A + B)$.

and 3-11, and realize that, except for the negations generated by the circuit in Fig. 3-11, the two circuits generate the same statement.

The combination of logic blocks needed to generate *Statement 3* is given in Fig. 3-12. This time, you try to trace through the block diagram to see how the statement is generated. Once more, notice the similarity between the diagrams in Figs. 3-6 and 3-12, and between the statements each produces.

After a logic block diagram has been set up to generate a Boolean statement, the next step is to design a circuit to replace the block diagram. It is necessary to design circuits that can perform logic addition, multi-

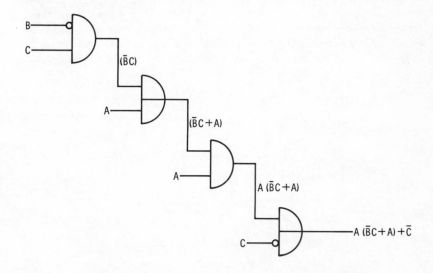

Fig. 3-12. The block diagram that generates the statement: $A(\overline{B}C + A) + \overline{C}$.

plication, and inversion. By examining a logic block diagram, the designer can estimate the number of electronic components that would be needed to replace each logic block. As you will learn in a later chapter, the component in question is usually a diode or transistor. A rule of thumb used for estimating the number of components required is: *Each input to a logic block requires its own component; every negation at the input of a logic block requires a component; the input to an inverter requires a component.* Look at Fig. 3-10, for example. There are two inputs to block **1**; and the circle at one of the inputs indicates one negation. Since there are two inputs and one negation, we can estimate that three electronic components are needed to generate the output of the block: $(B + \bar{C})$. Block **2** also has two inputs and again, one of the inputs is negated; to produce the output of block **2**, three more components are needed. So far, we have estimated that six components are required. Block **3** requires two components for its two inputs; and block **4**, the inverter, requires one component for its single input. Block **5** which generates the complete Boolean statement requires two components. The total number of components required to replace the logic block diagram in Fig. 3-10 is estimated to be eleven. This estimate can also be arrived at by examination of the Boolean statement instead of the logic block diagram that generates the statement. In the statement $\bar{A}(B + \bar{C}) + \overline{BC}$, the first term is composed of two parts: $\bar{A}$ and $(B + \bar{C})$. To generate $(B + \bar{C})$, three components are needed because there are two input variables and one negation. Then, A and $(B + \bar{C})$ become inputs, and the input A must be negated. This tells us that three more components are needed. The second term of the statement is $\overline{BC}$. B and C are input variables and require two components. The combination BC must be negated in an inverter, and for this we need another component. Finally, the two terms are inputs to a block that combines them by logic addition; therefore, two more components are used. The total number of components estimated by examining the statement itself is also eleven. The procedure for examining a statement is illustrated graphically in Fig. 3-13. The brackets

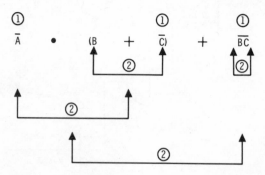

Fig. 3-13. The procedure used for estimating the number of components needed to generate a Boolean statement.

show which variables or combinations of variables are inputs to a logic block, and the encircled numbers accompanying the brackets indicate the number of components needed for each combination. The number of components required for the negation of variables or combinations of variables is also shown by encircled numbers. The Boolean statement used in this illustration is the same statement generated in Fig. 3-10. Review the preceding discussion on estimating the number of components required by examination of the Boolean statement, and refer to the illustration in Fig. 3-13 while doing so. You will then see how relatively simple the procedure is.

Since the same estimate of components can be made by examining either the Boolean statement or the corresponding logic block diagram, it is usually convenient to use the statement for this purpose, unless, of course, the block diagram has already been drawn for some other reason. You can check *Statements* 2 and 3, and Figs. 3-11 and 3-12, respectively, to see if you estimate the same number of components in both instances. Ten components are needed to generate both statements.

Determining the approximate number of electronic components needed to construct a logic circuit, has a very practical aspect. If a circuit is simple and is not used many times in the same system, the number of components in the circuit is not very critical. This, however, is usually not the case. Logic circuits, simple and complex, are generally used over and over again in a single system. If an unnecessary component is included in the original design of an individual circuit, there will be as many unnecessary components in the system as the number of times the circuit is used in the system. To keep the size and cost of electronic systems to a minimum, it is desirable to design logic circuits that will function properly using a minimum number of components. For example, look at the logic block diagram in Fig. 3-14A. This circuit requires only four electronic components, yet it functions exactly like the circuit requiring 25 components shown in Fig. 3-14B. The fact that these two circuits perform the same function is not a coincidence. In fact, by the use of Boolean algebra, it is possible to design relatively simple circuits to do the same job as more complex circuits. This is accomplished, as you will see in Chapter 4, by reducing Boolean statements to their simplest, equivalent form. For instance, the statements generated by the circuits in Fig. 3-14 are identical quantities, even though they look completely different: $AB\bar{C} + AC + \bar{A}B + \bar{A}B\bar{C} + \bar{A}\bar{B}C = \bar{A} + B + C$. After you learn the laws of combination in Boolean algebra, you will be able to simplify Boolean statements, and consequently, logic circuits, with considerable ease.

3-3. Laws of Combination

There are eight fundamental laws of combination in Boolean algebra; these are the laws of commutation, distribution, association, tautology, absorption, complementation and double complementation, and the laws of De Morgan. As these laws are explained, you will find that some of them are familiar to you from your experience with arithmetic and conventional

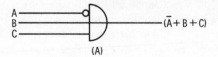

(A)

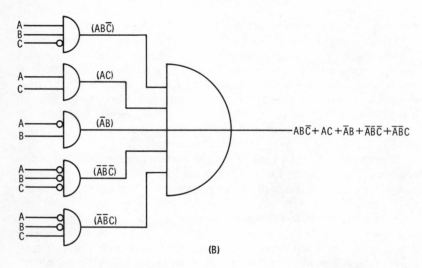

(B)

Fig. 3-14. A logical block diagram (A) after simplification and (B) before simplification.

algebra, and that some of them are very simple and seemingly obvious. Nevertheless, it is necessary to enumerate and explain each law as it applies in Boolean algebra to insure your complete understanding of the mathematical operations and simplifications.

Law of Commutation. By logical reasoning, we would agree that a verbal statement such as, the man is "old and wise" has the same meaning as the statement, the man is "wise and old." We would also agree that a statement such as, a man is "weak or strong" has the same meaning as the statement, a man is "strong or weak." These are two examples of the law of commutation which is generally identified as a concept of quantitative mathematics. Although this identification is justified, the application of the law of commutation is not confined to this one area; among its other areas of application is logic mathematics, or Boolean algebra. The law of commutation states: *The result of the addition or multiplication of any number of quantities is the same regardless of the order in which they are added or multiplied.* You know this to be true in arithmetic where problems like 2 + 4 and 4 + 2 are both equal to 6; and 5 × 6 and 6 × 5 are both equal to 30. We can see why Boolean addition and multiplication are commutative operations by considering the verbal statements at the beginning of this paragraph.

If we assign the Boolean symbol A to the word *old*, and B to the word *wise*, we can write the first two statements symbolically as the identity:

$$AB = BA$$

In the simplest terms, this identity consisting of Boolean multiplications *is read* "old and wise" has the same meaning as "wise and old". Because both sides of the identity have the same meaning regardless of the order in which the variables are multiplied, Boolean multiplication is commutative.

If we assign the Boolean symbol C to the word *weak*, and D to the word *strong*, the second two statements in the first paragraph can be written symbolically as the identity:

$$C + D = D + C$$

In the simplest terms, this identity consisting of Boolean additions *is read* "weak or strong" has the same meaning as "strong or weak." Since both sides of the identity have the same meaning regardless of the order in which the variables are added, Boolean addition is commutative.

Law of Distribution. If the sum of two or more quantities (multiplicand) is multiplied by another quantity (multiplier), the product is equal to the sum of the products obtained by multiplying each term of the multiplicand by the multiplier. Symbolically, this law is written: $A(B + C) = AB + AC$. The application of the Law of Distribution to arithmetic is in problems like $2 \times (3 + 4) = 2 \times 3 + 2 \times 4$. Both sides of this equation are equal to 14. We can show how the Law of Distribution applies in Boolean algebra by substituting verbal statements for each term in the equation. If we let A represent the word *fresh*, B represent the word *rye*, and C represent the word *white*, the left side of the equation would read, "fresh, and rye or white." According to the Law of Distribution, the right side of the equation would read "fresh and rye, or fresh and white." By logical reasoning, we would agree that the statement, "fresh, and rye or white" has the same meaning as the statement, "fresh and rye, or fresh and white."

The Law of Distribution is also given by the identity, $(A + B)(B + C) = B + AC$, where the quantity, $(A + B)$, is the multiplier, and the quantity, $(B + C)$, is the multiplicand. The distributive property of this identity is not apparent at first glance; however, it can be shown by operating on the equation by the rules of Boolean algebra. Since you are not yet familiar with enough of the Boolean manipulations, the proof of this identity will be shown in a later chapter (*see* Section 5-2).

Law of Association. Whenever several quantities are added or multiplied, the sum or product is the same regardless of how the quantities are grouped. For example, if several quantities are being added, the same sum is obtained when the first quantity is added to the second, and the third quantity is added to the sum of the first two, as when the second and third quantities are added, and the first quantity is then added to the sum of the last two. The same is true if the quantities are multiplied. Using Boolean symbols, we can use this problem as an example:

$$S = A + B + C$$

The sum, S, is the same whether the quantities are combined in this order:

$$S = (A + B) + C$$

or in this order:

$$S = A + (B + C)$$

If you substitute numbers into the two equations above, as in arithmetic, you will see that the sum is the same in both instances.

Law of Tautology. If a variable, or combination of variables, is added to, or multiplied by, itself, the result is the original variable or combination of variables. If a boy has a book or a book, no matter how you look at it, the boy has a book. This is the same as saying, $B + B = B$. If a piggy bank is full of pennies and pennies, no matter how you look at it, the bank is full of pennies. This is the same as saying, $P \cdot P = P$. This example and the preceding example seem to be just repetitious statements; in fact, the definition of tautology is *useless repetition*. The law of tautology, as stated earlier, applies in Boolean algebra regardless of the number of times a variable is used. For instance, $A + A + A + A + A + A = A$, or $A \cdot A \cdot A \cdot A \cdot A \cdot A = A$. It does not apply to the arithmetic or conventional algebraic operations of addition and multiplication. (The fact that 1×1 is equal to 1 is not necessarily a consequence of the law of tautology.)

Law of Absorption. This is another law of combination that is true for Boolean algebra and not for arithmetic or conventional algebra; and it is best introduced symbolically:

$$A + AB = A \quad \text{and} \quad A(A + B) = A$$

The symbols A and B, in these equations can be replaced by any other Boolean variable or combination of variables; only the form of the equations must be retained if they are to conform to the law of absorption. The proof of these equations is given in Section 4-4; however, the relationship between these two forms of the law of absorption is interesting and can be developed now. Since $A + AB$ and $A(A + B)$ are both equal to A, they are equal to each other:

$$A + AB = A(A + B)$$

If we multiply the two terms in the right side of the equation, we have:

$$A + AB = AA + AB$$

According to the law of tautology, $AA = A$; therefore,

$$A + AB = A + AB$$

Hence, the two symbolic forms of the law of absorption are one and the same.

Law of Complementation. The law of complementation is a more formal name for a concept to which you have already been introduced. This concept is negation, or complementation. It is logical that such a concept should exist in Boolean algebra. We would not bother to classify a person as being rich unless we were aware of the fact that not rich (poor) people also existed in the world. We wouldn't bother to classify an object as round if we didn't know that objects that are not round existed. In Boolean algebra, for every condition or variable that exists in the universe K, there is also an opposite condition or variable in the universe. For instance, if there are fat people in the universe, there are also not fat (skinny) people in the universe. If there is a happy person in the universe, there is also a not happy (unhappy) person in the universe. Symbolically, for every A, B, C, etc., in the universe K, there is a corresponding $\bar{A}$, $\bar{B}$, $\bar{C}$, etc., also in the universe. Two identities that are associated with the law of complementation are:

$$A + \bar{A} = I \quad \text{and} \quad A\bar{A} = \phi$$

The *all* element, I, is a quantity that always exists; and we can see that either A or $\bar{A}$ exists. The *null* element, ϕ, is a quantity that never exists in the universe; and we can see that A and $\bar{A}$ can never exist in the universe simultaneously.

Law of Double Complementation. Consider the verbal statement, "I do not have nothing." Juggling this idea around in your mind, you would quickly come to the conclusion that it means, "I have something." Now suppose someone said to you, "I am not unhappy." Ignoring his use of a double negative, you would immediately interpret the statement to mean, "I am happy." In Boolean algebra, the equivalent of this double negative in verbal statements is called double complementation; and it may be stated: *The negation of a negated variable, or group of variables, results in the original variable, or group of variables.* Symbolically, this law is written:

$$\bar{\bar{A}} = A \quad \text{or} \quad \overline{\overline{(A + B)}} = (A + B) \quad \text{or} \quad \overline{\overline{AB}} = AB$$

The Laws of De Morgan. Two of the most powerful laws in Boolean algebra are the laws of De Morgan for they often prove invaluable in finding the solution and simplification of Boolean equations. De Morgan's laws are usually stated symbolically as:

$$\overline{A \cdot B} = \bar{A} + \bar{B}$$

and

$$\overline{A + B} = \bar{A} \cdot \bar{B}$$

It is important to realize that the terms $\overline{A \cdot B}$ and $\bar{A} \cdot \bar{B}$ are not the same quantity; $\overline{A \cdot B}$ means, *not the quantity A* AND *B*, whereas $\bar{A} \cdot \bar{B}$ means not A AND not B. The logic of these two laws can be seen more readily when verbal statements are substituted for the Boolean symbols. If we let A represent *food*, and B, represent *money*, we can expand each term: if a man does *not* have *food* and *money*, then it must be true that he does *not* have *food or* that he does *not* have *money*. This statement illustrates the first law. If a man does *not* have either *food or money*, then it must be true that he does *not* have *food and* that he does *not* have *money*. This statement illustrates the second law of De Morgan. You will see just how useful these laws are in succeeding chapters where many of the Boolean simplifications rely on the laws of De Morgan.

3-4.   Summary of Boolean Identities

Throughout this chapter, you were introduced to many Boolean identities by way of the postulates, definitions, and laws of combination. (In other literature, these identities are often treated as theorems.) For convenience, the identities explained in the preceding sections are listed here in their most general forms. In addition to these identities, some additional and very helpful relationships are included. You can confirm the truth of any of the additional relationships with which you are not familiar by using the identities you learned in this chapter. You will notice that, instead of using A's, B's, C's etc., as we did in previous sections, all of the following identities are in terms of X and Y and Z. By doing this, we do not confine each relationship to be applicable to single variables. In other words, the X's, Y's and Z's do not represent only a single variable such as A, B, or C, but they may represent combinations of variables such as $(A + B)$, $(AB + CD)$, etc. It very often happens that a Boolean statement such as $\overline{AB}$ $+ \overline{AB}C$ can be simplified immediately to $\overline{AB}$ if you recognize that it is in the form of $X + XY = X$. Here, $\overline{AB}$ is represented by X, and C is represented by Y.

Your ability to manipulate Boolean equations will depend largely on your familiarity with these identities:

$X + 0 = X$ (ϕ is always 0) $X \cdot Y = Y \cdot X$

$X + 1 = 1$ (I is always 1) $X + (Y + Z) = (X + Y) + Z$

$X + X = X$ $X(Y \cdot Z) = (X \cdot Y)Z$

$X + \overline{X} = 1$ $X(Y + Z) = X \cdot Y + X \cdot Z$

$X \cdot 1 = X$ $X + X \cdot Y = X$

$X \cdot 0 = 0$ $X(X + Y) = X$

$X \cdot X = X$ $X + Y \cdot Z = (X + Y)(X + Z)$

$X \cdot \overline{X} = 0$ $X + \overline{X} \cdot Y = X + Y$

$X + Y = Y + X$ $\overline{X \cdot Y} = \overline{X} + \overline{Y}$

$\overline{\overline{X}} = X$ $\overline{X + Y} = \overline{X} \cdot \overline{Y}$

$X \cdot \overline{Y} + X \cdot Y = X$

3-5.   Problems

1. In the universe of horses, there are black horses, white horses, and brown horses. Represent each class of horses symbolically.

2. What is the primary difference between Boolean algebra and conventional algebra? How do addition and multiplication in these systems of algebra differ?

3. $T = A + \overline{B}$. If A is 1, and B is 0, what is the value of T?

4. Constants and variables exist in Boolean algebra as they do in conventional algebra. State some examples of Boolean constants and variables.

5. Write the verbal statements that are represented symbolically by:
   (a) $\overline{A} + A\overline{B} + \overline{A}B$ (b) $\overline{(A + B)}(A + \overline{C})$
   (c) $\overline{(A + B)} + \overline{A} \cdot \overline{B}$ (d) $B(A + C) + A\overline{C}$

6. Draw the logic block diagrams needed to generate the following Boolean statements:

   (a) $\overline{AB} + C(BC + A)$ (b) $(AC + B)(AB + C)$
   (c) $A\overline{B} + B\overline{C} + \overline{(A + B)}$ (d) $\overline{A}BC + A\overline{B}C + AB\overline{C} + \overline{A}B\overline{C}$

7. If A is 1, B is 0, and C is 1, what is the value of the output in each of the logic block diagrams in **Problem 6**?

8. Using two methods, estimate the number of electronic components needed to generate each of the Boolean statements in **Problem 6**.

9. Using X's, Y's, and Z's, restate the eight fundamental laws of combination in Boolean algebra.

10. Each of the following statements, given in terms of variables A, B, and C, is in the form of an identity. Determine the identity to which each statement corresponds by substituting X, Y, and Z for the appropriate variable or combination of variables.

    (a) $A\overline{B}\overline{C} + ABC$ (b) $(BC + A)(BC + AC)$
    (c) $BC + A\overline{B}\overline{C}$ (d) $\overline{A}(\overline{A} + BC)$

4

Visual Aids In Boolean Algebra

Venn and Veitch diagrams are visual devices that are used to explain the somewhat abstract concepts of Boolean algebra. It is often true, especially when dealing with abstract mathematical concepts, that visual aids tend to clarify these concepts. In conventional algebra, for example, the multiplication of X by itself is X^2. To represent this visually, all that has to be done is to let one side of a square be represented by X; consequently, the area of the square will be X^2. In this example, a visual device has been used to represent a mathematical concept. In a similar manner, the concepts of Boolean algebra can be visualized by the use of Venn and Veitch diagrams which are also geometrical figures.

4-1. Venn Diagrams

The Venn diagram derives its name from its originator, John Venn, who was a contemporary of George Boole. Primarily, Venn was a philosopher and logician. He endeavored to and succeeded in explaining the concepts of Boolean algebra by making use of geometrical areas to represent Boolean statements. In Venn diagrams, a universe is illustrated by a rectangular area. As was explained in Chapter 3, a universe is a totality in which a class of elements is encompassed. For example, the universe of colors is that universe that has all the colors in it.

In Fig. 4-1 is a universe represented by a rectangle. In this universe will be placed circles that will represent certain classes of people. All the classes of people placed in this universe will exist in this universe only. The sum of all the classes of people who exist in this universe is represented symbolically by I, which always has the value of 1. The symbol I (the *all* element) simply means that the sum of all the elements contained in the universe is the universe itself. Now, let the universe of people be subdivided into classes of people. First, let there be in the universe a class of small people, and let this class be represented by a circle. When this circle is placed into the rectangle, there will exist a circle and an area external to the circle but inside the rectangle. This is illustrated in Fig. 4-2.

Fig. 4-1. A rectangle which is used to represent a universe.

The shaded circle represents the class of small people, and the unshaded area inside the rectangle represents the class of people who are not small. Since the total rectangular area consists of the circle plus the area outside the circle but inside the rectangle, it follows that the area, S plus the area $\overline{S}$ is the total area of the universe. Therefore, by the use of the Venn diagram, we have shown that the Boolean statement, $S + \overline{S}$ is equal to I or 1.

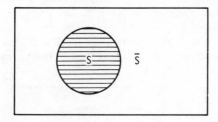

Fig. 4-2. In this universe, the shaded circle represents a class of small people; the unshaded area represents all the people who are not small.

All of the area outside the universe is void (does not exist) insofar as this universe is concerned; and it is represented symbolically by ϕ, which always has the value of 0. Recall that ϕ is the null element. Since the class of small people must be contained in the universe of people, it cannot be placed outside the universe. It follows, then, that a class of small people, and a nonexisting class of people (a class whose value is always 0) cannot exist. This observation tends to show visually why the Boolean statement, $S \cdot 0 = 0$, is true.

When the circle was placed inside the rectangle in Fig. 4-2, there occurred a superimposition of areas. In the Venn diagram, this superimposition of areas is equivalent to an AND statement in Boolean algebra. Furthermore, the superimposition of the areas in Fig. 4-2 is equivalent to the Boolean statement, S AND 1. It was stated in Chapter 3 that $S \cdot 1$ is equal to S. You can see in this figure that the area containing both S and 1 is entirely within the circle. Since the circle represents S, $S \cdot 1 = S$.

To show visually that the Boolean statement $S \cdot \overline{S} = 0$ requires imagination as well as a thorough understanding of what zero is. Zero means that something cannot exist; and the statement $S \cdot \overline{S} = 0$ tells us that a condition cannot exist that permits the area S to be superimposed on the area $\overline{S}$. You may think at first that this can be done by moving the circle to a new position. But if this is done, a new area of $\overline{S}$ is established; try as one may to superimpose these two areas, he will find, much to his dismay, that this cannot be done.

To show by the use of the Venn diagram that the Boolean statement, $S + 1$ is equal to 1 is not very difficult. This is an exercise that is left to the imagination of the reader.

4-2. Two-Variable Venn Diagrams

In the universe of people, we have placed a class of small people only. Let us now define a class of thin people, and designate this class by the letter T. Since there are now thin people in the universe, there are also people who are not thin (stout). These people are symbolized as $\overline{T}$. As was done for the class of small people, a circle shall be used to represent the class of thin people in the Venn diagram. To distinguish between the two circles, we have shaded the circle representing small people with horizontal lines, and the circle representing the thin people, with vertical lines. This is shown in Fig. 4-3.

In Fig. 4-3, the area that contains only horizontal lines is the area that represents *small* AND *not thin* people. This is true because all the area

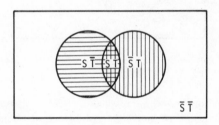

Fig. 4-3. A universe containing two classes of people: small and thin.

outside the circle representing thin people is the area that represents the not thin class of people. Some of this area overlaps the area representing the class of small people. Therefore, the area containing only horizontal lines is labeled $S\overline{T}$.

The area containing both horizontal and vertical lines represents the small and thin classes of people, ST. This is true because of the superimposition of the areas that represent these classes of people.

The area in Fig. 4-3 that contains only vertical lines represents the people who are thin and not small, $T\overline{S}$. This is true because all of the area outside the horizontally-lined circle represents not small people, and some of this area overlaps the circle representing the class of thin people.

The area of the rectangle that is completely external to both of the circles represents the people that are not small and not thin, $\overline{S}\overline{T}$. This area is all the area inside the rectangle that is not shaded.

4-3. De Morgan's Theorems Illustrated by the Venn Diagram

By the use of the Venn diagram, De Morgan's theorems can be shown visually. First, De Morgan's theorem stating that $\overline{(S + T)} = \overline{S} \cdot \overline{T}$ will be shown. As illustrated in Fig. 4-4, the area inside the circles is $S + T$. This area is NOT the area outside the circles. Since the area outside the circles is $\overline{S} \cdot \overline{T}$, $\overline{(S + T)} = \overline{S} \cdot \overline{T}$. Figure 4-4 is a simplification of Fig. 4-3 and it illustrates clearly the first of De Morgan's theorems.

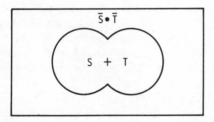

Fig. 4-4. A Venn diagram illustrating De Morgan's theorem, $\overline{S + T} = \overline{S} \cdot \overline{T}$.

The second of De Morgan's theorems states that $\overline{S \cdot T} = \overline{S} + \overline{T}$. This theorem is clearly illustrated by the Venn diagram shown in Fig. 4-5. The total area outside of the area representing S is $\overline{S}$; the total area outside of the area representing T is $\overline{T}$. The sum of these areas is $\overline{S}$ plus $\overline{T}$; and the area $\overline{S} + \overline{T}$ is outside the area labeled $S \cdot T$. You can see from Fig. 4-5 that the area that is NOT $S \cdot T$, $\overline{(ST)}$, is the area $\overline{S}$ plus $\overline{T}$; hence, we have shown with the aid of a Venn diagram that, $\overline{S \cdot T} = \overline{S} + \overline{T}$.

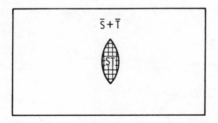

Fig. 4-5. A Venn diagram showing De Morgan's theorem, $\overline{S \cdot T} = \overline{S} + \overline{T}$.

4-4. Simplifying Boolean Statements by Venn Diagrams

There are essentially two important reasons for using Venn diagrams. The first, as you have seen, is that they help in visualizing the concepts of Boolean algebra; the second is that they show some of the manipulations of Boolean algebra. For example, the Boolean statement, $S\bar{T} + ST$, can be shown to be simply S. By the use of Boolean algebra, the steps in proving this are:

Step 1: $S\bar{T} + ST = S(\bar{T} + T)$ (Law of Distribution)

Step 2: $\bar{T} + T = 1$ (P-5)

Step 3: $S \cdot 1 = S$ (P-2b)

In the Venn diagram of Fig. 4-3, you can see immediately that the area $S\bar{T}$ plus the area ST is the total area that constitutes the original area, S. Thus, the Venn diagram has been used to show a simplification or manipulation of a Boolean statement.

The Boolean statement, $S + ST = S$, which you should recognize as the law of absorption, can easily be shown using a Venn diagram. In fact, this statement is very similar to the statement just discussed. Refer to Fig. 4-3 where you can see that the area ST is a part of the circle representing S. It is obvious in the figure that the area representing S plus the area ST is still the original area, S.

The two preceding statements are relatively simple when compared to a statement such as: $S\bar{T} + ST + \bar{S}T = S + T$. The proof of this statement involves extensive manipulation by Boolean algebra:

Step 1: $S\bar{T} + ST + \bar{S}T = S(\bar{T} + T) + \bar{S}T$ (Law of Distribution)

Step 2: $S(\bar{T} + T) + \bar{S}T = S + \bar{S}T$ (Law of Tautology)
$T + \bar{T} = 1$

Step 3: $S + \bar{S}T = \overline{\overline{S + \bar{S}T}}$ (Law of Double Complementation)

Step 4: $\overline{\overline{S + \bar{S}T}} = \overline{\bar{S} \cdot \overline{\bar{S}T}}$ (Law of Double Complementation and De Morgan's Theorem)

Step 5: $\overline{\bar{S} \cdot \overline{\bar{S}T}} = \overline{\bar{S}(\bar{\bar{S}} + \bar{T})}$ (De Morgan's Theorem)

Step 6: $\overline{\bar{S}(\bar{\bar{S}} + \bar{T})} = \overline{\bar{S}(S + \bar{T})}$ (Law of Double Complementation)

Step 7: $\overline{\bar{S}(S + \bar{T})} = \overline{\bar{S} \cdot \bar{T}}$ (Distribution and Complementation)

Step 8: $\overline{\bar{S} \cdot \bar{T}} = \bar{\bar{S}} + \bar{\bar{T}}$ (De Morgan's Theorem)

Step 9: $\bar{\bar{S}} + \bar{\bar{T}} = S + T$ (Law of Double Complementation)

Although this procedure is very systematical and logical, it is somewhat cumbersome. By inspection of Fig. 4-3, you can see that the sum of the areas that are represented by $S\bar{T}$, ST, and $\bar{S}T$ is the original area S plus the area T. You can see that, by the use of the Venn diagram, complex Boolean derivations can be easily visualized.

4-5. Three-Variable Venn Diagrams

A three-variable Venn diagram is shown in Fig. 4-6. We shall introduce as the third variable a class of people who are rich. The symbol we shall use to designate this class is R. Those people who are not rich shall,

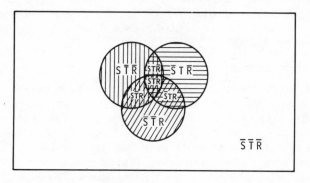

Fig. 4-6. A three-variable Venn diagram representing eight classes of people.

therefore, be symbolized by $\bar{R}$. Since there are now three classes of people, and since each class can either exist or not exist, there is a total of eight possible combinations of classes.

Combination	Description	Symbol
1	Small, Thin, and Rich	STR
2	Small, Thin, and not Rich	$ST\bar{R}$
3	Small, not Thin, and Rich	$S\bar{T}R$
4	Small, not Thin, and not Rich	$S\bar{T}\bar{R}$
5	Not Small, Thin, and Rich	$\bar{S}TR$
6	Not Small, Thin, and not Rich	$\bar{S}T\bar{R}$
7	Not Small, not Thin, and Rich	$\bar{S}\bar{T}R$
8	Not Small, not Thin, and not Rich	$\bar{S}\bar{T}\bar{R}$

In Fig. 4-6, the area that is shaded by only vertical lines represents the class of people who are small, not thin, and not rich. The area shaded with only horizontal lines represents the class of people who are not small, thin, and not rich. The area shaded by only slanted lines represents the class of people who are not small, not thin, and rich.

The area shaded with only horizontal and vertical lines represents the class of people who are small, thin, and not rich. The area shaded with only vertical and slanted lines represents the class of people who are small, not thin, and rich. The area that contains only horizontal and slanted lines represents the class of people who are not small, thin, and rich.

The area shaded with horizontal, vertical and slanted lines represents the small, thin, and rich class of people. Finally, the area that is completely external to the three shaded circles but that is still in the rectangle represents the not small, not thin, not rich class of people.

A three-variable Venn diagram, such as the one shown in Fig. 4-6, can be used to show many simplifications of Boolean algebra. For example, the original area S can be seen to be the sum of the areas $ST\bar{R}$ plus $ST\bar{R}$ plus STR plus $S\bar{T}R$. Similarly, the original area T can be seen to be the sum of the areas $\bar{S}T\bar{R}$, $\bar{S}TR$, STR, and $ST\bar{R}$. Also, the original area R can be seen to be the sum of the areas $\bar{S}\bar{T}R$, $S\bar{T}R$, STR, and $\bar{S}TR$. Many other simplifications can also be shown using Fig. 4-6; these, however, will be left to the imagination of the reader.

4-6. Veitch Diagrams

One of the shortcomings of Venn diagrams is that a Boolean statement containing more than three variables cannot be easily shown; that is, it is difficult to construct a Venn diagram for more than three variables. The Veitch diagram, which is similar to the Venn diagram, has the distinction of being easier to construct for more than three variables.

Like the Venn diagram, the Veitch diagram makes use of a rectangle, but it does not use any other geometrical figures. The rectangle in the Veitch diagram also represents the universe, and this universal rectangle is subdivided into smaller rectangles which represent the different classes that exist in the universe. The number of subdivisions depends, as you will see, on the number of variables being represented.

The simplest of the Veitch diagrams is the single-variable diagram such as illustrated in Fig. 4-7. In this figure, the rectangle is divided into two equals parts: the area at the left of the rectangle represents the variable,

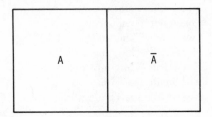

Fig. 4-7. A single-variable Veitch diagram is divided into two equal parts.

A, and the area at the right of the rectangle represents the negation of the variable, $\bar{A}$. Since the area of the rectangle representing the universe is the sum of A and $\bar{A}$, we have shown by the Veitch diagram that $A + \bar{A} = 1$.

To introduce another variable, B, a two-variable Veitch diagram must be constructed. Figure 4-8 shows the single-variable Veitch diagram for B. Notice that the rectangle is divided horizontally; this is done with the intention of superimposing this diagram over the diagram in Fig. 4-7. The superimposition of the two rectangles yields a two-variable Veitch diagram. The two-variable Veitch diagram, which consists of four rectangular areas, is shown in Fig. 4-9. Each area is the result of superimposing the two single-

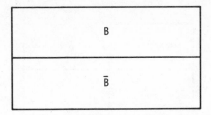

B		
$\bar{B}$		

Fig. 4-8. A single-variable Veitch diagram. The upper rectangular area is designated as B, and the lower area is $\bar{B}$.

	A	$\bar{A}$
B	A B	$\bar{A}$ B
$\bar{B}$	A $\bar{B}$	$\bar{A}$ $\bar{B}$

Fig. 4-9. A two-variable Veitch diagram is constructed by superimposing the diagram in Fig. 4-8 on that in Fig. 4-7.

variable diagrams. For example, the area designated as AB is the result of superimposing the area B in Fig. 4-8 on the area A in Fig. 4-7. As was explained previously, any superimposition yields an AND statement such as $A \cdot B$. The other areas in Fig. 4-9, $\bar{A}B$, $A\bar{B}$, and $\bar{A} \cdot \bar{B}$, are produced in like manner.

4-7. Simplifying Boolean Statements by Veitch Diagrams

Keeping in mind that the two-variable Veitch diagram in Fig. 4-9 was constructed by superimposing the single-variable Veitch diagrams for A and B, we can now show how the Veitch diagram is used for simplifying Boolean statements.

Let us take as our first statement, $AB + \bar{A}B = B$. In Fig. 4-9, the area consisting of AB plus $\bar{A}B$ is the area that was originally only B in Fig. 4-8. Thus, it has been shown that $AB + \bar{A}B = B$. The formal proof of this statement by Boolean algebra is shown quite simply. First, factor out the B: $B(A + \bar{A}) = B$. Since $A + \bar{A} = 1$, it follows that $AB + \bar{A}B = B$.

Notice that two rectangular areas were needed to show that $AB + \bar{A}B = B$. The process of "picking up" these two areas is referred to as *coupling*. In the last example, areas AB and $\bar{A}B$ were "picked up"; they are said to be *coupled*.

The concept of couples is illustrated in Fig. 4-10. The ovals shown between each two adjacent areas represent the couples that can be taken. For example, the areas AB and $\bar{A}B$ are coupled by the oval placed between

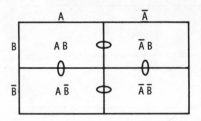

Fig. 4-10. A two-variable Veitch diagram that illustrates the concept of "couples."

them. Similarly, the area AB is coupled to $A\bar{B}$; $A\bar{B}$ is coupled to $\bar{A} \cdot \bar{B}$; and $\bar{A} \cdot \bar{B}$ is coupled to $\bar{A}B$. Only areas that are horizontally or vertically adjacent can be coupled; it is not correct to couple areas that are diagonally positioned such as areas $\bar{A}B$ and $A\bar{B}$. The reason for this is that two areas can be combined or coupled only if they give back the original area when they are combined. For example, when area $A\bar{B}$ is coupled with AB, their sum will yield the original area A. Observe, however, that the summing of the diagonal areas $\bar{A}B$ and $A\bar{B}$ does not yield any of the original areas.

Figure 4-11 illustrates one of De Morgan's theorems: $\overline{A + B} = \bar{A} \cdot \bar{B}$. The shaded area consists of the area A plus the area B, or $A + B$. (This can be more clearly seen by referring to Figs. 4-7 and 4-8.) However, this area

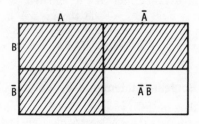

Fig. 4-11. The use of a Veitch diagram to illustrate De Morgan's theorem, $\overline{A + B} = \bar{A} \cdot \bar{B}$.

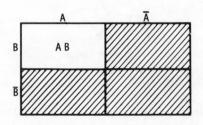

Fig. 4-12. This Veitch diagram illustrates De Morgan's theorem, $\overline{A \cdot B} = \bar{A} + \bar{B}$.

is *not* the unshaded area, $\overline{A} \cdot \overline{B}$. Therefore, by the use of the Veitch diagram, De Morgan's theorem, $\overline{A + B} = \overline{A} \cdot \overline{B}$, has been proved.

The second of De Morgan's theorems, $\overline{A} + \overline{B} = \overline{A \cdot B}$, is illustrated in Fig. 4-12. The shaded area represents the sum of the areas $\overline{A}$ and $\overline{B}$; the unshaded area is the area AB. Since the unshaded area is *not* the shaded area, $\overline{A} + \overline{B} = \overline{A \cdot B}$.

4-8. Three-Variable Veitch Diagrams

The three single-variable Veitch diagrams that are superimposed to form a three-variable Veitch diagram are shown in Fig. 4-13. The diagrams for A and B have already been discussed. The diagram for the third vari-

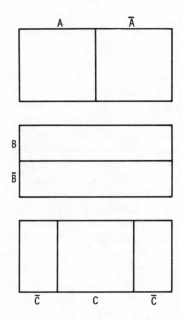

Fig. 4-13. The basis of a three-variable Veitch diagram.

able, C, is constructed in the same way as the diagram for the variable, A, except that the area for $\overline{C}$ is divided into two parts as shown in the figure. This must be done because there are eight combinations that can exist when three variables are used. By dividing the area for $\overline{C}$ in the manner shown, we can represent all eight combinations in the three-variable Veitch diagram. Figure 4-14 shows a three-variable Veitch diagram. This diagram, which contains eight areas representing the eight combinations of variables, is obtained by superimposing the single-variable diagram for C over the two-variable diagram for A and B.

The concept of coupling for a three-variable Veitch diagram is the same as that for a two-variable Veitch diagram. However, because $\overline{C}$ is posi-

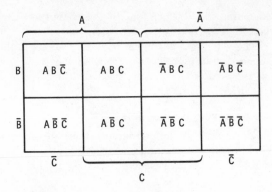

Fig. 4-14. A three-variable Veitch diagram showing all of the eight possible combinations.

tioned at the extreme right and left sides of the diagram, it is possible to couple at the ends of the diagram as shown in Fig. 4-15. In this figure, for example, the upper corners (and the lower corners) are coupled. Couple **1** embraces the areas $AB\overline{C}$ and $\overline{A}B\overline{C}$. Using formal Boolean algebra, we can simplify the Boolean statement, $AB\overline{C} + \overline{A}B\overline{C}$, represented by these areas. Factoring the quantity $B\overline{C}$, we obtain: $AB\overline{C} + \overline{A}B\overline{C} = B\overline{C}(A + \overline{A})$. Since $A + \overline{A} = 1$, the term on the right side of the equation is simply $B\overline{C}$. Thus, the statement, $AB\overline{C} + \overline{A}B\overline{C}$, given by couple **1**, is independent of the variable, A. This can also be observed in Fig. 4-15: the areas taken in by couple **1** lie in the horizontal section of the universal rectangle that represents B, but not $\overline{B}$; these areas also lie completely in the vertical section of the universal rectangle that represents $\overline{C}$, but not C. However, the two areas of couple **1** lie partially in the section representing A, and partially in the section representing $\overline{A}$; hence, the couple is independent of the variable A. We can conclude, therefore, that the couple consists of the original area, B, superimposed upon the original area, $\overline{C}$.

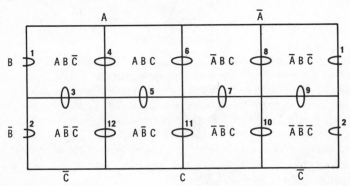

Fig. 4-15. A three-variable Veitch diagram showing all the possible couples that can be made.

The two lower corners in Fig. 4-15 are also coupled; and they represent the areas $A \cdot \bar{B} \cdot \bar{C}$ and $\bar{A} \cdot \bar{B} \cdot \bar{C}$. It can be observed that this couple is also independent of the variable, A, because the couple lies partially in the section of the universal rectangle representing A, and partially in the section representing $\bar{A}$. Since the two lower corners do not both contain either A or $\bar{A}$, the couple is independent of A.

All of the possible couples that can be made on a three-variable Veitch diagram are shown in Fig. 4-15. Couples 1 and 2 have already been explained. The areas contained in couple 3 are the original area, A and $\bar{C}$. Furthermore, these coupled areas are independent of the variable B: as you can see in the figure, one of the coupled areas contains B, and the other contains $\bar{B}$. That couple 3 is independent of B can also be proved by Boolean algebra. The Boolean statement represented by couple 3 is $A \cdot B \cdot \bar{C} + A \cdot \bar{B} \cdot \bar{C}$. Factoring the quantity, $A\bar{C}$ gives, $A\bar{C}(B + \bar{B})$. Since $(B + \bar{B})$ is 1, $A \cdot B \cdot \bar{C} + A \cdot \bar{B} \cdot \bar{C} = A\bar{C}$.

Couple 4, which represents the Boolean statement $AB\bar{C} + ABC$, can be simplified to AB. Again, this is true because the two areas in the couple consist of the original area B superimposed on the original area A. Couple 4 is independent of the variable C because in area $AB\bar{C}$, $\bar{C}$ exists and in the other area, ABC, the variable C exists.

Couple 5 consists of the original area C superimposed on the area A. This couple is independent of the variable B because B exists in one of the coupled areas while $\bar{B}$ exists in the other. The Boolean statement, $ABC + A\bar{B}C$, represented by couple 5 can be simplified to AC.

Using the same reasoning, we can simplify the remaining couples into the following original quantities:

Couple	Boolean Statement	Simplification
6	$ABC + \bar{A}BC$	BC
7	$\bar{A}BC + \bar{A}\bar{B}C$	$\bar{A}C$
8	$\bar{A}BC + \bar{A}B\bar{C}$	$\bar{A}B$
9	$\bar{A}B\bar{C} + \bar{A}\bar{B}\bar{C}$	$\bar{A}\bar{C}$
10	$\bar{A}\bar{B}C + \bar{A}\bar{B}\bar{C}$	$\bar{A}\bar{B}$
11	$A\bar{B}C + \bar{A}\bar{B}C$	$\bar{B}C$
12	$A\bar{B}\bar{C} + \bar{A}\bar{B}\bar{C}$	$\bar{A}\bar{B}$

Veitch diagrams are not limited to couples of two areas only. As shown in Fig. 4-16, the sum, or couple of four areas yields an original variable. For example, the sum of areas $AB\bar{C}$, ABC, $\bar{A}BC$, and $\bar{A}B\bar{C}$ is the original area, B. In this figure, this summation is indicated by the elongated oval labeled 1. This simplification can also be obtained using Boolean algebra: $AB\bar{C} + ABC + \bar{A}BC + \bar{A}B\bar{C} = AB(C + \bar{C}) + \bar{A}B(C + \bar{C}) = AB + \bar{A}B = B(A + \bar{A}) = B$. In the same manner, it can be shown that the other groups of four areas in the figure yield the following original areas:

Sum	Boolean Statement	Simplification
2	$A\bar{B}\bar{C} + A\bar{B}C + \bar{A}\bar{B}C + \bar{A}\bar{B}\bar{C}$	$\bar{B}$
3	$AB\bar{C} + \bar{A}B\bar{C} + A\bar{B}\bar{C} + \bar{A}\bar{B}\bar{C}$	$\bar{C}$

Sum	Boolean Statement	Simplification
4	$AB\bar{C} + ABC + A\bar{B}\bar{C} + A\bar{B}C$	A
5	$ABC + \bar{A}BC + A\bar{B}C + \bar{A}\bar{B}C$	C
6	$\bar{A}BC + \bar{A}B\bar{C} + \bar{A}\bar{B}C + \bar{A}\bar{B}\bar{C}$	$\bar{A}$

By understanding, using, and mastering Veitch diagrams, you can avoid many unnecessary steps in simplifying Boolean statements. Also, the simplest form of a Boolean statement can be easily obtained by using a Veitch diagram. For instance, the simplest form of the statement, $AB\bar{C} + ABC + \bar{A}BC + \bar{A}B\bar{C} + A\bar{B}\bar{C} + A\bar{B}C$, is $A + B$. This can be seen at a glance in Fig. 4-15 where the sum of these areas give the original area, $A + B$.

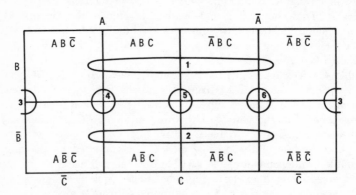

Fig. 4-16. Each sum of four areas yields an original variable. As shown, there are six possible sums.

4-9. Four-Variable Veitch Diagrams

Before we can construct a four-variable Veitch diagram, a fourth variable must be introduced. Let this variable be D. Since there are now four variables, there are sixteen possible combinations, and to construct a Veitch diagram with sixteen possible combinations, the single-variable Veitch diagram for D must be divided as shown in Fig. 4-17. This figure also shows the other single-variable diagrams of which the four-variable Veitch diagram is composed. When these rectangles are superimposed on each other, the result is a diagram that gives all the possible combinations of the four variables as illustrated in Fig. 4-18.

Figure 4-18 can very easily be used to show the simplications of Boolean statements. For example, the eight areas at the left of the diagram comprise a total area that was originally the area A. You can see, therefore, that these eight areas, $AB\bar{C}\bar{D}$, $ABC\bar{D}$, $AB\bar{C}D$, $ABCD$, $A\bar{B}\bar{C}D$, $A\bar{B}CD$, $A\bar{B}\bar{C}\bar{D}$, and $A\bar{B}C\bar{D}$, when summed together, are equal to A. This simplification can be obtained by using Boolean algebra, but it is much easier to use the Veitch diagram. The formal proof is $AB\bar{C}\bar{D} + ABC\bar{D} + AB\bar{C}D + ABCD + A\bar{B}\bar{C}D + A\bar{B}CD + A\bar{B}\bar{C}\bar{D} + A\bar{B}C\bar{D} = AB\bar{D} + ABD + A\bar{B}D + A\bar{B}\bar{D} = AB + A\bar{B} = A(B + \bar{B}) = A$.

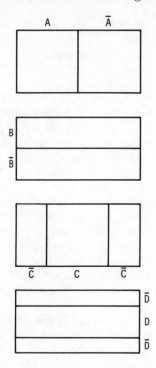

Fig. 4-17. The basis for constructing a four-variable Veitch diagram.

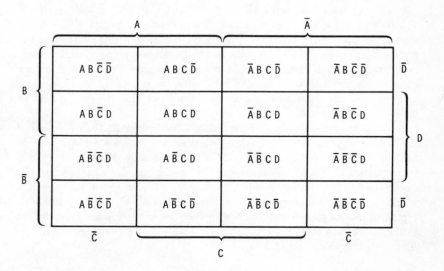

Fig. 4-18. A four-variable Veitch diagram showing all of the 16 possible combinations.

Now consider the eight areas at the right of the diagram in Fig. 4-18. These areas comprise the original area, $\bar{A}$. Consequently, if all these eight areas are summed up, they will yield the original area, $\bar{A}$. If the upper eight areas are summed up, they will result in the original area, B. If the lower eight areas are summed up, they will give the original area, $\bar{B}$. Again, these simplifications can be obtained by using Boolean algebra, but notice how simple it is when the Veitch diagram is used.

The sum of the four upper left areas in Fig. 4-18 is the original area, AB. This is true because this area is simply the overlap of area B on area A. Similarly, the sum of the upper four right areas is the original area, $\bar{A}B$. The lower left four areas yield the area $A\bar{B}$; and the lower right four areas yield the area $\bar{A}\bar{B}$.

The concept of coupling is also used very effectively for the four-variable Veitch diagram. By coupling the upper left two rectangles, for example, $AB\bar{C}\bar{D}$ and $ABC\bar{D}$ result in $AB\bar{D}$. Notice that in one of these rectangles, the area C exists, while in the other, $\bar{C}$ exists. Because of this, the sum of the two rectangles is independent of the variable C. Also, if the upper right two rectangles, $\bar{A}BC\bar{D}$ and $\bar{A}B\bar{C}\bar{D}$, are summed together, the resulting simplest form is $\bar{A}B\bar{D}$. You can see this by inspecting the four-variable Veitch diagram of Fig. 4-18.

A couple can be made by joining the upper two outer areas, $AB\bar{C}\bar{D}$ and $\bar{A}B\bar{C}\bar{D}$. This couple yields the simpest form, $B\bar{C}\bar{D}$. These two areas, as you can see, are independent of the variable A. As another example, the areas, $\bar{A}BC\bar{D}$ and $\bar{A}B\bar{C}\bar{D}$, can be coupled to give the result, $\bar{A}C\bar{D}$. You can see from the figure that the two areas in this couple are independent of the variable B.

For the Boolean statement, $AB\bar{C}\bar{D} + ABC\bar{D} + \bar{A}BCD + \bar{A}\bar{B}CD + \bar{A}\bar{B}C\bar{D}$, what is the simplest form? The first two quantities of this statement are represented by the two uppermost left areas in Fig. 4-18, and the remaining four quantities are represented by the four areas in the lower right corner of the diagram. Using the four-variable Veitch diagram, we can simplify the first two quantities into $AB\bar{D}$; the remaining four quantities simplify into $\bar{A}B$. Therefore, the simplest form for this Boolean statement is $AB\bar{D} + \bar{A}B$.

Another example of how four-variable Veitch diagrams can be used is the visual simplification of Boolean statements. For instance, the simplification of $A\bar{B}\bar{C}D + A\bar{B}\bar{C}\bar{D} + \bar{A}\bar{B}\bar{C}D + \bar{A}\bar{B}\bar{C}\bar{D}$ can be determined directly by inspection of the Veitch diagram. The four rectangles representing this statement are located in the lower right and left corners of the diagram. These rectangles are composed from the original areas $\bar{B}$ and $\bar{C}$, and they represent the simplest form, $\bar{B}\bar{C}$. Notice that the four areas are independent of the variables A and D; the simplest Boolean statement represented by the four areas is independent of A and D.

4-10. Five-Variable Veitch Diagrams

The basis for a five-variable Veitch diagram is shown in Fig. 4-19.

The fifth variable, E, is represented by a rectangle divided in such a way that when it is superimposed upon the other four diagrams, all of the 32 possible combinations of the five variables are represented. The rectangle for E is subdivided so that it does not exactly overlap the rectangle for the variable C. Needless to say, if both rectangles were subdivided identically, all of the 32 combinations would not be had. It is immaterial

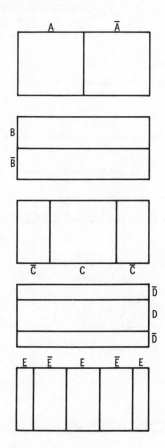

Fig. 4-19. The basis for constructing a five-variable Veitch diagram.

whether the rectangle for E is divided horizontally or vertically. If it is divided horizontally, the same technique is used, but the rectangle would be divided so that it is not identical to the rectangle for the variable D.

For convenience, the 32 combinations are numbered in Fig. 4-20. If we were to write the table for a five-variable diagram, beginning with $ABCDE$ and ending with $\bar{A}\bar{B}D\bar{C}\bar{E}$, then the table would be the same as the numbers in Fig. 4-20.

It was mentioned earlier that the main function of Veitch diagrams is to illustrate the concepts of simplification of Boolean statements. If a Boolean statement consisted of the sum of the combinations numbered from **1** to **8** in Fig. 4-20, the simplest form of that statement would be *AB*. This is true because, when these eight areas are summed together, they yield the original area that results from superimposing the area *B* on that of *A*. It is true, of course, that the same conclusion can be reached by using Boolean algebra; but it is so much easier to obtain the simplification from the Veitch diagram by inspection.

As another example, assume that the combinations numbered **1, 3, 17** and **19** in Fig. 4-20 are summed together. What is the simplest Boolean statement? Again referring to the figure, you can see that the simplest statement is *BCE*, and that these four areas are independent of the variables

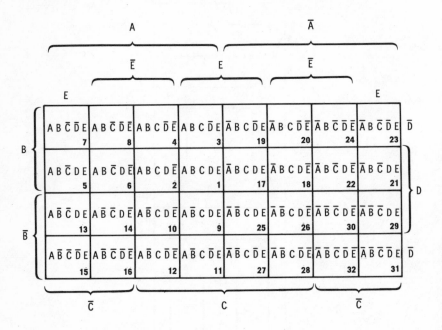

Fig. 4-20. A five-variable Veitch diagram showing all of the 32 possible combinations.

A and *D*. The reason that the simplest form is *BCE* is that two of the four areas contain the variable *A*, and the other two areas contain $\bar{A}$. Also, two of these areas contain *D*, while the other two contain $\bar{D}$. You have seen over and over again that, whenever any area contains both the quantity and not the quantity, the statement represented by the area is independent of the quantity (variable).

From Fig. 4-20, the following observations can be made:

1. Whenever a couple is picked up, one of the variables can be eliminated. An example of this is the couple consisting of the areas labeled

1 and **2**. The simplest form of the statement represented by these areas is *ABCD* because the couple is independent of the variable *E*.

2. Whenever four adjacent areas are summed together, the simplest statement will be a three-variable AND statement. For example, assume that the areas labeled **3**, **4**, **8**, and **7** are summed together. For these areas, the simplest statement is $AB\overline{D}$.

3. Whenever eight adjacent areas are summed together, the simplest statement will be a two-variable AND statement. For example, assume that the areas numbered from **1** through **8** are summed together. The simplest statement for these areas is *AB*.

4. Whenever 16 adjacent areas are summed up, the resulting simplest statement will contain only one variable. For example, assume that the areas **1** through **16** are summed. For these, the resulting simplest statement is *A*.

5. Whenever combinations that are *not* all adjacent are summed together, the resulting statement will be a mixed statement, i.e., a statement that contains both AND and OR statements. For example, assume that the areas labeled **5** and **6** as well as those labeled **9** and **10** were summed up. For areas **5** and **6**, the simplest statement is $AB\overline{C}D$; and for **9** and **10**, the simplest statement is $A\overline{B}CD$. The complete Boolean statement for the four areas is $AB\overline{C}D + A\overline{B}CD = AD(B\overline{C} + \overline{B}C)$.

4-11. Summary

Venn and Veitch diagrams are devices that help explain and visualize the somewhat abstract concepts of Boolean algebra. Venn diagrams are mostly useful for explaining how Boolean statements can be simplified; they are well-suited for simplifying two- and three-variable statements, but they are difficult to construct when four or more variables are encountered. Veitch diagrams are also useful for explaining how Boolean statements can be simplified; however, they are well-suited for simplifying statements containing two, three or more variables. For the most part, Veitch diagrams are used more extensively than Venn diagrams.

Venn and Veitch diagrams, when studied thoroughly, can help one to visualize and simplify Boolean statements much faster than by using conventional Boolean algebra. It is strongly recommended that when a Boolean statement is given in conventional Boolean form, a Veitch diagram be drawn; the Veitch diagram usually shows immediately whether or not the given Boolean statement can be simplified; and if it can be simplified, the diagram shows what the simplest statement is.

4-12. Problems

1. What geometric figure is used to represent the universe in Venn diagrams? In Veitch diagrams? How are the variables represented in Venn diagrams? In Veitch diagrams?

2. Explain the *null* element and the *all* element in terms of Venn and Veitch diagrams.

3. How is a two-variable Venn diagram constructed? What is the practical limit to the number of variables easily represented in a Venn diagram?

4. The Venn diagram in Fig. 4-6 represents the universe of people. Name five or six universes of other elements.

5. Using the Venn diagram, show that the following identities are true:
   (a) $X + XY = X$ (b) $X(X + Y) = X$
   (c) $X + \overline{X}Y = X + Y$ (d) $X \cdot 0 = 0$

6. What is the advantage of a Veitch diagram over a Venn diagram? Can the same conclusions be reached using either diagram, or does each diagram perform a different function?

7. How are multivariable Veitch diagrams constructed? What happens if two single-variable Veitch diagrams used to construct a multivariable Veitch diagram are subdivided in the same way?

8. In your own words, explain the process of coupling. How are couples indicated on a Veitch diagram?

9. Which areas in a Veitch diagram can be simplified by coupling? Which areas cannot be simplified by coupling?

10. How many combinations exist in a two-variable Veitch diagram? In a three-, four-, and five-variable Veitch diagram?

11. Construct a six-variable diagram. Use F as the sixth variable and construct the single-variable Veitch diagram for F so that the rectangle is divided horizontally.

12. For a couple to be independent of the variable A, what variables *must* the terms of the couple contain?

13. What is the result of summing areas **17** through **32** in Fig. 4-20? Write the Boolean statement that is represented by these areas.

14. In Fig. 4-20, write the Boolean statement represented by areas:
    (a) **5, 2, 6, 1**   (b) **22, 23, 26, 27**
    (c) **31, 32**   (d) **9, 10, 25, 26**
    (e) **21, 29**   (f) **6, 7, 10, 11, 25**

15. Which of the combinations in **Problem 15** can be simplified? Why can't the remaining problems be simplified?

16. Simplify the following Boolean statements using a Veitch diagram:
    (a) $A\overline{B}\overline{C} + ABC$ (b) $(BC + A)(BC + AC)$
    (c) $AB\overline{C}DE + \overline{A}B\overline{C}DE + \overline{C}(\overline{ABDE})$ (d) $ABC + \overline{A}BC + A\overline{B}C$
                                                       $+ \overline{A}\overline{B}C$

    (e) $BC + (\overline{BC})(A\overline{B}C)$ (f) $AC + \overline{A}B + AB\overline{C}$
                                                         $+ \overline{A}B\overline{C} + \overline{A}\overline{B}C$

5

Truth Tables and Designation Numbers

In the previous chapters, the basic concepts of Boolean algebra, and Venn and Veitch Diagrams were discussed. We saw how simple, everyday concepts can be put into a logical algebraic form.

In this chapter, we will show how it is possible to develop tables which will aid in telling us whether Boolean statements are either true or false. Also, we will show how to write Boolean statements from truth tables, and what designation numbers are. Finally, we will show how designation numbers are used to write and simplify Boolean statements.

5-1. The Development of a Truth Table

What is a truth table? A truth table is a systematical tabulation of statements that are given in the original argument, and the confirming or the denying of the *truth* of these statements. In a truth table, all possible combinations of the truth of statements are explored, and then the confirming or the denying of the truth of these statements is shown.

As a simple example of a development of a truth table, let us use the concept of the logic AND statement. As was explained in Chapter 3, an AND statement is one that has a number of variables, and which occurs only when all of the variables exist at the same time. If, for example, X and Y are the two variables under discussion, then the truth of the AND statement will occur when both X and Y exist. Let us assume that the variable X can either exist or not exist. The symbol that we shall use for the fact that X exists will be a 1, and the symbol we shall use for the fact that it doesn't exist shall be a 0. In like manner, let us assume that the variable Y can either exist or not exist, and let 1 be the symbol for when it exists and 0 be the symbol for when it doesn't exist. Now that we have the original statement and the symbols that are to be used for the existence and the non-existence of this statement, let us develop the truth table.

Since there are only two variables, X and Y, and since further these variables can either exist or not exist, then there can be only four combinations that must be considered. The first of these combinations is that both X and Y do not exist. The second is that X exists and Y does not exist. The third is that X does not exist and Y does exist. And the fourth is that both X and Y exist. The tabulation of the combinations that were just discussed is given in Table 5-1. In this table, the variable X is placed in the upper left-hand corner, and the variable Y is placed in the lower left-hand

TABLE 5-1. POSSIBLE COMBINATIONS
OF TWO VARIABLES

			COLUMN			
			1	2	3	4
ROWS	1	X	0	1	0	1
	2	Y	0	0	1	1

corner. The first vertical column next to the symbols X and Y consists of 0,0. These two zeros symbolically represent the first combination of the two variables, namely that X does not exist, and that Y does not exist. The second vertical column after the variables shows that X is 1, and Y is 0. This column represents the fact that X exists, and that Y does not exist. The third vertical column next to the variables shows that X is 0, and that Y is 1. This represents the fact that X does not exist, and that Y exists. The fourth vertical column next to the variables shows that X is 1, and Y is 1. This column shows that both X and Y exist.

Now that we have shown the tabulation of the variables, X and Y, as well as all the combinations that can exist for these variables, let us see how the truth table of the AND statement is developed. In order to do this, another row must be added to that of Table 5-1. The heading for this row will be the AND statement in symbolic form, namely XY. We should recall at this time that the AND statement for X and Y can exist only when both X and Y exist simultaneously. For all other combinations of X and Y, such as when X does exist and Y does not exist, then the truth will be a 0, which simply means that X AND Y does not exist.

Table 5-2 illustrates the truth table for the AND statement of X and Y.

TABLE 5-2. TRUTH TABLE OF "AND" STATEMENT XY

			COLUMN			
			1	2	3	4
ROWS	1	X	0	1	0	1
	2	Y	0	0	1	1
	3	XY	0	0	0	1

The first column shows variables X and Y as well as the AND statement for X AND Y, XY. The next column has all zeros in it. These zeros mean that X does not exist, Y does not exist, and that XY does not exist. The next column shows a 1 in the X row, and zeros in the Y and XY rows. This combination means that X exists, Y does not exist, and that XY does not exist. The next column shows zeros in the X and XY rows, and a 1 in the Y row. This combination represents the fact that XY cannot exist because X does not exist. The last column shows a 1 in all of the rows. This combination means that XY does exist because X exists and Y exists. That XY exists for the last combination can be clearly seen because both X and Y exist simultaneously. Thus, we see how the truth table for the AND statement is developed.

A few basic rules can be given for the development of a truth table. First, make as many rows as there are variables. Second, make as many vertical columns as there are combinations for the variables. If, for example, there are three variables, then there will be eight vertical columns. Third, make a row for the truth that is to be proved, such as XY in the previous discussion. Fourth, place zeros and ones in the rows for the variables, making sure that all combinations are considered. A simple trick is to alternate the topmost row with zeros and ones, beginning first with a zero. The next row will have two successive zeros followed by two successive ones, and this will continue on in the same alternation depending on the number of variables. The third row down will have four successive zeros followed by four successive ones, and this will continue depending on the number of variables. The fourth row will have eight successive zeros followed by eight successive ones, and this will continue depending on the number of variables. Also, it should be observed that the tabulation of the zeros and ones in the rows of the variables is nothing more than a conventional binary count reading from bottom to top and from left to right. Table 5-3 illustrates this principle for three variables.

TABLE 5-3. TRUTH TABLE WITH ALL THE COMBINATIONS FOR THREE VARIABLES

			COLUMN							
			1	2	3	4	5	6	7	8
ROWS	1	X	0	1	0	1	0	1	0	1
	2	Y	0	0	1	1	0	0	1	1
	3	Z	0	0	0	0	1	1	1	1

The development of a truth table for a two-variable OR statement is shown in Table 5-4. Here again the two variables are designated as X and Y. In Chapter 3, the OR concept was clearly defined. It should be recalled that the conditions for the OR states are three. Namely, the truth of the OR exists when either one variable, or the other variable, or both of the variables exist. In Table 5-4, notice that when X and Y are both zeroes that the row of X + Y is zero. The reason for this condition is that neither X nor Y exists, therefore, X + Y cannot exist. In the next three columns for the X + Y row,

TABLE 5-4.   TRUTH TABLE FOR TWO-VARIABLE
"OR" STATEMENT

			COLUMN			
			1	2	3	4
ROWS	1	X	0	1	0	1
	2	Y	0	0	1	1
	3	X+Y	0	1	1	1

notice that there are ones. The reason for this condition is that in these three columns either X, or Y, or both X and Y exist. Therefore, the truth table for the OR statement shows that X OR Y exists when either X or Y, or both X and Y exist.

Let us now proceed to develop the truth table for an exclusive OR statement. We must first redefine an exclusive OR statement. An exclusive OR statement is one that exists only when one variable or the other exists. Notice the difference between the exclusive OR statement and the OR statement. The difference lies in the fact that the exclusive OR statement does not exist when both of the variables exist. Now that we have defined the exclusive OR statement, let us develop its truth table for two variables. Let us once again select X and Y as the variables. Since there are only two variables, there will be only four combinations. These variables are tabulated once again the same as was done for the AND and OR statements. This is shown in Table 5-5. Notice that the uppermost row is an alternation of zeroes and ones, and that the row underneath it contains first two zeroes

TABLE 5-5.   TRUTH TABLE FOR AN EXCLUSIVE
"OR" STATEMENT

			COLUMN			
			1	2	3	4
ROWS	1	X	0	1	0	1
	2	Y	0	0	1	1
	3	X⊕Y	0	1	1	0

and then two ones. This will yield all of the possible combinations. The lowermost row contains the truth row for the exclusive OR statement. In order to tell the difference between the exclusive OR and the OR, the exclusive OR will be symbolically represented by $X \oplus Y$. Since the truth of the exclusive OR is that it exists only when either X or Y exists, then a 1 is placed in this row whenever a 1 is present in the X or Y row.

5-2. Proving Identities with Truth Tables

One of the most useful functions of the truth table is to prove that two

Boolean statements are identical. It is true that this can be done by using the concepts of conventional Boolean algebra, but it is much easier to show this by using truth tables.

In order to make use of the truth table to prove that two or more Boolean statements are identical, a systematic procedure is followed. First, make rows for the variables that are under consideration. In these rows, tabulate all of the possible combinations that can exist for the variables. This is done in the same manner as that described for setting up a truth table. The next step is to set up rows for all the combinations of the variables. The last step is to set up rows for the two Boolean statements under consideration. If the rows of the Boolean statements under consideration are identical, then the Boolean statements are identical. If the rows are not identical, then the Boolean statements are not identical.

TABLE 5-6.   TRUTH TABLE FOR EQUIVALENCE OF
$X + Y$ AND $X + \bar{X}Y$

			COLUMN			
			1	2	3	4
ROWS	1	X	0	1	0	1
	2	Y	0	0	1	1
	3	$\bar{X}$	1	0	1	0
	4	$\bar{X}Y$	0	0	1	0
	5	$X+\bar{X}Y$	0	1	1	1
	6	$X+Y$	0	1	1	1

An example of this will clarify how this is done. Let us prove by using the concept of the truth table that the Boolean statement $X + Y$ is identical to the Boolean statement $X + \bar{X}Y$. Notice that there are only two variables under consideration, namely X and Y. Therefore, the first step is to make rows for X and Y showing all of the possible combinations for these variables. The uppermost rows of Table 5-6 show the variables X and Y as well as all the combinations that can exist for these two variables. Since in one of the Boolean statements there is $\bar{X}$, then a row for it is necessary. Referring once again to Table 5-6, notice that the third row consists of $\bar{X}$. As was explained in Chapter 3, $\bar{X}$ is the negation of X. Notice that this row is a negation of the uppermost row, which means changing zeroes to ones and vice versa. The fourth row is an AND statement that consists of ANDing $\bar{X}$ and Y. This is done by ANDing the second and third rows. The fifth row consists of the OR statement $X + \bar{X}Y$. This row consists of ORing the first row with the fourth row. The last row consists of the OR statement $X + Y$. This was done by ORing the first row with the second row. The crux of this is to observe that the fifth and sixth rows are identical. Since this is the case, it is true that the Boolean statement $X + Y$ is identical to the Boolean statement $X + \bar{X}Y$.

The truth table, Table 5-7, shows that $X + YZ$ is equivalent to $(X + Y)$ $(X + Z)$. You should recognize this identity as the law of distribution that was discussed in Chapter 3. Since the identity is a function of X, Y, and Z, the truth table includes all of the eight possible combinations that can exist for the three variables. In the fourth row of Table 5-7, the truth of YZ

TABLE 5-7. TRUTH TABLE FOR EQUIVALENCE OF
X+YZ AND (X+Y)(X+Z)

		COLUMN							
		1	2	3	4	5	6	7	8
ROWS	1 X	0	1	0	1	0	1	0	1
	2 Y	0	0	1	1	0	0	1	1
	3 Z	0	0	0	0	1	1	1	1
	4 YZ	0	0	0	0	0	0	1	1
	5 X+YZ	0	1	0	1	0	1	1	1
	6 (X+Y)	0	1	1	1	0	1	1	1
	7 (X+Z)	0	1	0	1	1	1	1	1
	8 (X+Y)(X+Z)	0	1	0	1	0	1	1	1

is shown. Notice that a 1 is recorded in the rows in which both Y and Z also contain a 1. The left side of the identity is $X + YZ$ and the truth for this statement is obtained by ORING the first row and the fourth row. As you can see, a 1 is placed in every column for which either an X, YZ, or both also contain 1's. The truth of $X + YZ$ is, therefore, 01010111. Now we have to determine the truth of the right side of the identity. In the sixth row, a 1 is placed in every column for which either an X, Y, or both exist. Thus, the truth of $(X + Y)$ is obtained. In the seventh row, a 1 is placed in every column for which either an X, Z, or both exist; thus, the truth of $(X + Z)$ is obtained. Finally, in row eight, the truth of the right side of the identity is determined by ANDING rows 6 and 7. A 1 is placed in the columns for which both rows 6 and 7 contain a 1. As shown in the truth table, the truth of $(X + Y)(X + Z)$ is 01010111. This truth is identical to the truth of $X + YZ$; hence, we can conclude that $X + YZ = (X + Y)(X + Z)$.

As another example of how the truth table can prove that two Boolean statements are identical, let us prove the identity for the following two Boolean statements: $XYZ + XY\overline{Z} = XY$. Since there are three variables in these statements, a three-variable truth table must be used. In Table 5-8, the top three rows show these variables with all of the possible combinations. Observe that one of the two Boolean statements that are to be proved to be identical contains $\overline{Z}$. Therefore, a row for it must be included. Notice that this row is nothing more than a negation of the third row, Z. The fifth row shows the AND statement of XYZ. This row is simply a logic ANDING of rows 1, 2, and 3. The sixth row consists of the AND statement $XY\overline{Z}$. This row is simply the logic ANDing of rows 1, 2, and 4. The seventh row consists of the Boolean statement $XYZ + XY\bar{Z}$. This row consists of logic ORing rows 5 and 6. The eighth row consists of the AND statement XY. This row consists of logic ANDing rows 1 and 2. Now, notice that the last two rows are identical, which proves that these two Boolean statements are identical.

To end this section, let us get a little more daring by proving, with the aid of a truth table, that the following two Boolean statements are identical:

$$\bar{X}YZ + X\bar{Y}Z + XY\bar{Z} + XYZ = XY + XZ + YZ$$

This identity has three variables. It is, therefore, necessary to construct a truth table that will contain the three variables. This is the first step in the construction of the truth table. The next step is to tabulate the negation of X, Y, and Z to satisfy the Boolean statements that we are proving to be identical. After having done this, make rows in the truth table for all of the AND statements that are present in the Boolean statements that we are proving to be identical. After this is done, make a row for one of the Boolean statements that is to be proved identical. And finally, make a row in the truth table for the other Boolean statement.

TABLE 5-8. TRUTH TABLE FOR EQUIVALENCE OF $XYZ + XY\bar{Z} = XY$

		COLUMN							
		1	2	3	4	5	6	7	8
ROWS	1	X	0	1	0	1	0	1	0	1
	2	Y	0	0	1	1	0	0	1	1
	3	Z	0	0	0	0	1	1	1	1
	4	$\bar{Z}$	1	1	1	1	0	0	0	0
	5	XYZ	0	0	0	0	0	0	0	1
	6	$XY\bar{Z}$	0	0	0	1	0	0	0	0
	7	$XYZ + XY\bar{Z}$	0	0	0	1	0	0	0	1
	8	XY	0	0	0	1	0	0	0	1

This procedure has been followed in the construction of Table 5-9. For simplicity of explanation, the rows have been numbered from 1 to 15. Rows 1, 2, and 3 contain the variables X, Y, and Z, respectively. Rows 4, 5, and 6 contain the negation of rows 1, 2, and 3, respectively. Row 7 was constructed by logic ANDing rows 4, 2, and 3. Notice that zeroes are contained in all of the columns in this row except one. The reason for this is that the logic ANDing of all of the columns of the individual quantities, $\bar{X}$, Y, and Z will yield a zero in all columns except in that column where $\bar{X}$, Y, and Z are all ones. Row 8 was constructed by logic ANDing rows 1, 5, and 3. Again observe that this row contains zeroes in all of the columns except one. This is true for the same reason that was given above when we were discussing row 7. Row 9 consists of the logic ANDing of rows 1, 2, and

TABLE 5-9. TRUTH TABLE FOR EQUIVALENCE OF $\bar{X}YZ + X\bar{Y}Z + XY\bar{Z} + XYZ = XY + XZ + YZ$

		COLUMN							
		1	2	3	4	5	6	7	8
	1	X	0	1	0	1	0	1	0	1
	2	Y	0	0	1	1	0	0	1	1
	3	Z	0	0	0	0	1	1	1	1
	4	$\bar{X}$	1	0	1	0	1	0	1	0
	5	$\bar{Y}$	1	1	0	0	1	1	0	0
	6	$\bar{Z}$	1	1	1	1	0	0	0	0
ROWS	7	$\bar{X}YZ$	0	0	0	0	0	0	1	0
	8	$X\bar{Y}Z$	0	0	0	0	0	1	0	0
	9	$XY\bar{Z}$	0	0	0	1	0	0	0	0
	10	XYZ	0	0	0	0	0	0	0	1
	11	XY	0	0	0	1	0	0	0	1
	12	XZ	0	0	0	0	0	1	0	1
	13	YZ	0	0	0	0	0	0	1	1
	14	$\bar{X}YZ + X\bar{Y}Z + XY\bar{Z} + XYZ$	0	0	0	1	0	1	1	1
	15	$XY + XZ + YZ$	0	0	0	1	0	1	1	1

6. Row 10 consists of logic ANDing rows 1, 2, and 3. Row 11 consists of logic ANDing rows 1 and 2. Notice that in this row there are two ones. The reason for this is that in two columns will the logic ANDing of rows 1 and 2 result in a one. Row 12 consists of logic ANDing rows 1 and 3. Row 13 consists of logic ANDing rows 2 and 3. Row 14, which is the row that contains one of the Boolean statements, is the result of logic ORing rows 7, 8, 9, and 10. Notice that a 1 is contained in this row, whenever a 1 is present in either rows 7, 8, 9, or 10. Row 15, which contains the other Boolean statement that is to be proved to be identical, consists of logic ORing rows 11, 12, and 13. Again it is to be observed that a 1 will be present in this row, in any column that a one is contained for either rows 11, 12, or 13. Upon inspecting rows 14 and 15, one observes that the columns for these rows are identical. Since these rows contain zeroes and ones in the same columns, then it must be true that these two Boolean statements are identical.

It is true that these two Boolean statements could have been proved to be identical by using conventional Boolean algebra, but unless one is well versed at manipulating the conventional algebra, he will find it a somewhat difficult task. As to which method, either the conventional algebra or the use of truth tables, is easier is a question that only can be answered by you alone. There is no question that for a two-variable Boolean statement, by and large the conventional algebra is easier, but when three- or more variable Boolean statements are to be proved to be identical, the truth table method is undoubtedly faster and easier.

5-3. Developing Boolean Statements from Truth Tables

An equally useful function of the truth table is to develop a Boolean statement. This is necessary because, at first, the logics designer of a digital computer is confronted with a verbal statement. What he must do is to transform the verbal statement into Boolean form so that he can design a circuit that will fulfill the verbal statement requirements. The truth table is a valuable aid in going from the verbal statement to the Boolean form. It is true that the truth table method will not necessarily yield the simplest form for the Boolean statement. However, once this Boolean statement is available, various means are at his disposal for determining the simplest Boolean statement in order to design a circuit with the least number of components. For the present, however, let us restrict ourselves to the truth table method for finding a Boolean statement from a verbal statement.

As an example, let us assume the following: It is desired that a Boolean statement be written which will yield an exclusive OR statement for two variables. Verbally, the exclusive OR statement is one that desires an existence *if and only if* one or the other of the variables exists. The first step is to make a truth table which will show the variables, and all of the possible combinations. In this example, there are two variables; hence, there will be ony four combinations. The variables in this case will, once again, be designated as X and Y.

Table 5-10 shows the truth table that has been developed for the exclusive OR statement. Notice that rows 1 and 2 contain the variables X and Y, and all the possible combinations. Row 3 symbolically shows the exclusive

TABLE 5-10. TRUTH TABLE FOR AN EXCLUSIVE "OR" STATEMENT

			COLUMN		
			1	2	3	4
ROWS	1	X	0	1	0	1
	2	Y	0	0	1	1
	3	X⊕Y	0	1	1	0

OR. In column 1 of this row, you will notice a 0. What is the reason for placing a 0 in this column? The reason is that both X and Y are 0, and this combination is one that we do not desire to exist for the exclusive OR statement. Since we do not desire this condition to exist, and since further it has been desired to use the symbol 0 for a condition of nonexistence, then a 0 is placed in this column for the exclusive OR row.

In column 2 of the exclusive OR row, there is a 1. The reason for this is that we desire this condition to exist. Notice that for this column, X is 1, and Y is 0. This condition causes a 1 in column 2 of the exclusive OR row. That this is true can be seen from the original verbal statement, which was that the exclusive OR will have an existence only when either X, or Y exists. Since X exists in this column, then a 1 is placed in it.

Column 3 of the exclusive OR again contains a 1 because Y is 1, and X is 0. This, once again, is a condition that is desired for the exclusive OR. Since this is a desired condition, then a 1 must be placed in the column of this row.

Column 4 of the exclusive OR row contains a 0 because both X and Y contain ones. The fact that both X and Y contain ones is a condition that is not desired. Since this a condition that is not desired, a zero is placed in this column of this row.

All that we have done is to logically designate whether a 1 or a 0 should be placed in the columns of the exclusive OR row. Now that we have this, let us see how we can write the Boolean statement from this truth table. When we study the truth table of Table 5-10, we observe that a 1 is present in columns 2 and 3. Therefore, these two columns are important because they give us an insight as to what we want. When we look up these columns, we will have the conditions that must exist to meet the requirements for the existence of the exclusive OR. In column 2, X is 1, and Y is 0. This, then, is one condition for the existence of the exclusive OR; namely that X exists, and, simultaneously, Y does not exist. In column 3, X is 0, and Y is 1. This is the second condition that must exist in order that there be an existence in the exclusive OR row. This last condition states that X does not exist, and, simultaneously, Y does exist.

Because there are two conditions for the existence of the exclusive OR, there must be two conditions in the Boolean statement that we are developing. It is to be noted that the conditions for the exclusive OR exist when either the first OR the second condition exists. For the first condition, we observe that X exists, and Y does not exist. Symbolically, the Boolean statement for this condition is $X\overline{Y}$. However, the exclusive OR exists when either the first OR the second condition exists. Therefore, the final Boolean statement will be the ORing of the first condition with the second. Symbolically, this is $X\overline{Y} + \overline{X}Y$. We have now accomplished what we set out to do: namely, to write a Boolean statement from a verbal statement making use of the truth table.

A method that is suggested to be followed to develop a Boolean statement from a verbal statement is systematically presented in the following steps:

1. Determine the number of variables that are given in the original verbal statement.

2. Construct a truth table that will consist of all of the variables, and all of the possible combinations. When this truth table is constructed, make provisions for constructing one more row. The purpose for this row is to tabulate the conditions that are to be met in the verbal statement.

3. In the row that is constructed for the resulting conditions of the verbal statement, place a 0 in all columns where the conditions of the verbal statement are not desired, and place a one in those columns where the resulting conditions of the verbal statement are desired.

4. All the columns of the row that the resulting conditions of the verbal statement contain ones are the important columns, because from these columns the Boolean statement will be written.
5. Write the AND statement for the columns that contain ones of the rows for which the resulting Boolean statement is being written.
6. OR all of the AND statements of step 5. This will yield the final Boolean statement.

Let us once again develop a Boolean statement from a verbal one, making use of the steps. The verbal statement follows: There are three variables X, Y, and Z. It is desired to write a Boolean statement for the conditions that will exist only when two of the variables exist.

Using step 1, we see that there are three variables X, Y, and Z.

Table 5-11 is the result of step 2. Notice that the variables and all of

TABLE 5-11. TRUTH TABLE FROM A VERBAL STATEMENT

			COLUMN							
			1	2	3	4	5	6	7	8
ROWS	1	X	0	1	0	1	0	1	0	1
	2	Y	0	0	1	1	0	0	1	1
	3	Z	0	0	0	0	1	1	1	1
	4	?	0	0	0	1	0	1	1	0

their possible combinations are placed in the uppermost three rows. In the heading of row 4 is placed a question mark because we do not know as yet what the Boolean statement for this row will be.

Making use of step 3, the zeroes and ones are placed in the row that we are writing the Boolean statement. Let us carefully study why the zeroes and ones of this row are placed where they are. In the first column, each of the variables contains a 0. Verbally, this means that none of the variables exist. Since this is the case, and, since the condition for existence of the original verbal statement specified that in order to have existence, two of the variables must exist, a 0 must be placed in row 4 of column 1. Column 2 of row 4 also contains a zero because only one of the variables (X) exists in this column. For the same reason, except that variable Y exists, there is a zero in the column 3 of row 4. In column 4 of row 4, there is placed a 1 because X and Y both exist, and this is the condition for the existence of the resulting Boolean statement. In column 5, only Z exists, therefore, a 0 is entered. Column 6 of row 4 contains a 1 because both X and Z exist. Column 7 contains a 1 in the row 4 because Y and Z exist. Finally, column 8 contains a 0 because all of the variables exist which is not a condition for the existence of the resulting Boolean statement.

Using step 4, we see that columns 4, 6, and 7 are the important columns. The reason for this is that in these columns we will find the conditions of the variables in order to write the resulting Boolean statement.

In column 4, X and Y exist, and Z does not exist. Symbolically, this is $XY\overline{Z}$. In column 6, X and Z exist, and Y does not exist. Symbolically, this is $X\overline{Y}Z$. In column 7, Y and Z exist, and X does not exist. Symbolically, this is $\overline{X}YZ$. Having done this, step 5 has been accomplished.

Step 6 tells us to OR all of the AND statements that were written in step 5. This is necessary because there are three conditions that will yield an existence for the original verbal statement. Therefore, the final Boolean statement will be $XY\overline{Z} + X\overline{Y}Z + \overline{X}YZ$. We now have the Boolean statement that will fulfill the original verbal statement. Now that the Boolean statement is found, one can simplify it. However, the purpose of this section was to show how to write Boolean statements from verbal ones using truth tables. In a subsequent section of this chapter, simplification of a Boolean statement will be shown.

5-4. Introduction to Designation Numbers*

The concept of the designation number was evolved from the truth table, for the designation number is the extension of the truth table. As we shall see, we can do much more by using the designation number than by the truth table alone. As was explained in a previous section of this chapter, usually a designer of a logic circuit is first confronted with a verbal statement, and he must convert this verbal statement into a Boolean statement so that he can finally design the logic circuit for the original statement. The designation number concept is an aid to him in determining quickly what the Boolean statement for a verbal statement will be.

What, then, is a designation number? A designation number is nothing more than the representation of a Boolean statement in bit (0,1) form. For example, let us assume that we are considering a two-variable verbal statement. Let X represent one variable, and Y the other. Assuming that these two variables can either exist or not exist, there will be four possible combinations for these variables. Let the symbol, #, represent "the designation number of." Then $\#X$ symbolizes the designation number of X, and $\#Y$ symbolizes the designation number of Y. The $\#X$ when represented by bits, 0 and 1, will be the same as if we placed X in the top row of a truth table. Therefore, the $\#X$ is 0101. The $\#Y$ will be 0011 because it will be the same as when it is in the bottom row of a truth table. This is shown in Table 5-12.

TABLE 5-12. DESIGNATION NUMBERS FOR X AND Y

			COLUMN		
			0	1	2	3
ROWS	1	# X	0	1	0	1
	2	# Y	0	0	1	1

---

* Ledley, R. S., *Digital Computer and Control Engineering*, New York: McGraw-Hill Book Company, 1960, pp. 320-365.

The "basis" for a designation number is the tabulation of all the variables, and the combination of bits that they contain. Thus, the tabulation of the designation numbers X and Y in Table 5-12 is the basis for two variables. It is important that once the basis for a given number of variables is defined, it should not be altered because the operations that are going to be performed on these variables will depend on the assumption of the basis.

The basis for the designation numbers of three variables is shown in Table 5-13. Notice that the $\#X$ consists of alternating zeroes and ones.

TABLE 5-13. DESIGNATION NUMBERS FOR THREE VARIABLES

			COLUMN							
			0	1	2	3	4	5	6	7
ROWS	1	#X	0	1	0	1	0	1	0	1
	2	#Y	0	0	1	1	0	0	1	1
	3	#Z	0	0	0	0	1	1	1	1

Notice also that these bits are in groups of four bits. This is strongly suggested because it will be an aid in the writing of Boolean statements from designation numbers. The second row, containing $\#Y$, is also grouped in four bits, and it consists of an alternation of two zeroes and two ones. The third row, containing $\#Z$ also consists of groups of four bits, and it has four zeroes and four ones.

The basis for the designation numbers of four variables is shown in Table 5-14. Since there are four variables, there will be sixteen possible

TABLE 5-14. DESIGNATION NUMBERS FOR FOUR VARIABLES

			COLUMN														
			0	1	2	3	4	5	6	7	8	9	10	11	12	13	14	15
ROWS	1	#W	0	1	0	1	0	1	0	1	0	1	0	1	0	1	0	1
	2	#X	0	0	1	1	0	0	1	1	0	0	1	1	0	0	1	1
	3	#Y	0	0	0	0	1	1	1	1	0	0	0	0	1	1	1	1
	4	#Z	0	0	0	0	0	0	0	0	1	1	1	1	1	1	1	1

combinations. These combinations are numbered from zero to fifteen. These decimal numbers are also the numbers of the columns. Observe that this tabulation is simply the binary tabulation of the decimal numbers from zero to fifteen. For this reason, the columns are labeled in this manner.

5-5. Determining the Designation Number of a Boolean Statement

There are two points that have been brought out so far in reference to the concept of the designation number. The first is that the designation number is an extension of the truth table concept, and the second is that Boolean statements can be written from designation numbers. The former has already been shown; the latter will be shown in this section.

In order to show how a designation number can be used to write a Boolean statement, let us once again use the basic AND function. The AND function entails the logic multiplication of two variables. This simply means that when both of the two variables exist, i.e., when they both contain ones, *then and only then* will the AND function exist. For simplicity, let us, once again, use two variables, and let these be symbolized by X and Y. Let $\#X = 0101$, and let $\#Y = 0011$. The designation number of XY, $\#(XY)$, will, therefore, be 0001. The reason for this is that $\#(XY)$ will contain zeroes whenever X or Y contains a 0, and it will contain a 1 when X and Y both contain ones. Hence the designation number of XY, $\#(XY)$, will be 0001. Table 5-15 shows the $\#X$ and $\#Y$ as well as the $\#(XY)$. From this we can

TABLE 5-15.   DESIGNATION NUMBERS FOR
X "AND" Y, OR # XY

		COLUMN			
		0	1	2	3
ROWS	1 # X	0	1	0	1
	2 # Y	0	0	1	1
	3 # (XY)	0	0	0	1

see that whenever two variables are considered, if we were to see the designation number 0001, then we know that the Boolean statement will be the AND function.

As another example of how to write the designation number for a Boolean statement, let us develop the designation number of X OR Y, $\#(X + Y)$. The OR function entails the logic addition of variables. If we assume that we are considering two variables, then the OR function is a logic addition of these two variables because when one or the other of the variables exists or when both of them exist, then the OR function will also exist; that is, it will contain a 1. Table 5-16 shows the development of the designation number for X OR Y. Notice that the designation number of X OR Y, $\#(X + Y)$, contains a 1 in columns 1, 2, and 3. This is true because when we

TABLE 5-16.   DESIGNATION NUMBER FOR AN "OR" FUNCTION

		COLUMN			
		0	1	2	3
ROWS	1 # X	0	1	0	1
	2 # Y	0	0	1	1
	3 # (X + Y)	0	1	1	1

logic add #X and #Y, we will obtain the ones in these columns. Notice that when column 3 is logic added, it will contain a 1, for when we logic add 1 to 1 there will result a sum of 1.

The designation number of the exclusive OR is shown in Table 5-17. It should be remembered that the exclusive OR will exist, i.e., it will contain a 1 when X or Y exists, and not when they both exist.

TABLE 5-17. DESIGNATION NUMBER FOR AN EXCLUSIVE"OR"STATEMENT

			COLUMN			
			0	1	2	3
ROWS	1	# X	0	1	0	1
	2	# Y	0	0	1	1
	3	# (X⊕Y)	0	1	1	0

Table 5-18 shows the designation number of $\overline{X}$, and the designation number of $\overline{Y}$. Since negation is done by simply changing ones to zeros, and zeros to ones, the #$\overline{X}$ is the negation of #X, and the #$\overline{Y}$ is the negation of #Y. Here we also see the importance of the basis of a designation number. Notice that the designation of $\overline{X}$, depends on what designation number we have assigned to #X. Also, the #$\overline{Y}$ depends on what designation number we have assigned to #Y.

TABLE 5-18. DESIGNATION NUMBERS FOR $\overline{X}$ AND $\overline{Y}$

			COLUMN			
			0	1	2	3
ROWS	1	# X	0	1	0	1
	2	# Y	0	0	1	1
	3	# $\overline{X}$	1	0	1	0
	4	# $\overline{Y}$	1	1	0	0

TABLE 5-19. DESIGNATION NUMBER FOR X+$\overline{Y}$Z

			COLUMN							
			0	1	2	3	4	5	6	7
ROWS	1	# X	0	1	0	1	0	1	0	1
	2	# Y	0	0	1	1	0	0	1	1
	3	# Z	0	0	0	0	1	1	1	1
	4	# $\overline{Y}$	1	1	0	0	1	1	0	0
	5	# ($\overline{Y}$Z)	0	0	0	0	1	1	0	0
	6	# (X + $\overline{Y}$Z)	0	1	0	1	1	1	0	1

Table 5-19 shows the development for the $\#(X + \overline{Y}Z)$. The first three rows contain the designation numbers of X, Y, and Z. The fourth row contains the designation number of $\overline{Y}$, $\#\overline{Y}$. This row is simply a negation of row 2, $\#Y$, which is found in the Boolean function. The fifth row contains the designation number of $\overline{Y}Z$, also found in the Boolean function. The sixth row contains the designation number of the Boolean function. This designation number is formed by logic adding rows 1, and 5. Hence the $\#(X + \overline{Y}Z)$ is 0101 1101.

5-6. Writing Boolean Functions from Designation Numbers

So far, we have seen how to write the designation number for a Boolean function. We are now going to show how to write Boolean functions once the designation number is given. There are various ways of doing this, and three of these will be shown. These three shall be called: (1) the first canonical or minterm form, (2) the second canonical or maxterm form, and (3) the simplest sum-of-products form.

The First Canonical or Minterm Form. The first canonical form consists of writing AND-TO-OR Boolean functions. To explain this, let us assume two variables, X and Y. Let us start by writing the designation numbers for the variables X and Y. This is done in the first two rows of Table 5-20.

TABLE 5-20.   THE DEVELOPMENT OF THE FIRST CANONICAL
FORM FOR TWO VARIABLES

			COLUMN			
			0	1	2	3
ROWS	1	# X	0	1	0	1
	2	# Y	0	0	1	1
	3	# $(\overline{X}\overline{Y})$	1	0	0	0
	4	# $(X\overline{Y})$	0	1	0	0
	5	# $(\overline{X}Y)$	0	0	1	0
	6	# (XY)	0	0	0	1
	7	# $(\overline{X}\overline{Y} + X\overline{Y} + \overline{X}Y + XY)$	1	1	1	1

What we do next is to write the designation number for the ANDing of each of the columns. Thus, when the first column is ANDed, it will yield the designation number for $\overline{X}\overline{Y}$. Notice that a 1 is placed in the column for when this condition exists, and that a 0 is placed in all of the other columns. Thus, the designation number for $\overline{X}\overline{Y}$ is 1000. This is shown in the third row of Table 5-20. The fourth row shows $\#(X\overline{Y})$. The reason that $\#(X\overline{Y})$ is equal to 0100 is that in the column labeled with the decimal 1 (above the tabulation of the designation numbers), X exists and Y does not exist, i.e., X is 1, and Y is 0. Therefore, in this column $X\overline{Y}$ exists, and it is labeled with a 1. In all of the other columns of this row there are zeros, because $X\overline{Y}$ does not exist in all of these columns. The fifth row shows the designation number of $\overline{X}Y$, #($\overline{X}Y$). The #($\overline{X}Y$) is 0010 because only in column 2 will $\overline{X}Y$ exist. In all of the other columns of this row, $\overline{X}Y$ does not exist, and they will be zeroes. The sixth row shows the #(XY), which is 0001 because only in the column labeled 3 will XY exist. Thus, it will be a 1 only in this column. The last row shows the designation number of the first canonical form for two variables. Notice that this row consists of ORing rows 3, 4, 5, and 6. Thus, the first canonical form for two variables has been developed.

Each of the AND statements, $\overline{X}\overline{Y}$, $X\overline{Y}$, $\overline{X}Y$, and XY is referred to as either an elementary product or a minterm. From the development of this two-variable, first canonical form we can make the following observations:

1. Each elementary product, or minterm, contains both of the variables, and these variables can be with or without the negation.
2. The final first canonical form for the Boolean statement consists of ORing all of the elementary products or minterms.

These two observations can be used for generalizing any number of variables. Namely, the first canonical form of any number of variables consists of the minterms of all of the variables which are logically added together.

As an example of the use of the first canonical form, let us write the first canonical form for the following designation number: 0011. From Table 5-20, we can see that a 1 in column 2 will yield $\overline{X}Y$, and 1 in column 3 will yield XY. Thus, the Boolean statement in the first canonical form for the designation number 0011 will be $\overline{X}Y + XY$.

The development for the first canonical form for three variables is shown in Table 5-21. It is developed using the same concepts as were used in developing the two-variable first canonical form. As an example of how to write a Boolean statement of the first canonical form for three variables,

TABLE 5-21. THE DEVELOPMENT OF THE FIRST CANONICAL FORM FOR THREE VARIABLES

		COLUMN							
		0	1	2	3	4	5	6	7
ROWS	1	#X							
	1	#X	0	1	0	1	0	1	0	1
	2	#Y	0	0	1	1	0	0	1	1
	3	#Z	0	0	0	0	1	1	1	1
	4	#($\overline{X}\overline{Y}\overline{Z}$)	1	0	0	0	0	0	0	0
	5	#($X\overline{Y}\overline{Z}$)	0	1	0	0	0	0	0	0
	6	#($\overline{X}Y\overline{Z}$)	0	0	1	0	0	0	0	0
	7	#($XY\overline{Z}$)	0	0	0	1	0	0	0	0
	8	#($\overline{X}\overline{Y}Z$)	0	0	0	0	1	0	0	0
	9	#($X\overline{Y}Z$)	0	0	0	0	0	1	0	0
	10	#($\overline{X}YZ$)	0	0	0	0	0	0	1	0
	11	#(XYZ)	0	0	0	0	0	0	0	1

let us write the first canonical form for the following designation number: 1100 1100. From Table 5-21, it can be seen that this designation number yields a 1 in columns 0, 1, 4, and 5. Note that the minterms that will yield ones in these columns will be $\bar{X}\bar{Y}\bar{Z} + X\bar{Y}\bar{Z} + \bar{X}\bar{Y}Z + X\bar{Y}Z$. It should be seen that this Boolean statement is not in its simplest form. As a matter of fact, the simplest form for this is $\bar{Y}$. However, the point that is being made here is how to write the first canonical form of a designation number, and not how to simplify.

The Second Canonical Form. The second canonical form consists of writing an OR to AND Boolean statement. An example of an OR to AND statement is $(\bar{X} + \bar{Y})(X + Y)$. Notice that the variables are first ORed together, and then they are ANDed together. The second canonical form can be developed from the first canonical form. This can be done by taking the first canonical from and applying De Morgan's theorem to it. Recalling that $\overline{XY} = \bar{X} + \bar{Y}$ and $\overline{X + Y} = \bar{X}\bar{Y}$, let us apply the theorem to the first canonical form. The steps to be followed in order to do this are:

Step 1:

$\#(\bar{X}\bar{Y} + X\bar{Y} + \bar{X}Y + XY) = 1111$ 　　　　　(First Canonical Form)

Step 2:

$\#\overline{(\bar{X}\bar{Y} + X\bar{Y} + \bar{X}Y + XY)} = \overline{1111}$ 　　　　　(Negation)

Step 3:

$\#(\overline{\bar{X}\bar{Y}} \cdot \overline{X\bar{Y}} \cdot \overline{\bar{X}Y} \cdot \overline{XY}) = 0000$ 　　　　　(De Morgan's Theorem)

Step 4:

$\#[(X + Y)(\bar{X} + Y)(X + \bar{Y})(\bar{X} + \bar{Y})] = 0000$ 　　(De Morgan's Theorem)

Step 4 shows the designation number for the second canonical form. Observe that the designation number for the second canonical form is all zeroes, and that the Boolean statement for this form is an OR to AND statement.

Before proceeding to show how to write the second canonical form from a designation number, let us define a "maxterm," or an "elementary sum." A maxterm, or an elementary sum, consists of a logic addition or ORing of two variables. These variables may or may not be negated. Thus, examples of elementary sums, or maxterms, are $(X + Y)$, $(\bar{X} + Y)$, $(X + \bar{Y})$, and $(\bar{X} + \bar{Y})$. Now that we have defined the elementary sum or maxterm, let us proceed to develop the second canonical form from a designation number.

In Table 5-22, notice that the designation number of any maxterm has only one zero in it. Thus, for example, $\#(X + Y)$ is 0111. It is also to be observed that the designation number for the second canonical form contains all zeroes. Therefore, when writing a Boolean statement in the second canonical form of a designation number, if the column in the designation

TABLE 5-22. DESIGNATION NUMBER FOR THE SECOND
CANONICAL FORM FOR TWO VARIABLES

				COLUMN			
				0	1	2	3
ROWS	1	# X	=	0	1	0	1
	2	# Y	=	0	0	1	1
	3	# $\overline{X}$	=	1	0	1	0
	4	# $\overline{Y}$	=	1	1	0	0
	5	# (X+ Y)	=	0	1	1	1
	6	# ($\overline{X}$+ Y)	=	1	0	1	1
	7	# (X+ $\overline{Y}$)	=	1	1	0	1
	8	# ($\overline{X}$+ $\overline{Y}$)	=	1	1	1	0
	9	# $[(X+Y)(\overline{X}+Y)(X+\overline{Y})(\overline{X}+\overline{Y})]$	=	0	0	0	0

number that we are writing the Boolean statement contains a zero, we write the maxterm of that column.

As an example, let us write the second canonical form for the following designation number: 1001. Notice that in columns 1 and 2 there are zeroes. From Table 5-22, we observe that the zero of column 1 yields the maxterm of $(\overline{X} + Y)$, and that the zero of column 2 yields the maxterm of $(X + \overline{Y})$. Thus, the Boolean statement in the second canonical form for the designation number 1001 is $(\overline{X} +Y)(X + \overline{Y})$. This can be proved by observing that $(\overline{X} + Y)(X + \overline{Y})$ is the same as $\overline{X}Y + XY$, which is the first canonical form for the designation number 1001. Needless to say, we should get the same Boolean statement for the same designation number regardless of what form we use. Since we have shown this to be the case, then we have proved that either of these forms will yield the same Boolean statement though the form is different.

The Simplest Sum-of-Products Form. In order to find the simplest sum-of-products form, we must first define the term. A Boolean statement is said to be in the simplest sum-of-products form when it is in an AND-to-OR form which cannot be simplified any further. For example, the Boolean statement $\overline{X}YZ + X\overline{Y}Z + XY\overline{Z} + XYZ$ has, in Section 5-2, been proved to be $XY + XZ + YZ$. The latter Boolean statement is the simplest sum-of-products of the original Boolean statement.

The simplest sum-of-products form for a given designation number can be found by making use of the Veitch diagram. What we shall do is to construct a special Veitch diagram which will take into consideration all of the variables as well as all of the possibilities of the variables.

Figure 5-1 illustrates a Veitch diagram for a two variable designation number. The designation number of X, $\#X$, is in standard form and so is the designation number of Y, $\#Y$. The standard form for these variables is shown once again for convenience.

Column: 0123
#X 0101
#Y 0011

The bold decimal numbers, 0, 1, 2, 3, which are inside the rectangles of Fig. 5-1 represent the columns of the designation numbers. The Boolean statements inside each of the boxes represent those for each column of the

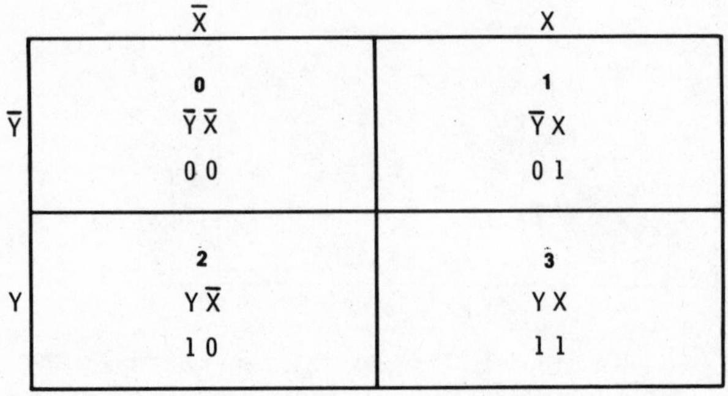

	$\overline{X}$	X
$\overline{Y}$	**0** $\overline{Y}\,\overline{X}$ 0 0	**1** $\overline{Y}\,X$ 0 1
Y	**2** $Y\,\overline{X}$ 1 0	**3** $Y\,X$ 1 1

Fig. 5-1. A Veitch diagram arranged for two-variable designation numbers.

designation number. The binary numbers under the Boolean statements represent the binary numbers found in a particular column of the designation numbers. For example, the column labeled with the decimal 2 shows that X is 0, and Y is 1. The fact that X is zero means that X does not exist; the fact that Y is 1 means that Y exists. Hence, the Boolean statement for this column is $Y\overline{X}$. Notice that the variable Y has been placed before $\overline{X}$. The reason for this is to keep the binary representation (10) and the decimal number of the column the same.

As an example, let us find the simplest sum-of-products form for the

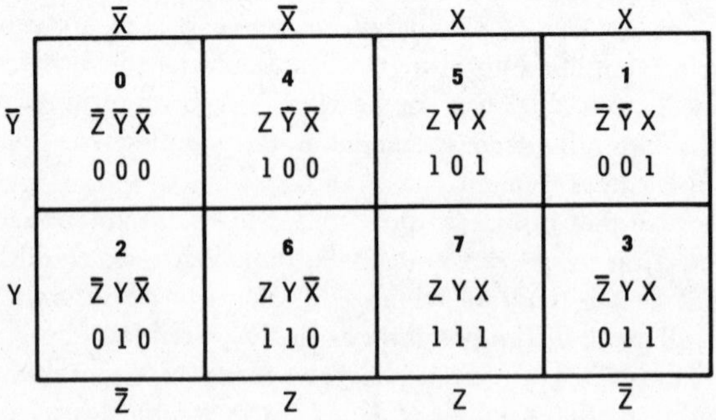

	$\overline{X}$	$\overline{X}$	X	X
$\overline{Y}$	**0** $\overline{Z}\,\overline{Y}\,\overline{X}$ 0 0 0	**4** $Z\,\overline{Y}\,\overline{X}$ 1 0 0	**5** $Z\,\overline{Y}\,X$ 1 0 1	**1** $\overline{Z}\,\overline{Y}\,X$ 0 0 1
Y	**2** $\overline{Z}\,Y\,\overline{X}$ 0 1 0	**6** $Z\,Y\,\overline{X}$ 1 1 0	**7** $Z\,Y\,X$ 1 1 1	**3** $\overline{Z}\,Y\,X$ 0 1 1
	$\overline{Z}$	Z	Z	$\overline{Z}$

Fig. 5-2. A three-variable Veitch diagram that is applicable for designation numbers.

following designation number: 1100. Using the first canonical form, we find that the Boolean statement for this designation number is $\overline{X}\overline{Y} + \overline{Y}X$. This is true because there are ones in columns 1 and 2 of the designation number tabulation. Looking at Fig. 5-1, we see that this designation number consists of the upper boxes which are coupled together. Since these two boxes are coupled together, there must be a simpler form. From this Veitch diagram, we see that this couple consists only of $\overline{Y}$. Therefore, the simplest sum-of-products for this designation number is $\overline{Y}$.

In Fig. 5-2, there is a Veitch diagram that is applicable for designation numbers for three variables. The arrangement of this diagram has been so designed as to make the numbering of the columns in a three-variable designation number tabulation simple. For convenience, the tabulation for a three-variable designation number shall be repeated:

$$\text{Column: } 0123 \ 4567$$
$$\#X \ 0101 \ 0101$$
$$\#Y \ 0011 \ 0011$$
$$\#Z \ 0000 \ 1111$$

As was done for the two-variable Veitch diagram, the decimal numbers inside each rectangle represent the number of the columns in the designation number tabulation. The Boolean statements inside of each rectangle represent those for the columns. The binary numbers represent those for the columns. It is to be noted that the binary numbers are read from bottom to top in the tabulation of the designation number table. It was for this reason that the Boolean statements began with the variable Z, and not with the variable X. This design for the Veitch diagram is simpler than the conventional Veitch diagram, for it makes it easy to remember where the columns of the designation number are placed. Notice the symmetry that exists in the placement of the column numbers. The four outer rectangles contain the first four columns of the designation number table, and the four inner rectangles contain the last four columns of the designation number table.

As an example, let us develop the simplest sum-of-products form for the following designation number: 1100 0011. The first two ones in the designation number are represented in the Veitch diagram of Fig. 5-2 as the upper corner rectangles. These are the ones that are labeled with the column numbers 0,1. Notice that these two rectangles can be coupled together as was explained in Chapter 4. As can be seen, these two rectangles are independent of the variable X, for in one of these rectangles $\overline{X}$ is present, while in the other one, X is present. Since these two rectangles can be coupled together, and since they are independent of the variable X, then the simplest Boolean statement for these first two ones will be $\overline{Y}\overline{Z}$.

The 1's in columns 6 and 7 can also be coupled together. These are the lower, inner rectangles of Fig. 5-2. When these two rectangles are coupled, they will be independent of the variable X because in rectangle 6 there is $\overline{X}$, while in rectangle 7 there is X. Therefore, the simplest Boolean statement for these two 1's will be YZ. Consequently, the simplest sum-of-products form for the designation number 1100 0011 is $\overline{Y}\overline{Z} + YZ$.

As another example, let us write the simplest sum-of-products form for the following designation number: 1010 1010. Notice that in this designation number there are 1's in columns 0, 2, 4, and 6. Looking at the Veitch diagram of Fig. 5-2, we see that these four 1's comprise the four rectangles in the left side of the Veitch diagram. These four rectangles when coupled will yield $\overline{X}$ because, in the development of the three-variable Veitch diagram, this area was originally $\overline{X}$. Therefore, the simplest sum-of-products form for the designation number 1010 1010 is $\overline{X}$.

The designation numbers for four variables are tabulated in Table 5-23.

TABLE 5-23. DESIGNATION NUMBERS FOR FOUR VARIABLES

			COLUMN																
			0	1	2	3		4	5	6	7		8	9	10	11		12	13	14	15
ROWS	1	#W	0	1	0	1		0	1	0	1		0	1	0	1		0	1	0	1
	2	#X	0	0	1	1		0	0	1	1		0	0	1	1		0	0	1	1
	3	#Y	0	0	0	0		1	1	1	1		0	0	0	0		1	1	1	1
	4	#Z	0	0	0	0		0	0	0	0		1	1	1	1		1	1	1	1

The decimal numbers represent the columns. Notice the alternation principle that is followed. For example, #W has an alternation of zeros and ones; #X has an alternation of two zeros and two ones; #Y has an alternation of four zeros and four ones; and #Z has an alternation of eight zeros and eight ones.

A four-variable Veitch diagram for the designation numbers of four variables is shown in Fig. 5-3. The decimal numbers represent the columns, the Boolean statements represent those for the columns, and the binary numbers represent those for that particular column. For example, the rectangle labeled with the decimal number 9 shows the Boolean statement $Z\overline{Y}\overline{X}W$ and the binary number 1001. This rectangle represents column 9 in Table 5-23. This column is read from bottom to top in order to keep the proper sequence in the binary numbers. Notice that in this column, X and Y are both zeroes, while W and Z are ones. Since a zero represents that a variable does not exist, and since a 1 represents that a variable does exist, then the Boolean statement for this column is $Z\overline{Y}\overline{X}W$. All of the rectangles have been labeled using this concept.

With a careful study of the Veitch diagram of Fig. 5-3, one sees a pattern. Notice that the rectangles labeled with the decimal numbers 0 and 1 occupy the left, upper, and outermost two rectangles. The rectangles labeled 2 and 3 occupy the right, upper, and outermost two rectangles. These rectangles have the smaller number for the columns on top. The rectangles 4 and 5 are the lower, left, and outermost rectangles. Notice that

4 is underneath 5. Rectangles 6 and 7 occupy the lower, right, and outermost rectangles. Notice again that 6 is underneath 7. The rectangles 8, 9, 10, and 11 occupy the upper, center area, with rectangles 8 and 10 on top. The rectangles 12, 13, 14, and 15 occupy the lower and central area, with rectangles 12 and 14 on the bottom. This system of labeling the rectangles tends to make it somewhat easy to remember where the number for each column of the designation number is located.

	$\bar{X}$	$\bar{X}$	X	X	
$\bar{Y}$	0 $\bar{Z}\,\bar{Y}\,\bar{X}\,\bar{W}$ 0 0 0 0	8 $Z\,\bar{Y}\,\bar{X}\,\bar{W}$ 1 0 0 0	10 $Z\,\bar{Y}\,X\,\bar{W}$ 1 0 1 0	2 $\bar{Z}\,\bar{Y}\,X\,\bar{W}$ 0 0 1 0	$\bar{W}$
$\bar{Y}$	1 $\bar{Z}\,\bar{Y}\,\bar{X}\,W$ 0 0 0 1	9 $Z\,\bar{Y}\,\bar{X}\,W$ 1 0 0 1	11 $Z\,\bar{Y}\,X\,W$ 1 0 1 1	3 $\bar{Z}\,\bar{Y}\,X\,W$ 0 0 1 1	W
Y	5 $\bar{Z}\,Y\,\bar{X}\,W$ 0 1 0 1	13 $Z\,Y\,\bar{X}\,W$ 1 1 0 1	15 $Z\,Y\,X\,W$ 1 1 1 1	7 $\bar{Z}\,Y\,X\,W$ 0 1 1 1	W
Y	4 $\bar{Z}\,Y\,\bar{X}\,\bar{W}$ 0 1 0 0	12 $Z\,Y\,\bar{X}\,\bar{W}$ 1 1 0 0	14 $Z\,Y\,X\,\bar{W}$ 1 1 1 0	6 $\bar{Z}\,Y\,X\,\bar{W}$ 0 1 1 0	$\bar{W}$
	$\bar{Z}$	Z	Z	$\bar{Z}$	

Fig. 5-3. A four-variable Veitch diagram for four-variable designation numbers.

Now that we have explained the Veitch diagram for the designation numbers of four variables, let us show an example of how to write the simplest sum-of-products form for four variables.

Let us first state this example in the following verbal form: It is desired to write the simplest sum-of-products form for four variables that will produce an output from an electronic circuit whenever two or more of the variables exist simultaneously.

The first thing to do is to write the tabulation of the designation numbers for four variables. In order to write the designation number of the function that is desired, we must first give it a symbol. Let the symbol for this be f_d. Having assigned a symbol to the function desired, let us now proceed to write the designation number for it. From the verbal statement, we see that we desire an output whenever two or more of the variables exist simultaneously. Therefore, we proceed to look in our tabulation for the designation numbers of four variables, and whenever we see two or more ones in any column, we write a one in the row for the designation number of the function desired, $\#(f_d)$. Table 5-24 shows the tabulation of the designation numbers for the four variables as well as the designation number for the function desired. In the $\#(f_d)$ there are ones in 3, 5, 6, 7, 9, 10, 11, 12, 13, 14, and 15. We next construct a Veitch diagram for four variables, using the same method that was used in constructing the Veitch diagram of

TABLE 5-24. DESIGNATION NUMBER FOR A VERBAL STATEMENT

			COLUMN															
			0	1	2	3	4	5	6	7	8	9	10	11	12	13	14	15
ROWS	1	#W	0	1	0	1	0	1	0	1	0	1	0	1	0	1	0	1
	2	#X	0	0	1	1	0	0	1	1	0	0	1	1	0	0	1	1
	3	#Y	0	0	0	0	1	1	1	1	0	0	0	0	1	1	1	1
	4	#Z	0	0	0	0	0	0	0	0	1	1	1	1	1	1	1	1
	5	#(f_d)	0	0	0	1	0	1	1	1	0	1	1	1	1	1	1	1

Fig. 5-3 except that we do not put in the Boolean statements and the binary numbers, but we do put in the decimal numbers corresponding to the columns of the designation numbers. In order to easily locate the rectangles that have ones in the $\#(f_d)$, we shall shade in these rectangles. This is shown in Fig. 5-4.

The next step is to determine the coupling. When coupling, it should be borne in mind that the greatest number of boxes that are coupled gives the simplest form. The ellipses and circles that are drawn in Fig. 5-4 show the coupling that is to be used. Notice that each ellipse and circle encompasses four rectangles, so that the least number of variables can be obtained. Since

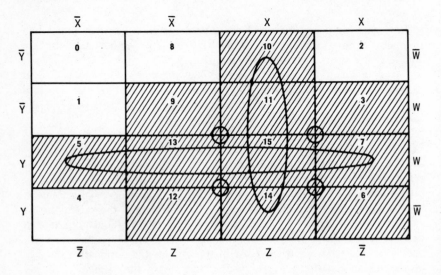

Fig. 5-4. A Veitch diagram explaining the problem in the text.

there are six couples, there will be six Boolean statements in the final Boolean expression. The couple consisting of rectangles 5, 13, 15, and 7 will yield the Boolean statement WY because these rectangles are independent of the other two variables. The rectangles 10, 11, 15, and 14 which are coupled will yield XZ. The rectangles 9, 11, 15, and 13 which are coupled will yield as the simplest Boolean statement WZ. The rectangles 11, 3, 7, and 15 will yield the Boolean statement WX. The rectangles 13, 15, 14, and 12 will yield YZ. The rectangles 15, 7, 6, and 14 will yield XY. Therefore, the simplest sum-of-products form for this example will be $WY + XZ + WZ + WX + YZ + XY$.

5-7. Problems

1. State in your own words the definition of a truth table.
2. What do the numbers 0 and 1 represent when used in a truth table?
3. How many combinations will there be for two variables? For 3? For 5? Construct a truth table for 5 variables.
4. Prove the following identities using a truth table.
   (a) $XY + X\bar{Y} = X$ (b) $X\bar{Y}Z + XYZ = XZ$
   (c) $\bar{X}Y\bar{Z} + XY\bar{Z} = Y\bar{Z}$ (d) $\overline{\bar{X}Y} + X\bar{Y} = \bar{X}Y \ \overline{X\bar{Y}}$
   (e) $XY\bar{Z} + X\bar{Y}Z + \bar{X}YZ = (\bar{X} + \bar{Y} + Z)(\bar{X} + Y + \bar{Z})(X + \bar{Y} + \bar{Z})$
5. Develop the Boolean statements from the following truth tables.

   (a) X 0101
        Y 0011
        ? 1001

   (b) X 01010101
        Y 00110011
        Z 00001111
        ? 01101100

   (c) X 01010101
        Y 00110011
        Z 00001111
        ? 01110110

   (d) X 01010101
        Y 00110011
        Z 00001111
        ? 11110000

   (e) W 0101010101010101
        X 0011001100110011
        Y 0000111100001111
        Z 0000000011111111
        ? 0110010001100001

6. Using truth tables, develop the Boolean function for the following: There are three variables, X, Y, and Z. It is desired to write the Boolean function for whenever any of the variables exists alone.
7. Using truth tables, develop the Boolean function for the following: There are four variables W, X, Y, and Z. It is desired to write the Boolean function for whenever any and only two of the variables exists simultaneously.
8. What is a designation number? Explain why it is important that the basis for a designation number be clearly defined.
9. Write the basis for a designation number that contains five variables.
10. Determine the designation numbers of the following:

(a) $X\overline{Y}$ (b) $\overline{XYZ}$

(c) $XY + \overline{XY}$ (d) $XY + \overline{X}\overline{Y}$

(e) $XYZ + \overline{X}Y\overline{Z} + \overline{X}YZ$

11. What is the first canonical or minterm form of a designation number? What is the second or maxterm form? What is meant by the simplest sum-of-products form of a designation number?

12. Derive the second canonical, or maxterm, form of a designation number from the first canonical, or minterm, form.

13. Write the first canonical, or minterm, form for the following:

(a) #X 0101   (b) #X 0101 0101
     #Y 0011   #Y 0011 0011
     #? 1001   #Z 0000 1111
                                         #? 1001 0110

(c) #X 0101 0101   (d) #W 0101 0101 0101 0101
     #Y 0011 0011   #X 0011 0011 0011 0011
     #Z 0000 1111   #Y 0000 1111 0000 1111
     #? 1101 0111   #Z 0000 0000 1111 1111
                                         #? 1010 0110 0011 1100

(e) #W 0101 0101 0101 0101
     #X 0011 0011 0011 0011
     #Y 0000 1111 0000 1111
     #Z 0000 0000 1111 1111
     #? 0011 1001 1111 0001

14. Write the second canonical or maxterm form for those given in **Problem 13**.

15. Write the simplest sum-of-products form for those given in **Problem 13**.

6

Problem Solving

In the preceding chapters, Boolean variables were represented by general symbols such as A, B, X, and Y. Because these symbols are general, they can be used in many different applications, and may represent any specific variable. When Boolean algebra is used in electronic applications, the variable quantity is usually a voltage; hence, in this chapter and in the chapters to follow, we will use voltage symbols such as e_1, e_2, etc., instead of the previously introduced symbols. Although a different notation is used, the same definitions, postulates, and identities of Boolean algebra apply. For example, if you see a Boolean statement that reads:

$$e_0 = e_1 + \bar{e}_1 e_2$$

you should immediately recognize that this statement has the same form as

$$T = X + \bar{X}Y$$

where T is a function of X and Y.

Since you know that $X + \bar{X}Y = X + Y$, you can apply this solution to the voltage statement:

$$e_1 + \bar{e}_1 e_2 = e_1 + e_2$$

or
$$e_0 = e_1 + e_2$$

6-1. Logic Blocks in Electronic Applications

The logic block circuit in Fig. 6-1A is the type of block diagram introduced in Chapter 3. The inputs to each block are general Boolean variables and the output, T, is a function of the input variables. In this general circuit, T exists only when a certain combination of input variables exists. For instance, the circuit in Fig. 6-1A is designed to have an output when $AB + CD$ exists. When $AB + CD = 1$, $T = 1$; or, $T = AB + CD$. If at any time A and C, for instance, are not available at the input, then neither AB nor CD exists. Consequently, there will be no output. This is the same as saying, if $AB + CD = 0$, $T = 0$. The same reasoning is applicable to the circuit in Fig. 6-1B. The only difference between this circuit and the one in Fig. 6-1A

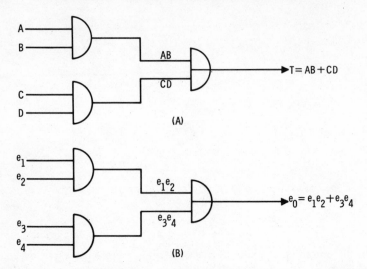

Fig. 6-1. Logic block circuits using (A) general variables A, B, C, and D; and (B) voltage variables e_1, e_2, e_3, and e_4. Otherwise, the circuits are identical.

is that, here, the inputs are specific voltages, and not general Boolean variables. This circuit is designed to have an output voltage, e_0, only when either e_1e_2 or e_3e_4 exists. Whenever an input voltage is missing from both terms at the same time, there can be no output voltage. In other words, if $e_1e_2 + e_3e_4$ is 0, e_0 is also 0.

We have ascertained, so far, that logic blocks can be designed to deliver an output voltage when certain voltages, or combinations of voltages are present at the input. Another important consideration in this discussion is that only two states of voltage are recognized in logic circuits. One state is usually zero or negative voltage; logically, this is a voltage that does not exist and it is represented, as you have learned, as $\bar{e}$. The other level is any voltage that is not zero. This voltage, *regardless of its amplitude,* is said to exist, and is represented logically as e.

Having reconciled electronic quantities to general Boolean quantities, we can proceed to design logic block circuits to produce voltage outputs under certain predetermined conditions. Furthermore, we can use the theorems of Boolean algebra to change the electronic block diagrams to their simplest form as we did in Chapter 4. In the following sections, we will write preliminary statements in terms of voltage and simplify the corresponding block diagrams by various methods. Then, to show that the simplified circuit will produce an output voltage under the same conditions imposed for the original circuit, we will check all of the solutions by using truth tables.

6-2.   Simplifying $e_0 = e_1 + e_1e_2$ by Veitch Diagram

The output voltage is a function of two variables, e_1 and e_2. Hence, as shown in Fig. 6-2, a two-variable Veitch diagram is required. The first step in simplifying the statement is to shade the squares of the diagram corresponding to the terms in the statement. The first term of the statement is e_1. The two squares at the right of the diagram contain e_1 so they are shaded. The second term of the statement is e_1e_2, and the only square that contains these two variables is the square at the lower right corner of the diagram. This square is shaded, and now has a crosshatch pattern. After all the terms

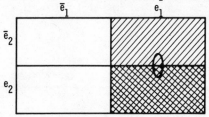

Fig. 6-2. A Veitch diagram shows that $e_1 = e_1 + e_1e_2$.

of the statement have been accounted for on the Veitch diagram, the next step is to choose couples. As you can see, there is only one couple to choose; when the two shaded squares are coupled, they yield the area e_1. This couple is independent of $\bar{e}_1$ and e_2; therefore, we can say that e_0 is equal to e_1.

To verify that $e_0 = e_1$, or $e_1 + e_1e_2 = e_1$, we can construct a truth table as shown in Table 6-1. Rows 1 and 2 list all of the possible combinations of e_1 and e_2. In the third row, the truth of the AND statement, e_1e_2, is recorded. Notice that a 1 appears in only the fourth column, where both e_1 and e_2 contain a 1. In the fourth row, the truth of the statement $e_1 + e_1e_2$ is re-

TABLE 6-1.   TRUTH TABLE VERIFYING THE SIMPLIFICATION

			COLUMN			
			1	2	3	4
ROWS	1	e_1	0	1	0	1
	2	e_2	0	0	1	1
	3	e_1e_2	0	0	0	1
	4	$e_0 = e_1 + e_1e_2$	0	1	0	1

corded. For this statement, a 1 is recorded only in the columns in which e_1 has a 1, or e_1e_2 has a 1. The row for $e_1 + e_1e_2$ reads 0101. But, notice that this is the same as the row for e_1, which also reads 0101. We have proved by the truth table that $e_1 = e_0 = e_1 + e_1e_2$.

Let us see how the simplification of the original statement affects the logic block diagram for the statement. In Fig. 6-3A, the logic block diagram required to generate an output for the original statement is shown. Notice that the e_1 input to the OR gate is taken from the e_1 input to the AND gate. Schematically, it can also be drawn as a separate input as is done occasionally. This diagram consists of an AND gate and an OR gate, and requires four electronic components. The simplified statement is $e_0 = e_1$, and you can

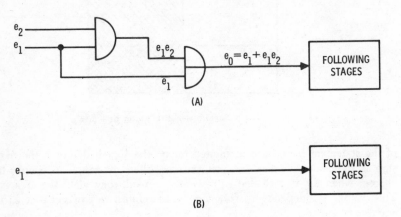

Fig. 6-3. The logic block diagrams needed to generate (A) the original statement, and (B) the simplified statement.

see by looking at this statement that no logic blocks are needed at all; hence, no electronic components are needed. The physical significance of this is that e_0 and e_1 are the same quantity; that whenever e_1 exists we have an output. This voltage may be used directly as an input to a following stage. Instead of feeding the output of the logic blocks to the next stage as shown in Fig. 6-3A, e_1 is fed directly to the following stage as shown in Fig. 6-3B. By simplifying the original statement, and consequently, the original logic diagram, we have saved four electronic components while still satisfying the requirements of the original circuit.

6-3. Simplifying $e_0 = e_1 + \bar{e}_1 e_2$ by Veitch Diagram

In this statement, e_0 is a function of two variables; therefore its simplification requires the use of a two-variable Veitch diagram. The Veitch diagram in Fig. 6-4A contains the two variables e_1 and e_2. The first term of the statement, e_1, is contained in the two rectangles at the right; these two rectangles are shaded. The second term, $\bar{e}_1 e_2$, is contained in the lower left rectangle; this area is also shaded. Having accounted for all the terms in the original statement, we apply the concept of couples to the diagram to find the simplest equivalent statement. The first couple takes in the two rectangles at the right of the diagram. This couple yields the area that is e_1,

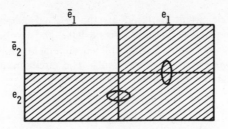

Fig. 6-4. Veitch diagram showing that $e_1 + \bar{e}_1 e_2 = e_1 + e_2$.

and it is independent of the variables e_2 and $\bar{e}_1$, as you can see. The only couple remaining is that between the two lower rectangles. This couple yields the area e_2, which is independent of e_1 and $\bar{e}_2$. By use of the Veitch diagram, therefore, the original statement has been simplified to $e_0 = e_1 + e_2$. Using the truth table of Table 6-2, the truth of the simplified statement can be tested. The first two rows of the truth table contain all the possibilities of the two variables. The third row contains the truth of $\bar{e}_1$, which is the negation of e_1. In the fourth row, the truth of the AND statement $\bar{e}_1 e_2$ is written, and, in the fifth row, the original statement is written. Finally, the truth of the simplified statement is recorded. The simplified

TABLE 6-2. TRUTH TABLE VERIFYING THE SIMPLIFICATION

		COLUMN			
		1	2	3	4
ROWS	1 $\quad e_1$	0	1	0	1
	2 $\quad e_2$	0	0	1	1
	3 $\quad \bar{e}_1$	1	0	1	0
	4 $\quad \bar{e}_1 e_2$	0	0	1	0
	5 $\quad e_0 = e_1 + \bar{e}_1 e_2$	0	1	1	1
	6 $\quad e_1 + e_2$	0	1	1	1

statement is $e_1 + e_2$. In the first column, neither variable exists; therefore, $e_1 + e_2$ is zero. In the second column, e_1 exists, and, in the third column, e_2 exists. A 1 is, therefore, recorded in the second and third columns for the simplified statement. In the fourth column, e_1 and e_2 exist; hence $e_1 + e_2$ exists, and a 1 is placed in the fourth column. The truth of $e_1 + e_2$ is 0111, and you can see that this is the same as the truth of the original statement. They are, therefore, equivalent.

The logic block circuit required for the original statement is shown in Fig. 6-5A; it uses an AND gate and an OR gate, and requires five electronic components. For the equivalent simplified statement, only one OR gate is required, and two electronic components. The circuit required to generate the simplified statement is shown in Fig. 6-5B.

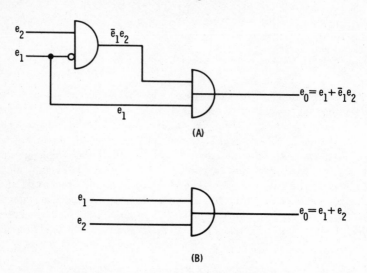

(A)

(B)

Fig. 6-5. The logic block diagrams needed to generate (A) the original statement, and (B) the simplified statement.

6-4.   Simplifying $e_0 = e_1 e_2 e_3 e_4 + e_1 \bar{e}_2 + e_1 \bar{e}_3 + e_2 e_3$ by Veitch Diagram

The output voltage, e_0, in this statement, is a function of four variables. In order to simplify the statement, a four-variable Veitch diagram is needed. A four-variable Veitch diagram is shown in Fig. 6-6. For the purpose of convenient reference, the rectangles have been arbitrarily numbered from 1 to 16. These numbers have no bearing on the problem.

The first term of the original statement is $e_1 e_2 e_3 e_4$, and it is contained only in rectangle 11 of the diagram; this rectangle is, therefore, shaded. The second term, $e_1 \bar{e}_2$, is contained in rectangles 3, 4, 7, and 8; each of these rectangles is shaded. The third term of the statement, $e_1 \bar{e}_3$, is contained in rectangles 4, 8, 12, and 16; and the fourth and last term of the statement, $e_2 e_3$, is contained in rectangles 10, 11, 14, and 15. Having accounted for all of the terms of the statement in the Veitch diagram, we can apply the concept of couples to obtain the simplified equivalent statement. As shown in the figure, one couple can be made to include the entire area of the eight rectangles in the right section of the Veitch diagram. This couple yields the term, e_1, which is independent of $\bar{e}_1$, and the variables e_2, e_3, and e_4. Another couple consisting of rectangles 10, 11, 14 and 15 can be made. This couple yields the term e_2e_3, and is independent of $\bar{e}_2$, $\bar{e}_3$, and the variables e_1 and e_4. A question might arise as to why the entire area of rectangles 10, 11, 14 and 15 were coupled rather than just rectangles 10 and 14. Remember that, the greater the number of rectangles that can be included in one couple, the fewer the variables contained in the resultant term. If only rectangles 10 and 14 were coupled, the statement obtained using this couple would not be in its simplest form. To prove this, let us use the couple consisting of rectangles 10 and 14 rather than the larger couple used originally. The smaller couple yields the term, $\bar{e}_1e_2e_3$; hence, the simplified statement would be $e_1 + \bar{e}_1e_2e_3$.

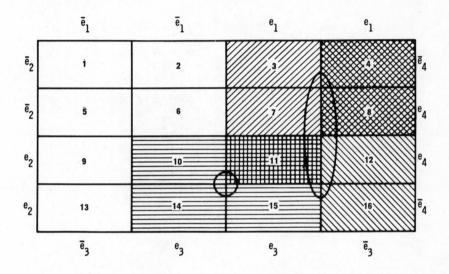

Fig. 6-6. Veitch diagram showing that $e_1e_2e_3e_4 + e_1\bar{e}_2 + e_1\bar{e}_3 + e_2e_3 = e_1 + e_2e_3$.

If you examine this statement carefully, you can see that it is in the form of $X + \bar{X}Y$, where X represents e_1, and Y represents e_2e_3. You know that $X + \bar{X}Y$ is equal to $X + Y$; therefore, $e_1 + \bar{e}_1e_2e_3$ is equal to $e_1 + e_2e_3$. This is exactly the statement that is obtained using the four-rectangle couple as we did originally.

To prove that the simplified statement obtained by the Veitch diagram is equivalent to the original statement, a truth table such as shown in Table 6-3 can be developed. In this truth table, the first four rows contain all the possibilties of the four variables. Following these rows are six rows in which the truth of each term in the original statement is developed. In the eleventh row, the truth of the entire original statement is written, and, in the last row, the truth of the simplified statement is tested. As you see, the truth values for the original and simplified statements are identically arranged; we can, therefore, conclude that the two statements are equivalent.

The logic block circuit needed to generate the original statement is shown

TABLE 6-3. TRUTH TABLE VERIFYING THE SIMPLIFICATION

ROWS			COLUMN															
			1	2	3	4	5	6	7	8	9	10	11	12	13	14	15	16
	1	e_1	0	1	0	1	0	1	0	1	0	1	0	1	0	1	0	1
	2	e_2	0	0	1	1	0	0	1	1	0	0	1	1	0	0	1	1
	3	e_3	0	0	0	0	1	1	1	1	0	0	0	0	1	1	1	1
	4	e_4	0	0	0	0	0	0	0	0	1	1	1	1	1	1	1	1
	5	$\bar{e}_2$	1	1	0	0	1	1	0	0	1	1	0	0	1	1	0	0
	6	$\bar{e}_3$	1	1	1	1	0	0	0	0	1	1	1	1	0	0	0	0
	7	$e_1 e_2 e_3 e_4$	0	0	0	0	0	0	0	0	0	0	0	0	0	0	0	1
	8	$e_1 \bar{e}_2$	0	1	0	0	0	1	0	0	0	1	0	0	0	1	0	0
	9	$e_1 \bar{e}_3$	0	1	0	1	0	0	0	0	0	1	0	1	0	0	0	0
	10	$e_2 e_3$	0	0	0	0	0	0	1	1	0	0	0	0	0	0	1	1
	11	$e_1 e_2 e_3 e_4 + e_1 \bar{e}_2 + e_1 \bar{e}_3 + e_2 e_3$	0	1	0	1	0	1	1	1	0	1	0	1	0	1	1	1
	12	$e_1 + e_2 e_3$	0	1	0	1	0	1	1	1	0	1	0	1	0	1	1	1

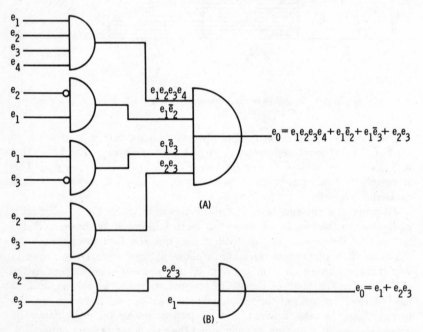

Fig. 6-7. The logic block diagrams needed to generate (A) the original statement, and (B) the simplified statement.

in Fig. 6-7A. This circuit uses four AND gates, two inhibitors, and one OR gate. This arrangement requires a total of 16 electronic components, including inhibitors. The logic block circuit in Fig. 6-7B is all that is required to generate the equivalent simplified statement. This circuit uses only one AND gate, and one OR gate, and requires four electronic components. Here is a very definite example of eliminating the need for excessive components by Boolean simplification. Although there is a substantial difference in the two circuits, they both produce an output under the same conditions.

6-5.   Simplifying $e_0 = e_1(e_1 + e_2)$ by Boolean Algebra

According to the law of distribution in Boolean algebra, $X(Y + Z) = XY + XZ$. Using this identity, we can write:

$$e_0 = e_1e_1 + e_1e_2$$

The first term of this statement, e_1e_1, can be simplified by the Law of Tautology. As you learned in Chapter 3, $X \cdot X = X$; therefore,

$$e_0 = e_1 + e_1e_2$$

According to the Law of Absorption, $X + XY = X$. This identity has the same form as our voltage statement; therefore, we can further simplify the

TABLE 6-4.   TRUTH TABLE FOR $e_1(e_1 + e_2) = e_1$

		COLUMN			
		1	2	3	4
ROWS	1 e_1	0	1	0	1
	2 e_2	0	0	1	1
	3 $e_1 + e_2$	0	1	1	1
	4 $e_1(e_1 + e_2)$	0	1	0	1

statement to read: $e_0 = e_1$. Recognize that this is essentially the same statement that was simplified in Section 6-2; it is reasonable, then, to expect the same solution. Nevertheless, let us use the truth table to verify this simplification.

The first two rows of Table 6-4 list all the combinations of the two variables. In the third row, the truth of the OR statement, $e_1 + e_2$, is recorded. A zero appears in the first column because $e_1 + e_2$ does not exist in this column. Each of the other three columns contains a 1 because $e_1 + e_2$ exists in these columns. Now, in the fourth row, the truth of $e_1(e_1 + e_2)$ is tested. A zero appears in the first and third columns because both e_1 and $(e_1 + e_2)$ do not exist in these columns. In the second and fourth columns, a 1 appears because both e_1 and $(e_1 + e_2)$ exist. We see that, for $e_0 =$

$e_1(e_1 + e_2)$, the whole truth table reads 0101. But, notice that the row for e_1 also reads 0101. This proves that the truth of $e_1(e_1 + e_2)$ and e_1 are the same; therefore, e_0 is equal to e_1, or $e_1(e_1 + e_2) = e_1$.

The logic block diagram for the original statement is shown in Fig. 6-8A. This block diagram uses an OR circuit, an AND circuit, and requires four electronic components. However, the circuit required for the simplified statement requires no logic blocks or electronic components. The voltage, e_1, is the same as e_0, or the original statement, and can be fed directly to the following stages as shown in Fig. 6-8B.

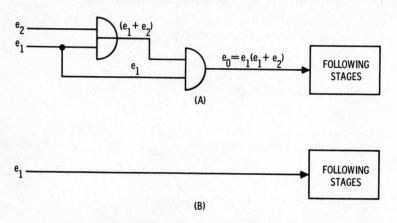

(A)

(B)

Fig. 6-8. (A) The logic block diagram required to generate the original statement, and (B) the logic block diagram required to generate the simplified statement.

As in the previous problem, by simplifying the original statement, we have eliminated the need for four electronic components while still satisfying the requirements of the original circuit. In other words, when e_1 exists, there is an input to the following stages; when $e_1(e_1 + e_2)$ exists, there is also an input to the following stages. The two statements, or circuits, are, therefore, equivalent.

6-6. Simplifying $e_0 = e_1\bar{e}_2 + e_2\bar{e}_3 + e_1e_3 + e_2$ by Boolean Algebra

Before applying the laws and identities of Boolean algebra to the statement, it will be easier to work with if some of the terms are rearranged. By changing the position of the terms, we can write:

$$e_0 = e_2 + e_2\bar{e}_3 + e_1\bar{e}_2 + e_1e_3 \qquad (6\text{-}1)$$

The first two terms of this statement are in the form:

$$X + XY = X$$

If we let X represent e_2, and Y represent $\bar{e}_3$, then we can say:

$$e_2 + e_2\bar{e}_3 = e_2$$

Substituting this into Eq. (6-1), we have:

$$e_0 = e_2 + e_1\bar{e}_2 + e_1e_3 \tag{6-2}$$

Now we can work on the first two terms of Eq. (6-2). Notice that $e_2 + e_1e_2$ is in the form:

$$X + \bar{X}Y = X + Y$$

If we let X represent e_2, and Y represent e_1, then we have:

$$e_2 + \bar{e}_2e_1 = e_1 + e_2$$

Substituting this equivalent term into Eq. (6-2), we have:

$$e_0 = e_1 + e_2 + e_1e_3$$

or

$$e_0 = e_1 + e_1e_3 + e_2 \tag{6-3}$$

The first two terms in Eq. (6-3) are in the form of $X + XY$, where X represents e_1, and Y represents e_3. Since $X + XY = X$, we can say that $e_1 + e_1e_3 = e_1$. Equation (6-3) can then be written:

$$e_0 = e_1 + e_2 \tag{6-4}$$

To verify this simplification by truth table, we develop the three-variable truth table of Table 6-5. The first three rows list all the possibilties for the three variables. The fourth and fifth rows contain the truth of $\bar{e}_2$ and $\bar{e}_3$; these are simply the negations of e_2 and e_3. In rows 6, 7, and 8, the truth of each term in the original statement is determined. The truth of the original statement is recorded in row 9. You have seen how the truth of a

TABLE 6-5. TRUTH TABLE FOR $e_1\bar{e}_2 + e_2\bar{e}_3 + e_1e_3 + e_2 = e_1 + e_2$

		COLUMN							
		1	2	3	4	5	6	7	8
1	e_1	0	1	0	1	0	1	0	1
2	e_2	0	0	1	1	0	0	1	1
3	e_3	0	0	0	0	1	1	1	1
4	$\bar{e}_2$	1	1	0	0	1	1	0	0
5	$\bar{e}_3$	1	1	1	1	0	0	0	0
6	$e_1\bar{e}_2$	0	1	0	0	0	1	0	0
7	$e_2\bar{e}_3$	0	0	1	1	0	0	0	0
8	e_1e_3	0	0	0	0	0	1	0	1
9	$e_1\bar{e}_2 + e_2\bar{e}_3 + e_1e_3 + e_2$	0	1	1	1	0	1	1	1
10	$e_1 + e_2$	0	1	1	1	0	1	1	1

(ROWS label spans rows 4–10 on the left side)

statement is obtained in the previous problems. In row 10, the truth of the simplified statement is written. Neither e_1 nor e_2 is present in the first column, so a zero is recorded in the first column for the simplified statement. Either e_1 or e_2 is present in columns 2, 3, and 4; hence a 1 is placed in the same columns of the simplified statement. In column 5, neither e_1 nor e_2 is present; therefore, a zero is recorded. In the last three columns, either e_1, e_2, or both exist; therefore, a 1 is recorded in each of these columns for the simplified statement. The truth of $e_1 + e_2$ is 01110111 which, as you can see, is identical to the truth for the original statement. The two statements are, therefore, equivalent.

Let us now examine the logic block circuits required to generate these two statements, and compare them. The logic circuit for the original statement is shown in Fig. 6-9A. This circuit uses three AND gates, an OR gate, and it requires 12 electronic components, including inhibitors. The extent of

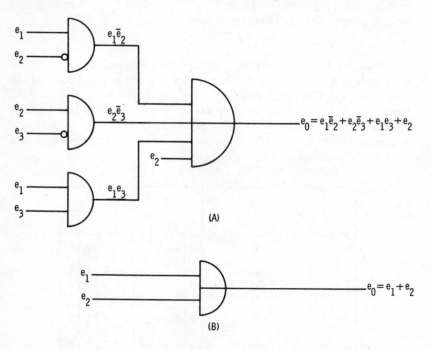

(A)

(B)

Fig. 6-9. The logic block diagrams needed to generate (A) the original statement, and (B) the simplified statement.

the simplification of the original statement becomes more apparent after seeing the logic circuit required for the simplified statement. In Fig. 6-9B, the equivalent circuit uses only one OR gate, and requires only two electronic components. Since these circuits are equivalent, they produce an output under the same condition.

6-7. Simplifying $e_0 = \overline{(e_1 + e_2)} + \overline{(e_1 + e_3)}$ by Boolean Algebra

At first glance, this statement seems rather difficult to simplify. Since both terms in this statement are negated, you may be at a loss for an idea of how to approach the problem. Do not forget De Morgan's theorem; it provides a simple method of attack here. According to De Morgan's theorem, $\overline{X} + \overline{Y} = \overline{X \cdot Y}$. Applying this theorem to the problem, you can write:

$$e_0 = \overline{(e_1 + e_2) \ (e_1 + e_3)} \tag{6-5}$$

Recognize that X may represent the term $(e_1 + e_2)$ and that Y may represent the term $(e_1 + e_3)$. Now that the form of the original statement has been changed, we can operate on the terms beneath the negation sign. The parentheses in the statement can be removed by applying the Law of Distribution:

$$e_0 = \overline{e_1 e_1 + e_1 e_3 + e_1 e_2 + e_2 e_3} \tag{6-6}$$

We can immediately reduce the first term in this statement to e_1 instead of $e_1 e_1$. The Law of Tautology justifies this simplification. The equation now reads:

$$e_0 = \overline{e_1 + e_1 e_3 + e_1 e_2 + e_2 e_3} \tag{6-7}$$

The first two terms of Eq. (6-7) are in the form of $X + XY$ which equals X. We can, therefore, say that $e_1 + e_1 e_3 = e_1$, and rewrite Eq. (6-7) to read:

$$e_0 = \overline{e_1 + e_1 e_2 + e_2 e_3} \tag{6-8}$$

The first two terms in Eq. (6-8) are also in the form of $X + XY = X$. As we did before, we can simplify the first two terms of Eq. (6-8) to simply e_1, and rewrite the equation:

$$e_0 = \overline{e_1 + e_2 e_3} \tag{6-9}$$

This is the simplest form into which the original statement can be changed. Using the truth table of Table 6-6, we can verify that the original statement, and Eq. (6-9) are equivalent. The first three rows of the truth table contain all the possibilities for the three variables. In rows 4 through 7, the truth of each term of the original statement is developed, and, in the eighth row, the truth for the original statement is written. In rows 9 and 10, the truth of each term of the simplified statement is developed and, finally, in the last row, the truth for the simplified statement is written. You can see that the truths for both the original and simplified statements are identical; therefore, the two statements are equivalent.

The logic block circuit for the original statement is shown in Fig. 6-10A. This circuit requires three OR gates, and two inverters. Altogether, eight electronic components are required. It is also possible to use inhibitors at the inputs to the last OR gate, instead of inverters, to negate the outputs of the first two OR gates. This, however, does not reduce the number of electronic components needed to generate the original statment. In Fig. 6-10B, one AND gate, one OR gate, and one inverter are used. This circuit, which produces an output under the same conditions as the circuit in Fig. 6-10A, requires only five electronic components.

TABLE 6-6. TRUTH TABLE FOR $\overline{(e_1+e_2)} + \overline{(e_1+e_3)} = \overline{(e_1+e_2e_3)}$

		COLUMN							
		1	2	3	4	5	6	7	8
1	e_1	0	1	0	1	0	1	0	1
2	e_2	0	0	1	1	0	0	1	1
3	e_3	0	0	0	0	1	1	1	1
4	e_1+e_2	0	1	1	1	0	1	1	1
5	$\overline{e_1+e_2}$	1	0	0	0	1	0	0	0
6	e_1+e_3	0	1	0	1	1	1	1	1
7	$\overline{e_1+e_3}$	1	0	1	0	0	0	0	0
8	$e_0 = \overline{(e_1+e_2)} + \overline{(e_1+e_3)}$	1	0	1	0	1	0	0	0
9	e_2e_3	0	0	0	0	0	0	1	1
10	$e_1+e_2e_3$	0	1	0	1	0	1	1	1
11	$e_0 = \overline{(e_1+e_2e_3)}$	1	0	1	0	1	0	0	0

(ROWS)

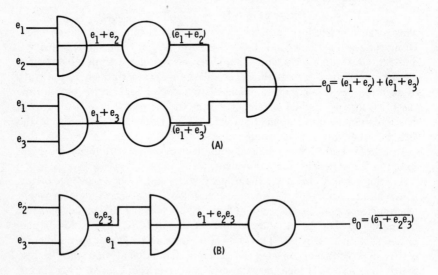

Fig. 6-10. The logic block diagrams needed to generate (A) the original statement, and (B) the simplified statement.

6-8. Simplifying $e_0 = \bar{e}_1\bar{e}_2e_3 + e_2e_3 + e_3$ by Designation Numbers

Since a Boolean statement, reduced to its simplest sum-of-products form, cannot be further simplified, we shall simplify the given statement by finding its simplest sum-of-products form. To do this, we construct the special Veitch diagram as shown in Fig. 6-11, and the designation numbers for the three variables in Table 6-7. The column numbers of the designation numbers for the variables are placed in the appropriate rectangles in the Veitch diagram. For example, in column 0, there are all zeroes, therefore, the AND statement for column 0 is $\bar{e}_1\bar{e}_2\bar{e}_3$. The rectangle in the upper left

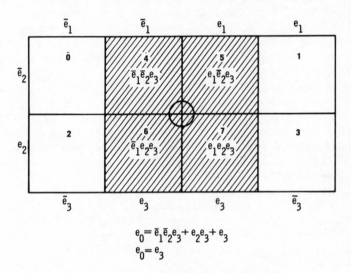

$$e_0 = \bar{e}_1\bar{e}_2e_3 + e_2e_3 + e_3$$
$$e_0 = e_3$$

Fig. 6-11. Finding the simplest sum-of-products form by Veitch diagram.

TABLE 6-7. SIMPLIFYING $\bar{e}_1\bar{e}_2e_3 + e_2e_3 + e_3$ BY DESIGNATION NUMBERS

			COLUMN							
			0	1	2	3		4	5	6	7
ROWS	1	# e_1	0	1	0	1		0	1	0	1
	2	# e_2	0	0	1	1		0	0	1	1
	3	# e_3	0	0	0	0		1	1	1	1
	4	# e_0	0	0	0	0		1	1	1	1

corner of the Veitch diagram contains $\bar{e}_1\bar{e}_2\bar{e}_3$; the 0 is, therefore, placed in this rectangle. After all the column designations have been located on the Veitch diagram, the rectangles are shaded. The first term of the statement is $\bar{e}_1\bar{e}_2e_3$. This term is represented in rectangle 4; hence this rectangle is shaded. The second term of the statement is e_2e_3, which is represented in rectangles 6, and 7. These rectangles are shaded. The third term of the statement is simply e_3, which is represented in rectangles 4, 5, 6, and 7. Since rectangles 4, 6, and 7 have already been shaded, only rectangle 5 remains to be shaded. Having accounted for all three terms of the original statement, we find that a couple can be made that takes in all four of the rectangles. This couple yields only the variable e_3; therefore, from the special Veitch diagram, $e_0 = e_3$. We know that the simplified statement is independent of $\bar{e}_3$ because none of the shaded rectangles contain $\bar{e}_3$. Also, if rectangles 5 and 7, or 4 and 6 were coupled, they would contain $e_2\bar{e}_2$ which is equal to 0; the simplified statement is, therefore, independent of the variable e_2. Similarly, if rectangles 4 and 5, or 6 and 7 were coupled, they would contain $e_1\bar{e}_1$ which is equal to 0; the simplified statement is, therefore, independent of the variable e_1.

Having found that $e_0 = e_3$, let us determine the designation number of e_0. From the Veitch diagram, we see that the area that is e_3 encompasses rectangles 4, 5, 6, and 7. To find the designation number of e_0, we record a 1 in the respective columns in the designation number of Table 6-7. In the remaining columns, zeroes are recorded. The designation number for e_0 is 0000 1111. We can also tell from the designation number that e_0 is equal to e_3 because $\#e_3 = 0000\ 1111$, and $\#e_0 = 0000\ 1111$.

To verify the simplification by designation numbers, the truth table, shown in Table 6-8 is developed. First, all the combinations of the three variables are written in the first three rows. In the fourth row, $\bar{e}_1$, which is the negation of e_1, is written; and, in the fifth row, $\bar{e}_2$, which is the negation of e_2, is written. The sixth row contains the truth of the AND

TABLE 6-8.   TRUTH TABLE VERIFYING THE SIMPLIFICATION

		COLUMN							
		1	2	3	4	5	6	7	8
	1	e_1	0	1	0	1	0	1	0	1
	2	e_2	0	0	1	1	0	0	1	1
	3	e_3	0	0	0	0	1	1	1	1
ROWS	4	$\bar{e}_1$	1	0	1	0	1	0	1	0
	5	$\bar{e}_2$	1	1	0	0	1	1	0	0
	6	$\bar{e}_1\bar{e}_2e_3$	0	0	0	0	1	0	0	0
	7	e_2e_3	0	0	0	0	0	0	1	1
	8	$\bar{e}_1\bar{e}_2e_3+e_2e_3+e_3$	0	0	0	0	1	1	1	1

statement $\bar{e}_1\bar{e}_2e_3$, and the seventh row contains the truth of the statement e_2e_3. Finally, in the eighth row, the truth of the original statement is written. Here, from the truth table, it is clear that the truth of e_3 is identical to that of $\bar{e}_1\bar{e}_2e_3 + e_2e_3 + e_3$; hence, we have verified that $e_0 = e_3$.

The logic block diagram needed to generate an output under the conditions of the original Boolean statement is shown in Fig. 6-12A. This diagram consists of two AND gates, one OR gate, and requires ten electronic compo-

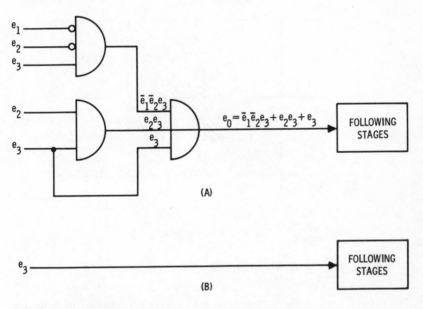

(A)

(B)

Fig. 6-12. The logic block diagrams needed to generate (A) the original statement, and (B) the simplified statement.

nents, including inhibtors. However, the equivalent statement as determined by the use of designation numbers shows that e_0 is the same as e_3; hence, whenever e_3 exists, e_0 exists. The circuit for the simplified statement requires no logic blocks, or no electronic components, and e_3 is fed directly to the following stages. In this problem, we have been able to save ten electronic components by simplifying the original statement.

6-9. Simplifying $e_0 = (e_1 + e_2)(e_1 + e_3)$ by Designation Numbers

Using the simplest sum-of-products technique to simplify this statement requires the use of a three-variable Veitch diagram. Such a diagram is shown in Fig. 6-13; the conventional designation numbers for the three variables are shown in Table 6-9. The best approach to representing the statement on the special Veitch diagram is to change the statement from the "OR to AND" form, in which it is presented, to the "AND to OR" form, which is easier to work with. This is accomplished very easily by applying the Law of Distribution:

$$(e_1 + e_2)(e_1 + e_3) = e_1 e_1 + e_1 e_3 + e_2 e_3 + e_1 e_2$$

or

$$e_0 = e_1 + e_1 e_2 + e_1 e_3 + e_2 e_3$$

Now we can take each term and locate it on the Veitch diagram. The first term, e_1, is contained in the entire area included under e_1 in the Veitch diagram. This area is made up of rectangles 1, 3, 5, and 7, and it is shaded.

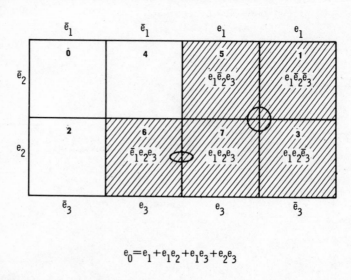

$$e_0 = e_1 + e_1 e_2 + e_1 e_3 + e_2 e_3$$

Fig. 6-13. Finding the simplest sum-of-products form by Veitch diagram.

The second term of the statement is $e_1 e_2$ and it is contained in rectangles 3 and 7. These have already been shaded. The third term, $e_1 e_3$, of the statement is contained in the area of rectangles 5 and 7. These rectangles have also been shaded. The last term of the statement, $e_2 e_3$, is contained

TABLE 6-9. SIMPLIFYING $e_1 + e_1 e_2 + e_1 e_3 + e_2 e_3$ BY DESIGNATION NUMBERS

			COLUMN							
			0	1	2	3		4	5	6	7
	1	# e_1	0	1	0	1		0	1	0	1
	2	# e_2	0	0	1	1		0	0	1	1
ROWS	3	# e_3	0	0	0	0		1	1	1	1
	4	# e_0	0	1	0	1		0	1	1	1
	5	# $(e_2 e_3)$	0	0	0	0		0	0	1	1
	6	# $(e_1 + e_2 e_3)$	0	1	0	1		0	1	1	1

TABLE 6-10. TRUTH TABLE VERIFYING THE SIMPLIFICATION

		COLUMN							
		1	2	3	4	5	6	7	8
ROWS	1 e_1	0	1	0	1	0	1	0	1
	2 e_2	0	0	1	1	0	0	1	1
	3 e_3	0	0	0	0	1	1	1	1
	4 $e_1 e_2$	0	0	0	1	0	0	0	1
	5 $e_1 e_3$	0	0	0	0	0	1	0	1
	6 $e_2 e_3$	0	0	0	0	0	0	1	1
	7 $e_1 + e_1 e_2 + e_1 e_3 + e_2 e_3$	0	1	0	1	0	1	1	1
	8 $e_1 + e_2 e_3$	0	1	0	1	0	1	1	1

in the area made up of rectangles 6 and 7. Since rectangle 7 has already been shaded, only rectangle 6 is shaded. The entire statement has now been accounted for on the Veitch diagram. The rectangles covered are 1, 3, 5, 7, and 6. To find the designation number of the original statement, a 1 is placed in each of the columns of e_0 for which a rectangle has been shaded. As you can see in Table 6-9, there is a 1 in columns 1, 3, 5, 6, and 7, and a zero in each of the remaining columns. Now, let us use the concept of couples on the Veitch diagram to see if e_0 can be represented by a simpler statement. The first couple takes in rectangles 1, 3, 5, and 7. These rectangles cover the area of e_1, and are independent of $\bar{e}_1$, and the variables e_2 and e_3. One term of the simplified statement is, therefore, e_1. The second couple, which accounts for the remainder of the rectangles, takes in rectangles 6 and 7. These cover the area containing e_2 and e_3. They are, however, independent of $\bar{e}_2$ and $\bar{e}_3$, and the variable e_1. Hence, the second and last term of the simplified statement is $e_2 e_3$. We can check the validity of the simplification by finding the designation number of the simplified statement, $e_0 = e_1 + e_2 e_3$. To find the designation numbers, we must first determine the designation number of e_2 and e_3, and logically add this number to the designation number of e_1. In the fifth row of designation numbers, the designation number of $e_2 e_3$ is recorded. This number contains a 1 in the sixth and seventh columns. Logically adding the designation number of $e_2 e_3$ to that of e_1, we record #$(e_1 + e_2 e_3)$ in the sixth row. We find that #$(e_1 + e_2 e_3)$ is 0101 0111. This is identical to the designation number of the original statement for e_0; hence, the two statements are equivalent.

The truth table of Table 6-10 has been developed to verify the validity of the simplified statement. Having used the truth table in the preceding problems for this purpose, you should be capable of following the develop-

134   Principles and Applications of Boolean Algebra

ment to see that the two statements are equivalent.

The logic block diagram needed to generate the original statement is shown in Fig. 6-14A, and the logic block diagram needed to generate the simplified, equivalent circuit is shown in Fig. 6-14B. The circuit in Fig. 6-14A uses three AND gates, an OR gate, and requires ten electronic components. The equivalent circuit produces an output for exactly the same conditions as the circuit in Fig. 6-14A, yet it uses one AND gate, one OR gate, and requires only four electronic components.

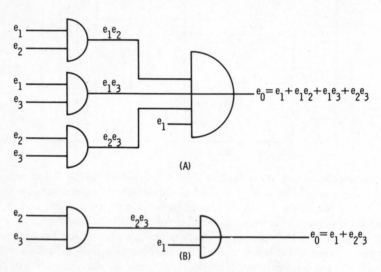

Fig. 6-14. The logic block diagrams needed to generate (A) the original statement, and (B) the simplified statement.

6-10.   Simplifying $e_0 = e_1\bar{e}_2\bar{e}_3 + \bar{e}_1e_2\bar{e}_3 + \bar{e}_1\bar{e}_2e_3 + e_1\bar{e}_2e_3 + e_1e_2\bar{e}_3$ by Designation Numbers

This statement can be reduced to an equivalent simpler form by the technique of simplest sum-of-products, and the use of the special three-variable Veitch diagram of Fig. 6-15. A table of designation numbers for the three variables is in Table 6-11. For convenience, the original statement shall be referred to as e_{o-o}, and the simplified statement shall be called, e_{o-s}.

The first step in this simplification is to locate each term of the original statement on the Veitch diagram. As shown in Fig. 6-15, each term is contained in one of the rectangles of the diagram, and, after all of the terms have been accounted for, six rectangles of the diagram are shaded. Once this has been done, we look at the numbers of the rectangles that have been used. In the corresponding columns of the table of designation numbers, we record a 1 in the e_{o-o} row. In the remaining columns, zeros are recorded. Now, the designation number of e_{o-o} has been determined.

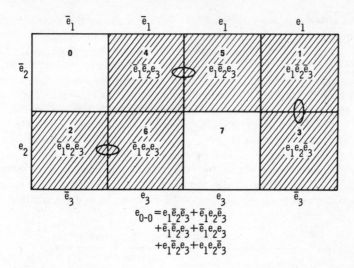

$$e_{0-0} = e_1\bar{e}_2\bar{e}_3 + \bar{e}_1 e_2\bar{e}_3$$
$$+ \bar{e}_1\bar{e}_2 e_3 + \bar{e}_1 e_2 e_3$$
$$+ e_1\bar{e}_2 e_3 + e_1 e_2\bar{e}_3$$

Fig. 6-15. Finding the simplest sum-of-products form by Veitch diagram.

TABLE 6-11. SIMPLIFYING $e_1\bar{e}_2\bar{e}_3 + \bar{e}_1 e_2\bar{e}_3 + \bar{e}_1\bar{e}_2 e_3 + \bar{e}_1 e_2 e_3 + e_1\bar{e}_2 e_3 + e_1 e_2\bar{e}_3$ BY DESIGNATION NUMBERS

			COLUMN							
			0	1	2	3	4	5	6	7
ROWS	1	$\# e_1$	0	1	0	1	0	1	0	1
	2	$\# e_2$	0	0	1	1	0	0	1	1
	3	$\# e_3$	0	0	0	0	1	1	1	1
	4	$\#(e_{0-0})$	0	1	1	1	1	1	1	0
	5	$\# \bar{e}_1$	1	0	1	0	1	0	1	0
	6	$\# \bar{e}_2$	1	1	0	0	1	1	0	0
	7	$\# \bar{e}_3$	1	1	1	1	0	0	0	0
	8	$\#(e_1\bar{e}_3)$	0	1	0	1	0	0	0	0
	9	$\#(\bar{e}_1 e_2)$	0	0	1	0	0	0	1	0
	10	$\#(\bar{e}_2 e_3)$	0	0	0	0	1	1	0	0
	11	$\#(e_{0-s})$	0	1	1	1	1	1	1	0

The simplified statement is found by coupling areas on the Veitch diagram. As shown in Fig. 6-15, couples can be formed between rectangles 4 and 5, 1 and 3, and 2 and 6. These couples yield the simplified statement, $e_{o-s} = e_1\bar{e}_3 + \bar{e}_1e_2 + \bar{e}_2e_3$. Now we must find the designation number of the simplified statement. To do this, we shall first determine the designation numbers for each of the terms in the simplified statement as shown in Table 6-11. Once this is done, we logically add the designation numbers of the three terms to obtain the designation number of e_{o-s}. As you see in the table, $\#e_{o-s}$ is 0111 1110; similarly, $\#e_{o-o}$ is 0111 1110. The two statements are, therefore, equivalent. A check by using a truth table is another way to verify the equivalency of the two statements, and this check is shown in Table 6-12. After listing all the possible combinations of the three variables in the first three rows, we use the next nine rows to find the truth of each

TABLE 6-12.   TRUTH TABLE VERIFYING THE SIMPLIFICATION

		COLUMN							
		1	2	3	4	5	6	7	8
1	e_1	0	1	0	1	0	1	0	1
2	e_2	0	0	1	1	0	0	1	1
3	e_3	0	0	0	0	1	1	1	1
4	$\bar{e}_1$	1	0	1	0	1	0	1	0
5	$\bar{e}_2$	1	1	0	0	1	1	0	0
6	$\bar{e}_3$	1	1	1	1	0	0	0	0
7	$e_1\bar{e}_2\bar{e}_3$	0	1	0	0	0	0	0	0
8	$\bar{e}_1e_2\bar{e}_3$	0	0	1	0	0	0	0	0
9	$\bar{e}_1\bar{e}_2e_3$	0	0	0	0	1	0	0	0
10	$\bar{e}_1e_2e_3$	0	0	0	0	0	0	1	0
11	$e_1\bar{e}_2e_3$	0	0	0	0	0	1	0	0
12	$e_1e_2\bar{e}_3$	0	0	0	1	0	0	0	0
13	e_{0-0}	0	1	1	1	1	1	1	0
14	$e_1\bar{e}_3$	0	1	0	1	0	0	0	0
15	$\bar{e}_1e_2$	0	0	1	0	0	0	1	0
16	$\bar{e}_2e_3$	0	0	0	0	1	1	0	0
17	e_{0-s}	0	1	1	1	1	1	1	0

(ROWS)

term in the original statement. In the thirteenth row, the truth of the original statement is written. In rows 14–16, the truth for each term of the simplified statement is developed. Finally, in the last row, the truth of the simplified statement is written. As you can see, it is identical to the truth of the original statement. We have verified by truth table that the two statements are equivalent.

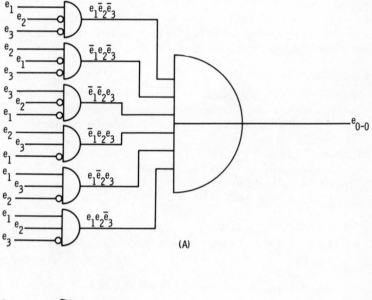

(A)

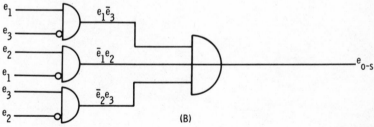

(B)

Fig. 6-16. The logic block diagrams needed to generate (A) the original state-ment, and (B) the simplified statement of Fig. 6-15.

Now let us look at the logic block diagram needed to generate both statements. Figure 6-16A is the circuit that generates the original state-ment. This circuit uses six AND gates, one OR gate, and requires 33 elec-tronic components, including inverters. The simplified circuit, however, requires only three AND gates, one OR gate, and requires only 12 electronic components. You'll agree that this is quite a reduction; the reduction in the number of components required is even more impressive when you consider that both circuits produce an output under exactly the same input conditions.

6-11. Summary

The nine solutions presented in this chapter should be sufficient to familiarize you with the methods of approaching and simplifying Boolean statements. Naturally, it is not possible to show every type of problem, but with the sample solutions you have seen here and with the basic information you've encountered in the preceding chapters, you are well equipped to solve any problem of simplification.

6-12. Problems

1. Simplify the following statements using Veitch diagrams. Then, show the logic block diagrams needed to generate both the original statements, and the simplified statements. Indicate the number of components used in each logic block diagram.
   (a) $A\bar{B} + \bar{A}B + \bar{A}\bar{B}$ (b) $A\bar{B}\bar{C} + \bar{A}B\bar{C} + \bar{A}\bar{B}\bar{C}$
   (c) $ABCD + A\bar{B} + A\bar{C} + BC + AB\overline{(CD)}$

2. Simplify the following statements using Boolean algebra:
   (a) $ABC + A\bar{B}\bar{C} + \bar{A}B\bar{C} + \bar{A}\bar{B}C$ (b) $AB + A\bar{C} + BC$
       $+ \bar{A}BC + A\bar{B}C$
   (c) $AB\bar{C} + BD(B + C) + \bar{C}(A + B)$

3. Simplify the following statements using designation numbers:
   (a) $e_1\bar{e}_3 + e_1e_2 + \bar{e}_1e_2\bar{e}_3\bar{e}_4$ (b) $e_1e_2e_3 + \bar{e}_1e_2\bar{e}_3 + \bar{e}_1\bar{e}_2e_3$
   (c) $(e_1 + e_2e_3)(e_1 + e_3)(e_1e_2)$

4. Prove the following equalities by using a truth table:
   (a) $XY + WZ = (X + W)(X + Z)(Y + W)(Y + Z)$
   (b) $X + \bar{Z} = XZ + \bar{X}\bar{Z} + X\bar{Z}$ (c) $\bar{X} + Y + Z = XY\bar{Z} + XZ$
                                                                $+ \bar{X}Y + \bar{X}\bar{Y}\bar{Z} + \bar{X}\bar{Y}Z$

7

Basic Concepts of D-C Principles

In order to fully understand and appreciate the application of Boolean algebra to electronic circuits, it is necessary to master some basic concepts in d-c circuitry. With this in mind, this chapter is intended as an introduction to d-c principles.

It is also advantageous to master a-c circuits, but in a book of this length it is almost impossible to present a complete discussion. It is assumed that the reader is somewhat familiar with a-c concepts, for a certain knowledge of them is necessary to understand the application of Boolean algebra to electronic circuits.

Since it is rare that inductors are used in computers, only d-c and RC circuits are going to be discussed.

7-1. Resistive D-C Circuitry

The most fundamental law in electronic circuitry is Ohm's Law, which states that the *current flowing in a closed loop that contains a voltage and a resistance is equal to the voltage divided by the resistance:*

$$I = E/R \qquad (7\text{-}1)$$

where I is the current in amperes, E is the voltage in volts, and R is the resistance of the circuit in ohms.

Equally as important as Ohm's Law are Kirchhoff's two laws. One of them is referred to as Kirchhoff's Voltage Law, and the other as Kirchhoff's Current Law. Kirchhoff's Voltage Law states that *the sum of the voltage drops in a closed loop is equal to the voltage applied to this loop.* Kirchhoff's Current Law states that *the sum of the currents leaving a junction is equal to the sum of the currents entering that same junction.*

7-2. Series Circuits

By definition, *a series circuit is one in which current can take only one path.* Such a circuit is shown in Fig. 7-1. The total resistance in a series circuit is the sum of the individual resistances:

$$R_T = R_1 + R_2 + R_3 \text{ etc.} \tag{7-2}$$

where R_T is the total resistance, and R_1, R_2, R_3 are the individual resistances. The current flowing in the circuit can be found by using Ohm's Law. Thus: $I = E/R$. The voltage drop across each resistor can be found by multiplying the current by the individual resistor. Thus,

$$V_{R1} = IR_1; \ V_{R2} = IR_2; \ V_{R3} = IR_3 \tag{7-3}$$

where V_{R1}, V_{R2}, and V_{R3} represent the voltage drops across resistors R_1, R_2, and R_3, respectively.

Applying Kirchhoff's Voltage Law, which states that the sum of the voltage drops across the resistors must equal to the applied voltage, we obtain:

$$E = V_{R1} + V_{R2} + V_{R3} \tag{7-4A}$$
$$E = IR_1 + IR_2 + IR_3 \tag{7-4B}$$

Let us now do an example in series circuits. For the circuit of Fig. 7-1,

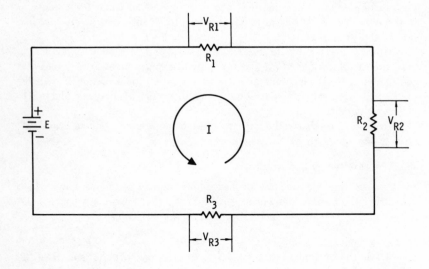

Fig. 7-1. A series circuit containing three resistors, and one source of emf. Also represented is the current flowing in the circuit, and the voltage drops across each resistor.

assume that $R_1 = 10$ ohms, $R_2 = 15$ ohms, $R_3 = 5$ ohms, and the applied voltage, E, is 6 volts. Determine the current flowing in the circuit, and the voltage drop across each resistor.

Solution: First find R_T.

$$R_T = R_1 + R_2 + R_3$$
$$R_T = 10 + 15 + 5 = 30 \text{ ohms}$$

Now find the current.

$$I = E/R_T = 6/30 = 0.2 \text{ amps}$$

Now find the voltage drops across each resistor.

$$V_{R1} = IR_1 = 0.2 \times 10 = 2 \text{ volts}$$
$$V_{R2} = IR_2 = 0.2 \times 15 = 3 \text{ volts}$$
$$V_{R3} = IR_3 = 0.2 \times 5 = 1 \text{ volt}$$

It will be noted that the sum of the voltage drops does equal to the applied voltage. $2 + 3 + 1 = 6$.

Whenever the voltage drop across a resistor is desired, a voltage proportionality can be set up. This will be given here, and the interested reader will find the derivation in the Appendix. This voltage proportionality states that the voltage drop across a resistor is equal to the applied voltage times the value of the resistor divided by the total resistance of the circuit. Thus,

$$V_{R1} = E(R_1/R_T) = ER_1/(R_1 + R_2 + R_3) \qquad (7\text{-}5\text{A})$$
$$V_{R2} = E(R_2/R_T) = ER_2/(R_1 + R_2 + R_3) \qquad (7\text{-}5\text{B})$$
$$V_{R3} = E(R_3/R_T) = ER_3/(R_1 + R_2 + R_3) \qquad (7\text{-}5\text{C})$$

The advantage of using these equations is that the voltage drops can be readily found without bothering to find the current.

As an example of the use of these equations, let us find the voltage drops across each resistor of the previous example.

$$V_{R1} = E(R_1/R_T) = 6(10/30) = 2 \text{ volts}$$
$$V_{R2} = E(R_2/R_T) = 6(15/30) = 3 \text{ volts}$$
$$V_{R3} = E(R_3/R_T) = 6(5/30) = 1 \text{ volt}$$

7-3. Parallel Circuits

By definition, *a parallel circuit is one where current can take more than one path, and where the voltage across each parallel resistor is the same.* Figure 7-2 illustrates a parallel circuit. The current flowing into junction A is the total current, and is designated I_T. Some of this current flows through R_1, and it is designated as I_1. Since some of the total current flows through R_1, the remaining current, $I_T - I_1$, flows to junction B. At this junction, some of the current flows through R_2. This is designated as I_2. The remaining current flows through R_3. Thus, the current flowing through R_3, which is also designated as I_3, is equal to $I_T - I_1 - I_2$. At junction C, the current flowing through R_3 joins with the current flowing through R_2 giving, as a result, the current $I_T - I_1$. This current as well as the current I_1 joins at junction D to give, as a result, the current I_T.

As was mentioned in the definition of a parallel circuit, the voltage drop is the same across each of the parallel resistors. Since this is the case, the currents flowing through each resistor can be found by taking the voltage drop, and dividing it by the value of the corresponding resistor. Thus,

$$I_1 = E/R_1 \qquad (7\text{-}6\text{A})$$

$$I_2 = E/R_2 \qquad\qquad (7\text{-}6\text{B})$$

$$I_3 = E/R_3 \qquad\qquad (7\text{-}6\text{C})$$

The equivalent resistance for resistors in parallel can be found by applying the following formula:

$$\frac{1}{R_T} = \frac{1}{R_1} + \frac{1}{R_2} + \frac{1}{R_3} \text{ etc.} \qquad (7\text{-}7)$$

or

$$R_T = \cfrac{1}{\cfrac{1}{R_1} + \cfrac{1}{R_2} + \cfrac{1}{R_3}}$$

where R_T is the equivalent resistance of the parallel combination, and R_1, R_2, R_3 are the individual resistors that are in parallel. For two resistors in parallel, the total or equivalent resistance can be found by taking their product, and dividing it by their sum. Thus,

$$R_T = (R_1 R_2)/(R_1 + R_2) \qquad (7\text{-}8)$$

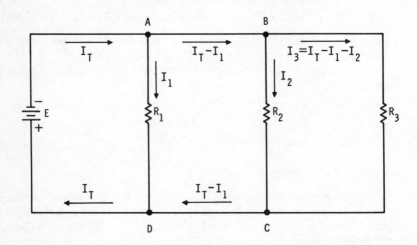

Fig. 7-2. A parallel circuit containing three resistors that are across a source of voltage, E. Also shown are the currents through each resistor, and the total current.

As an example of parallel circuits, assume that in Fig. 7-2, $R_1 = 10$ ohms, $R_2 = 20$ ohms, $R_3 = 30$ ohms, and $E = 60$ volts. Find the current flowing through each resistor, the total current, and the equivalent resistance of the parallel branch.

Solution:

$$I_1 = E/R_1 = 60/10 = 6 \text{ amps}$$

$$I_2 = E/R_2 = 60/20 = 3 \text{ amps}$$

$$I_3 = E/R_3 = 60/30 = 2 \text{ amps}$$

$$I_T = I_1 + I_2 + I_3$$

$$= 6 + 3 + 2 = 11 \text{ amps}$$

$$R_T = \cfrac{1}{\cfrac{1}{R_1} + \cfrac{1}{R_2} + \cfrac{1}{R_3}}$$

$$= \cfrac{1}{\cfrac{1}{10} + \cfrac{1}{20} + \cfrac{1}{30}} = \cfrac{1}{\cfrac{6+3+2}{60}}$$

$$R_T = 60/11 = 5.45 \text{ ohms}$$

This equivalent resistance if placed across 60 volts will cause a current of 11 amps to flow.

Check: $60 \div (60/11) = 11$ amps, which checks with the total current above.

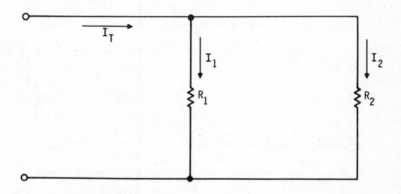

Fig. 7-3. A circuit that is used to illustrate the current inverse proportionality law.

When two resistors are placed in parallel, and the current entering into their junction is known, the current flowing through each resistor can be found by using the current inverse proportionality law. This law states that *to find the current flowing through one of the resistors, multiply the current entering the junction by the opposite resistor, and divide this product by the sum of the resistors.* Thus, in Fig. 7-3:

$$I_1 = I_T R_2 / (R_2 + R_1) \qquad (7\text{-}9)$$
$$I_2 = I_T R_1 / (R_2 + R_1) \qquad (7\text{-}10)$$

This is a useful law to remember, and it can save a great deal of time in solving for the currents flowing through two parallel resistors. As a matter of fact, this method can be used for any number of resistors in parallel. The thing to do in this case is to resolve resistances into equivalent resistances until only two resistors are left. For three resistors in parallel, for example, take any of them and resolve them into an equivalent resistor by using Eq. (7-8). Take this equivalent resistor and the third resistor, and treat them as if they were two resistors in parallel in order to find the current flowing through each resistor. Once the current flowing through the equivalent resistance is found, it becomes the current entering the junction of these two resistors. The current flowing through each of the individual resistors, which originally comprised this equivalent resistor, can be found, once again, using the current inverse proportionality law.

As an example of using the current inverse proportionality law, find the currents through each resistor in Fig. 7-4A.

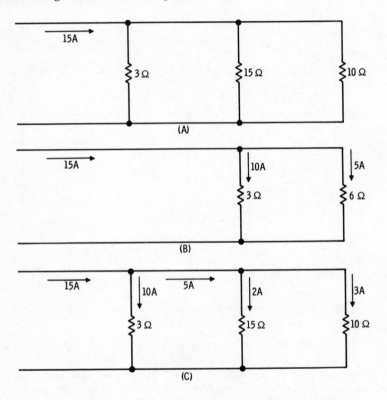

Fig. 7-4. An illustration of the use of the current inverse proportionality law for three resistors in parallel. (A) The original circuit, (B) the resulting circuit when the 10- and 15-ohm resistors are made into an equivalent 6-ohm resistor, and (C) the currents through each resistor.

Solution: First take the 10-ohm and 15-ohm resistors and find the equivalent resistance by using Eq. (7-8). Thus,

$$R_T = (10)(15)/(10 + 15) = 150/25 = 6 \text{ ohms}$$

This equivalent resistance is now in parallel with the 3-ohm resistor. The current through each resistor can now be found by using the current inverse proportionality law. Thus,

$$I_{3\,\Omega} = (15)(6)/(3 + 6) = 15(6/9) = 10 \text{ amps}$$
$$I_{6\,\Omega} = (15)(3)/(3 + 6) = 15(3/9) = 5 \text{ amps}$$

The circuit is now equivalent to the circuit in Fig. 7-4B. Since the 6-ohm resistor is the equivalent resistance of the 10- and 15-ohm resistors in parallel, we now know the current flowing into the junction of these resistors, namely 5 amps. To find the current flowing into each of these resistors, once again, use the current inverse proportionality law with 5 amps as the current into the junction, and with 10 ohms and 15 ohms as the parallel resistance by using Eq. (7-8). Thus,

$$I_{10\,\Omega} = (5)\,(15)/(10 + 15) = 5(15/25) = 3 \text{ amps}$$
$$I_{15\,\Omega} = (5)\,(10)/(10 + 15) = 5(10/25) = 2 \text{ amps}$$

The final circuit, which includes the currents, is shown in Fig. 7-4C.

7-4. Power

Power in a d-c circuit is defined as *the product of voltage times current.* Its unit is the watt. The basic equation for power is:

$$P = IE \tag{7-11}$$

where P is the power in watts, I is the current in amperes, and E is the voltage in volts. Since $I = E/R$, substituting this into Eq. (7-11) yields:

$$P = E^2/R \tag{7-12}$$

where R is the resistance in ohms. Also, since $E = IR$, then substituting this into Eq. (7-11) yields:

$$P = I^2R \tag{7-13}$$

There are, therefore, three formulas that can be used to determine the power that a resistor is dissipating. The choice of which equation to use depends on the circumstances of the problem. If, for example, the voltage drop across a resistor as well as the current flowing through that resistor were given, then the equation to use would be $P = IE$. If, on the other hand, the voltage drop across a resistor as well as its resistance value were given, then the formula to use will be $P = E^2/R$.

7-5. Combination Circuits

In this book, a *combination circuit* shall be defined as *any circuit other than a simple series or parallel circuit.* Often, combination circuits are referred to as series-parallel circuits. A basic combination circuit is shown in Fig. 7-5.

The solution of a combination circuit depends on the nature of the problem. There are no new equations for these solutions. If one fully understands Ohm's and Kirchhoff's laws, the solution for these circuits becomes somewhat easy. Experience is the best teacher in the solution of these circuits, and the more practice one acquires in solving these circuits, the easier their solutions become. A few examples will be given.

For the first example, assume that in Fig. 7-5, $R_1 = 2$ ohms, $R_2 = 6$ ohms, $R_3 = 12$ ohms, and $E = 18$ volts. Determine the current flowing through each resistor, the voltage drop across each resistor, the power dissipated by each resistor, and the total power dissipated by the resistors.

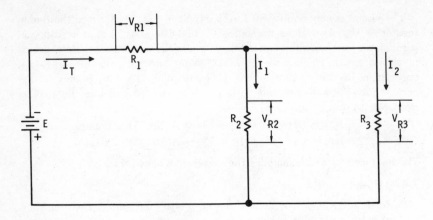

Fig. 7-5. A basic d-c combination circuit.

Solution: First find the total resistance of the circuit. This can be done by finding the equivalent resistance of the two resistors in parallel, and then adding this equivalent resistance to that of R_1. Thus, the equivalent resistance of R_2 and R_3 in parallel is their product over their sum.

$$R_{eq.} = (R_2 R_3)/(R_2 + R_3) = (6)(12)/(6+12) = 72/18 = 4 \text{ ohms}$$

Next find the total resistance of the circuit.

$$R_T = R_1 + R_{eq.} = 2 + 4 = 6 \text{ ohms}$$

Knowing the total resistance, we can now find the total current, I_T.

$$I_T = E/R_T = 18/6 = 3 \text{ amps}$$

The voltage drop across R_1, V_{R1}, can now be found.

$$V_{R1} = I_T R_1 = (3)(2) = 6 \text{ volts}$$

The voltage drop across R_2, V_{R2}, which is equal to the voltage drop across R_3, V_{R3}, can now be found by using Kirchhoff's voltage law.

$$E = V_{R1} + V_{R2}$$

Therefore, $V_{R2} = E - V_{R1} = 18 - 6 = 12 \text{ volts}$

The current flowing through R_2 as well as that flowing through R_3 can now be found.

$$I_2 = V_{R2}/R_2 = 12/6 = 2 \text{ amps}$$
$$I_3 = V_{R2}/R_3 = 12/12 = 1 \text{ amp}$$

As a check, $I_T = I_1 + I_2 = 1 + 2 = 3$ amps. The power dissipated by R_1, R_2, and R_3 can now be found.

$$P_{R1} = I_T V_{R1} = (3)(6) = 18 \text{ watts}$$
$$P_{R2} = I_2 V_{R2} = (2)(12) = 24 \text{ watts}$$
$$P_{R3} = I_3 V_{R3} = (1)(12) = 12 \text{ watts}$$

The total power dissipated by these resistors and which the battery must be able to supply is the sum of all of these powers:

$$P_T = P_{R1} + P_{R2} + P_{R3} = 18 + 24 + 12 = 54 \text{ watts}$$

As another example of combination circuits, assume that in Fig. 7-6, $R_1 = 8$ ohms, $R_2 = 12$ ohms, $R_4 = 6$ ohms, $R_5 = 9$ ohms, $I_3 = 5$ amps, and $V_{R2} = 48$ volts. Find: R_3, I_T, I_2, I_4, I_5, V_{R1}, V_{R3}, V_{R4}, and E.

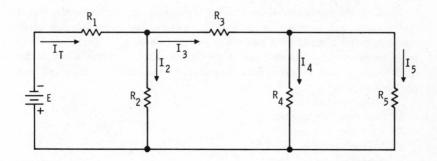

Fig. 7-6. A combination circuit showing all the currents through the resistors.

Solution: First find I_4 by using the current inverse proportionality law.

$$I_4 = I_3 R_5/(R_4 + R_5) = (5)(9)/(6+9) = 3 \text{ amps}$$

Next find I_5 by using Kirchhoff's Current Law.

$$I_3 = I_4 + I_5; \; I_5 = I_3 - I_4 = 5 - 3 = 2 \text{ amps}$$

The voltage drop across R_4, which is the same as the voltage drop across R_5, can now be found.

$$V_{R4} = I_4 R_4 = (3)(6) = 18 \text{ volts}$$

Since the voltage drop across R_2 is given, and since the voltage drop across R_4 is now known, then the voltage drop across R_3 can be found by using Kirchhoff's Voltage Law.

$$V_{R3} = V_{R2} - V_{R4} = 48 - 18 = 30 \text{ volts}$$

Knowing the voltage drop across R_3 and the current flowing through it, we can find its resistance by using Ohm's Law.

$$R_3 = V_{R3}/I_3 = 30/5 = 6 \text{ ohms}$$

The value of I_2 can be found because the voltage drop across it and the resistance of R_2 is known.

$$I_2 = V_{R2}/R_2 = 48/12 = 4 \text{ amps}$$

Now that I_2 and I_3 are known, the total current, which is the current flowing through R_1, can be found by using Kirchhoff's Current Law.

$$I_T = I_2 + I_3 = 4 + 5 = 9 \text{ amps}$$

The voltage drop across R_1 is next determined.

$$V_{R1} = I_T R_1 = (9)(8) = 72 \text{ volts}$$

Knowing the voltage drops across R_1 and R_2, we can determine the battery voltage by using Kirchhoff's Voltage Law.

$$E = V_{R1} + V_{R2} = 72 + 48 = 120 \text{ volts}$$

7-6. Network Theorems

So far in our discussion of d-c circuits, we have been dealing with circuits that contain only one source of emf. In solving logic circuits, one often encounters d-c circuits with more than one source of emf. There are many ways to solve these circuits, and some of the most common methods for their solutions shall be given here. The theorems that will be discussed here are the following:

1. Loop equations.
2. Superposition theorem.
3. Thevenin's theorem.
4. Norton's theorem.
5. Node voltage theorem.
6. Millman's theorem.

Loop Equations. A loop is a circuit where current can have a continuous path to flow. In Fig. 7-7, for example, one possible loop would be the

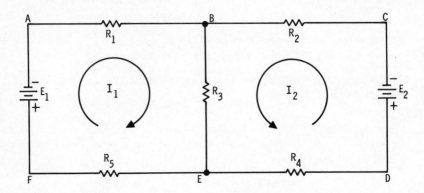

Fig. 7-7. A d-c circuit with two sources of emfs. Also shown are the two loop currents.

path ABEFA. Another possible loop would be the path CBEDC. Still another possible loop would be the path ABCDEFA. Thus, we see that there are three possible loops in Fig. 7-7.

The first step in using loop equations is to *arbitrarily* assign currents, and their directions through loops. Thus, in Fig. 7-7, the current I_1 flows through loop ABEFA, and the current I_2 flows through loop CBEDC. There is a common resistor in these two loops, namely R_3. Notice that the current

I_1, and the current I_2 flow in the same direction through R_3. It is important to notice this because the voltage drop across R_3 will be due to these currents. Also, the current through R_3 will be the algebraic sum of the currents, $I_1 + I_2$. It will be noticed that the term "algebraic sum of the currents" is used. This is so because one is not certain that the currents, I_1 and I_2, will flow in the directions that are assumed. If in the solution of the circuit, one of the currents is negative, then the actual current is going in the opposite direction to that which was at first designated.

Once the loops and the currents have been chosen, the next step is to write Kirchhoff's voltage equations for these loops. For Fig. 7-7, loop ABEFA has only one battery, E_1. This is the applied voltage to this loop. Since I_1 flows through resistors R_1, R_3, and R_5, we must multiply the sum of these resistors by this current to find the voltage drops in that loop. However, we also note that the current I_2 flows through R_3. Since I_2 flows through R_3, then the voltage drop across R_3 will not only depend on the current I_1 but also on the current I_2. Since these two currents are in the same direction, then the voltage drop across R_3 which is due to the current I_2 is considered as being a positive voltage drop. Therefore, the voltage equation for loop ABEFA is:

$$E_1 = (R_1 + R_3 + R_5)I_1 + R_3I_2 \tag{7-14}$$

Using the same line of reasoning for loop CBEDC, we obtain the following equation:

$$E_2 = R_3I_1 + (R_2 + R_3 + R_4)I_2 \tag{7-15}$$

Solving these two equations simultaneously, we can determine the currents I_1 and I_2.

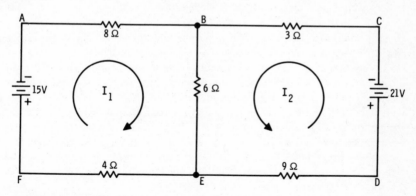

Fig. 7-8. A circuit that is set up so that it can be solved using loop equations.

As an example of the solution of a d-c circuit by loop equations, solve for the currents I_1 and I_2 of Fig. 7-7 given the following: $E_1 = 15$ volts, $E_2 = 21$ volts, $R_1 = 8$ ohms, $R_2 = 3$ ohms, $R_3 = 6$ ohms, $R_4 = 9$ ohms, and $R_5 = 4$ ohms as shown in Fig. 7-8.

Substituting these values into the loop equations, we obtain:

1. $$15 = (8 + 6 + 4)I_1 + 6I_2$$
2. $$21 = 6I_1 + (3 + 6 + 9)I_2$$

These equations now become:

1. $$15 = 18I_1 + 6I_2$$
2. $$21 = 6I_1 + 18I_2$$

If we divide Eq. **2** by three, we will now have:

1. $$15 = 18I_1 + 6I_2$$
2. $$7 = 2I_1 + 6I_2$$

In order to find I_1, subtract Eq. **2** from Eq. **1**. Thus,

$$16I_1 = 8; I_1 = 0.5 \text{ amps}$$

To find I_2, substitute the value of I_1 into Eq. **2**. Thus,

$$7 = 2(0.5) + 6I_2$$

From which we find that I_2 is 1 amp.

Now that we know the currents I_1 and I_2, the current through each resistor can be determined. The current I_1 flows through the 8- and 4-ohm resistors. The current I_2 flows through the 3- and 9-ohm resistors. The current flowing through the 6-ohm resistor will be the sum of the currents I_1 plus I_2 which is 1.5 amps.

Loop equations can be used for more than two loops. As a matter of fact, they are most commonly used when four, or five loops must be solved. The method for solving these is the same as the one outlined, except that there would be more equations to develop.

Superposition Theorem. The superposition theorem is a good theorem to use when a circuit contains two sources of emfs. The first step in using this theorem is to short out all sources of emf except one. This will reduce the circuit to a simple combination circuit. The magnitudes and the directions of the currents are now found. Next, the emf that was not shorted is now shorted, and one of the previously shorted emfs is returned. Again, the magnitudes and the directions of the currents are found. This process is continued until all of the emfs have been returned, and the currents for each condition have been found. The currents through each resistor can then be found once the magnitudes and the directions of the currents through each resistor are known.

As an example of this theorem, let us solve for the currents flowing through each resistor in Fig. 7-8. Since we have already solved for these currents by using loop equations, we know the currents flowing through each resistor. This will be used as a check and a guide when we solve this circuit using the superposition theorem.

First let us short the 21-volt battery. The resulting circuit is shown in Fig. 7-9A. The magnitude and direction of the currents flowing through each resistor is also shown in this figure. Having solved for these currents, now short the 15-volt source of emf, and return the 21-volt source. This is shown in Fig. 7-9B. Now the current and its direction flowing through each resistor can be found. For example, the resulting current flowing through the 8-ohm resistor will be due to a current flowing from A to B of 15/16 amperes (see Fig. 7-9A), and a current flowing from B to A of

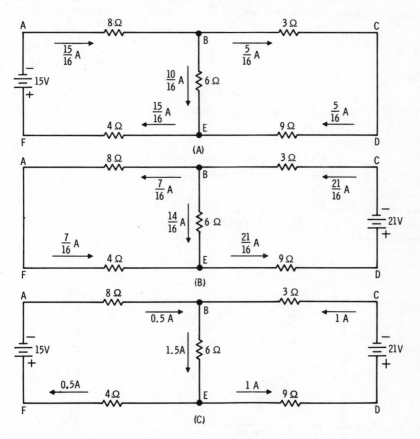

Fig. 7-9. A circuit that illustrates the superposition theorem. (A) The currents when the 21-volt supply is short-circuited, (B) the currents when the 15-volt supply is short-circuited, and (C) the currents through each resistor.

7/16 amperes (see Fig. 7-9B) which will be a resulting current of 0.5 amperes flowing from A to B. Figure 7-9C shows the resulting currents flowing through the resistors; these are the same currents and directions that we found by using loop equations.

Thevenin's Theorem. Thevenin's theorem is useful when the current or voltage drop through a variable resistor is desired, or when a current through only one resistor is desired. The reason for this is that the final Thevenin circuit is a simple series circuit which consists of a source of emf, an equivalent resistance, and the load resistor. In using this theorem, there are a number of steps to follow:

1. Disconnect the load resistor. We are determining the current for this resistor.

2. Find the voltage drop across the open terminals that now exist because of removing the load resistor from the circuit. Call this voltage V_{oc} which stands for the open-circuit voltage.

3. With the load resistor still disconnected, short all the sources of emf.

4. With the load resistor disconnected, and all the emfs short-circuited, find the resistance of the resulting network from the terminals of the removed load resistor. Call this resistance R_{oc}.

5. The resulting Thevenin circuit will be the open-circuit voltage, V_{oc}, in series with R_{oc} and the load resistor. This Thevenin circuit is shown in Fig. 7-10.

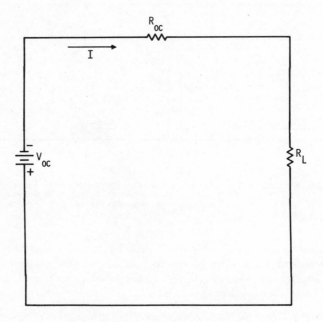

Fig. 7-10. The equivalent Thevenin's circuit.

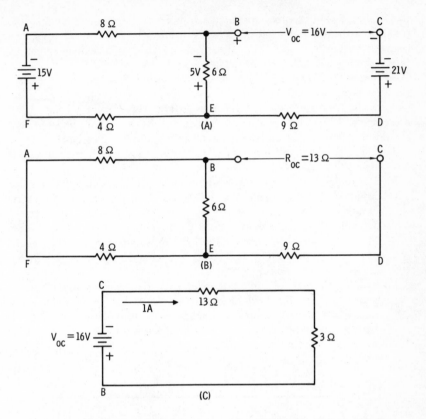

Fig. 7-11. A circuit that is used as an example of Thevenin's theorem. (A) The circuit to find V_{oc}, (B) the circuit to find R_{oc}, and (C) the equivalent Thevenin's circuit.

As an example of Thevenin's theorem, let us find the current flowing through the 3-ohm resistor of Fig. 7-8. We already know that this current is 1 ampere, for we solved for it by both loop equations and superposition theorem; but let us now solve for it using Thevenin's theorem.

First we disconnect the 3-ohm resistor. The next step is to find V_{oc}, which is the open-circuit voltage across terminals B and C of Fig. 7-11A. To do this, we must find the voltage drop across the 6-ohm resistor. This can be found by using the voltage proportionality law. Thus,

$$V_6 = 15 \ (6/18) = 5 \ \text{volts}$$

There will not be any voltage drop across the 9-ohm resistor because no current is flowing through it. Therefore, V_{oc} will be 16 volts with terminal B positive with respect to terminal C.

Next, R_{oc} must be found. To do this, the emfs (batteries) are short-circuited. Now the resistance R_{oc} can be found by finding the resistance between terminals B and C. This is shown in Fig. 7-11B. As can be seen,

154 PRINCIPLES AND APPLICATIONS OF BOOLEAN ALGEBRA

the 8- and 4-ohm resistors are in series, and this series combination is in parallel with the 6-ohm resistor. This makes the equivalent resistance between terminals B and C equal to 4 ohms. This equivalent resistance is in series with the 9-ohm resistor. Therefore, R_{oc} is 13 ohms.

The equivalent Thevenin's circuit is shown in Fig. 7-11C. As can be seen, the current flowing through the 3-ohm resistor will be 1 ampere.

Norton's Theorem. Norton's theorem is also very useful when solving d-c circuits. As we did for Thevenin's theorem, let us outline the steps that should be followed when solving a circuit using Norton's theorem:

1. Short the load resistor; this is the resistor for which the current is being determined.
2. Determine the current flowing through this short-circuited resistor using whatever theorem that one desires. Call this ,current the short-circuited current, I_{sc}.
3. Disconnect both the short and the load resistor.
4. Short all sources of emf, and find the resistance across the terminals of the load resistor. This is R_{oc} which is found in the same way as R_{oc} for a Thevenin's circuit.
5. The R_{oc} is now placed in parallel with the short-circuited current generator, and the load resistor is placed across this parallel combination. This is the Norton's equivalent circuit as shown in Fig. 7-12. The current flowing through the load resistor can now be found by using the current inverse law. Thus,

$$I_L = I_{sc}R_{oc}/(R_L + R_{oc}) \qquad (7\text{-}16)$$

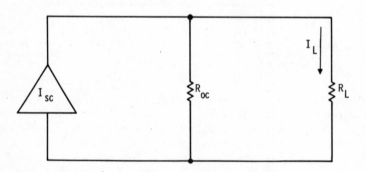

Fig. 7-12. The equivalent Norton's circuit.

As an example of Norton's theorem, let us find the current flowing through the 6-ohm resistor of Fig. 7-8. We already know that this current is 1.5 amps, for we have solved it previously. Let us find it by using Norton's theorem.

First we short the 6-ohm resistor. This is shown in Fig. 7-13A. Now we determine the current flowing through this short, which is the I_{sc}, by loop equations. Thus,

$$15 = 12I_1 + 0I_2$$
$$21 = 0I_1 + 12I_2$$

Therefore, $I_1 = 15/12 = 5/4$ amperes, and $I_2 = 21/12 = 7/4$ amperes. The short-circuited current will be the sum of I_1 plus I_2. Therefore, I_{sc} is 3 amps.

Next, we have to determine R_{oc}. To do this we short the emfs, and disconnect both the short and the 6-ohm resistor. This is shown in Fig. 7-13B.

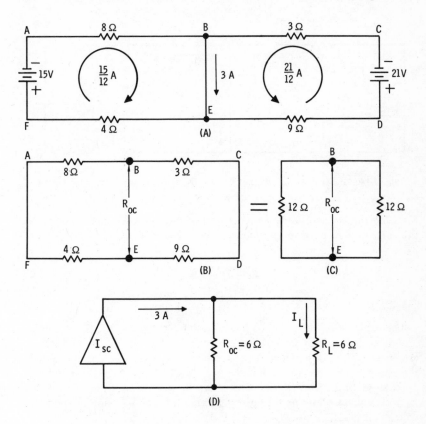

Fig. 7-13. A circuit that is used as an example of Norton's theorem. (A) The shorted load resistor and the resultant current flowing through the short, (B) the circuit for finding R_{oc}, (C) the simplified circuit for finding R_{oc}, and (D) the equivalent Norton's circuit.

From this figure, it is seen that the 8- and 4-ohm resistors are in series, and that the 3- and 9-ohm resistors are also in series. However, these series resistors are in parallel with each other as shown in Fig. 7-13C. Therefore, R_{oc} is 6 ohms.

The Norton's circuit is shown in Fig. 7-13D. As can be seen, the current going through the 6-ohm load resistor is 1.5 amperes.

Node Pair Voltage Theorem. The advantage of this theorem is that one need write one less equation than he would have to write if he solved a circuit using loop equations.

The first step in using this theorem is to designate a voltage drop across a resistor. This is done in Fig 7-14; the designated voltage drop is across R_3. Next, the voltage drops across R_1 and R_2 can easily be found. The voltage drop across R_1 is $E_1 - V_{R3}$, and the voltage drop across R_2 is $E_2 - V_{R3}$.

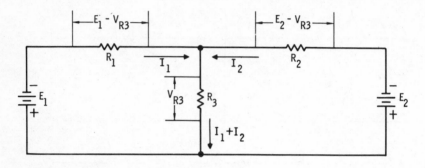

Fig. 7-14. One possible circuit that can be solved using the node pair voltage theorem.

Knowing the voltage drops across these resistors and their resistance values, the currents flowing through them can be found. Thus,

$$I_1 = (E_1 - V_{R3})/R_1 \qquad (7\text{-}17)$$
$$I_2 = (E_2 - V_{R3})/R_2 \qquad (7\text{-}18)$$
$$I_1 + I_2 = V_{R3}/R_3 \qquad (7\text{-}19)$$

Therefore, $(E_1 - V_{R3})/R_1 + (E_2 - V_{R3})/R_2 = V_{R3}/R_3 \qquad (7\text{-}20)$

The value of V_{R3} can now be found, assuming that E_1, E_2, R_1, R_2, and R_3 are given. Notice that since there is only one unknown, V_{R3}, only one equation need be written. Once V_{R3} is solved for, then the currents flowing through the resistors can be found.

As an example, let $R_1 = R_2 = 12$ ohms, $R_3 = 6$ ohms, $E_1 = 15$ volts, and $E_2 = 21$ volts. Determine the current flowing through R_3 using the node pair voltage theorem.

Solution: $(15 - V_{R3})/12 + (21 - V_{R3})/12 = V_{R3}/6$
$$15 - V_{R3} + 21 - V_{R3} = 2V_{R3}$$
$$36 = 4V_{R3}$$
$$V_{R3} = 9 \text{ volts}$$

Therefore, $I_{R3} = V_{R3}/R_3 = 9/6 = 1.5$ amperes.

Millman's Theorem. Millman's theorem is an especially useful theorem in the solution of diode logic circuits. In this section, the general expression will be given, plus a specific example where E_3 is equal to zero. The derivation is given in the Appendix.

In Fig. 7-15, let us determine the voltage across R_L using Millman's theorem. To do this, the formula for Millman's theorem is given:

$$E_o = V_{RL} = \frac{E_1/R_1 + E_2/R_2 + E_3/R_L}{1/R_1 + 1/R_2 + 1/R_L} \qquad (7\text{-}21)$$

Using this formula, we can easily find the voltage across R_L.

As an example of this theorem, let us find the voltage drop across the 6-ohm resistor of Fig. 7-8 which we already know to be 9 volts.

$$V_6 = \frac{15/12 + 21/12 + 0/6}{1/12 + 1/12 + 1/6} = \frac{36/12}{4/12} = 9 \text{ volts}$$

Notice how simple it was to find the voltage drop across the 6-ohm resistor by using Millman's theorem.

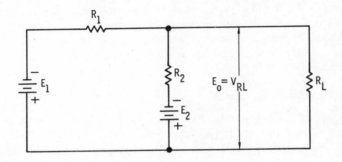

Fig. 7-15. A circuit where Millman's theorem can be applied.

7-7. Basic Concepts of Capacitors

In almost all computer circuits, one finds capacitors. These capacitors are usually used for forming pulses for a given circuit. It is necessary, therefore, to understand the concept of capacitance.

When a capacitor is placed across a d-c potential, a charge results. This charge, in coulombs, is designated as Q, and it can be computed by multiplying the voltage across the capacitor by the capacitance. Thus,

$$Q = CE \qquad (7\text{-}22)$$

This is the fundamental equation for capacitance. In this equation, C is the capacitance in farads, E is the voltage across the capacitor in volts, and Q is the charge in coulombs.

The current flowing in a capacitive circuit can be found by taking the capacitance and multiplying it by the rate of change of voltage across the capacitor. In equational form, the current is:

$$i = C \, \Delta e/\Delta t \qquad (7\text{-}23)$$

where i is the instantaneous current in amperes, C is the capacity in farads, and $\Delta e/\Delta t$ is the rate of change of voltage applied to the capacitor in

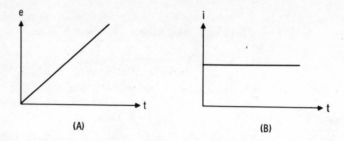

(A)   (B)

Fig. 7-16. Relation between (A) e and (B) i in a capacitative circuit when the rate of change of voltage is a constant.

volts/sec. Notice that if a sawtooth voltage were applied to a capacitor, the result would be a square wave of current flowing through that capacitor. This is true because the rate of change of voltage for a sawtooth voltage is a constant. Therefore, a constant or square wave of current would flow when a sawtooth of voltage is applied to a capacitor. This is illustrated in Fig. 7-16.

7-8. Capacitors in Series

Figure 7-17 illustrates a circuit for capacitors in series. When capacitors are placed in series, the overall capacity of the circuit decreases. This can be proved mathematically, but it should be observed that when capacitors

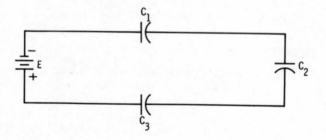

Fig. 7-17. A circuit that illustrates capacitors in series.

are placed in series, the overall distance between the plates increases which in turn decreases the total capacity. To find the total capacity of a number of capacitors in series, the following formula can be used:

$$C_T = \frac{1}{1/C_1 + 1/C_2 + 1/C_3} \qquad (7\text{-}24)$$

When two capacitors are in series, and across a d-c potential, the voltage drop across them can be found from the following formulas. Refer to Fig. 7-18. The derivations of these formulas are given in the Appendix.

$$V_{C1} = EC_2/(C_1 + C_2) \qquad (7\text{-}25A)$$
$$V_{C2} = EC_1/(C_1 + C_2) \qquad (7\text{-}25B)$$

As an example of these formulas, assume that in Fig. 7-18, C_1 is 1 μf, and C_2 is 9 μf. Assume also that the applied voltage is 100 volts. Determine the voltage drop across each capacitor.

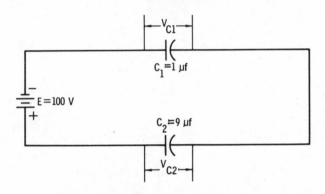

Fig. 7-18. A circuit that illustrates the voltage drops for two capacitors in series.

Solution:
$$V_{C1} = 100 \ (9/10) = 90 \text{ volts}$$
$$V_{C2} = 100 \ (1/10) = 10 \text{ volts}$$

7-9. Capacitors in Parallel

As is true for resistors in parallel, capacitors in parallel have the same voltage across them. There is a different charge on each capacitor depending on the voltage and the value of the capacitor. When capacitors are placed in parallel, the total capacity of the circuit increases. The reason is that the overall area of the plates increases. In order to find the total capacity, simply add the individual capacities. Thus,

$$C_T = C_1 + C_2 + C_3 \qquad (7\text{-}26)$$

7-10. Charging a Capacitor in Series With a Resistor

Figure 7-19 illustrates a series circuit consisting of a battery, switch, resistor, and a capacitor. It is assumed that there is no initial charge on the capacitor. The instant when the switch is closed shall be referred to as $t = 0$. At this instant, the capacitor behaves as a short circuit, and all of the applied voltage is across the resistor. At this instant, the current can be found by dividing the applied voltage, E, by the resistance of the circuit. Thus,

$$i\big|_{t=0} = E/R$$

After a long period of time, which depends on the time constant of the

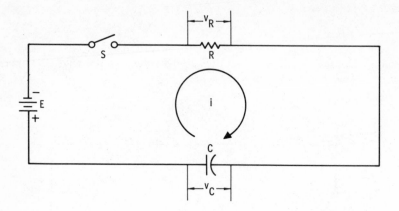

Fig. 7-19. Charging a capacitor from a d-c source.

circuit, the current flowing in the circuit will be 0. The reason for this is that the capacitor will become fully charged, and since the voltage across it will be equal to the applied voltage, no current can flow in the circuit. For any interval of time after the switch is closed until the capacitor becomes fully charged, the current flowing in the circuit can be found by using the following equation:

$$i = (E/R)e^{-t/RC} \tag{7-27}$$

where i is the instantaneous current in amperes, E is the applied voltage in volts, R is the resistance in ohms, e is epsilon whose value is approximately 2.72, C is the capacity of the circuit in farads, and t is the time in seconds.

The instantaneous voltage drop across the resistor can be found by multiplying the instantaneous current in the circuit by the resistance. Thus,

$$v_R = Ee^{-t/RC} \tag{7-28}$$

The instantaneous voltage drop across the capacitor is the difference in voltage between the applied voltage, E, and the voltage drop across the resistor. Thus,

$$v_C = E(1 - e^{-t/RC}) \tag{7-29}$$

The time, t, that it would take for the voltage drop across the resistor to reach a given value can be found by using the following equation:

$$t = 2.3 \log_{10} E/v_R \tag{7-30}$$

where t is the time in seconds, $\log_{10}$ is the common logarithm, 2.3 is a constant, E is the applied voltage, and v_R is the voltage drop across the resistor.

The plot of the voltage drop across the resistor, and the voltage drop across the capacitor is shown in Fig. 7-20. This plot clearly shows that at the instant when the switch is closed, the voltage drop across the resistor is at its maximum value of E volts; and the voltage drop across the capacitor is 0. It also shows that as time increases the current decreases, the voltage drop across the resistor decreases, and the voltage drop across the capacitor increases.

Let us now develop the concept of the time constant. At $t = 0$, the rate of change of current is starting to decrease, and its value is E/R^2C. The maximum current that flows in the circuit flows at this time, and is E/R. If the current were to decrease at the same rate as when $t = 0$, then it would take a certain time for the current to reach 0. This time, known as the

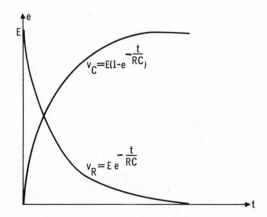

Fig. 7-20. Voltage relations when charging a capacitor from a d-c source.

time constant, can be found by dividing the maximum current by the rate of change of current at $t = 0$. Notice that current divided by the rate of change of current in amps/sec will yield time in seconds. Therefore,

$$T = (E/R)/(E/R^2C) = RC \tag{7-31}$$

Since the current does not continue to decrease at the same rate as when $t = 0$, what is the value of the current after one time constant? To find this, substitute RC for t in Eq. (7-27). With this substitution, it will be found that at $t = RC$, the current reaches 0.37 of its maximum value. After one time constant, the voltage drop across the resistor will be 0.37 of the applied voltage, E. This is true because the voltage drop across the resistor is the product of the current and resistance. Since the current at this instant is $0.37E/R$, then the voltage drop across the resistor will $(0.37E/R) \times R = 0.37E$.

The capacitor voltage is the difference between the applied voltage, E, and the voltage drop across the resistor. Therefore, to find the voltage drop across the capacitor after one time constant, subtract $0.37E$ from E, which is $0.63E$. Thus the voltage drop across the capacitor after one time constant is $0.63E$.

As an example, assume in Fig. 7-19 that R is 1 megohm, C is 1 μf, and E is 10 volts. Find: (a) the time constant of the circuit, (b) the current in the circuit after one time constant, (c) the voltage drop across the resistor after one time constant, and (d) the voltage drop across the capacitor after one time constant.

Solution:

(a) $T = RC = (10^6)(10^{-6}) = 1$ sec

(b) $i = 0.37E/R = 0.37\ (10)/(10^6) = 3.7$ microamps

(c) $v_R = iR = 3.7(10^{-6})(10^6) = 3.7$ volts

(d) $v_C = 0.63E = 0.63(10) = 6.3$ volts

Notice that at this instant of time as well as at any instant of time, the sum of the voltage drops across the resistor and the capacitor is equal to the applied voltage.

As another example, let's do the following: Using the same information that was given in the previous example, determine the time that it would take for the voltage drop across the resistor to reach half of the applied voltage

Solution:

$$v_R = 5 \text{ volts}$$
$$t = 2.3RC \log_{10}(E/v_R) = 2.3(1)\log_{10} 10/5$$
$$t = 2.3\ (1)\ (\log 2) = 2.3(1)(0.301) = 0.69 \text{ sec}$$

Therefore, it would take 0.69 second for the voltage across the resistor to reach 5 volts.

7-11. Current and Voltage Equations for an Initially Charged Capacitor

In Fig. 7-21A, a resistive-capacitive circuit with an initial charge on the capacitor is shown. The polarity of the voltage across the capacitor is important, and its value is E_0. The basic Kirchhoff voltage equation for this circuit is:

$$E = V_R + v_C \tag{7-32}$$

Notice that the initial voltage across the capacitor opposes the battery, and for this reason the initial voltage applied to the circuit will be the difference between the battery voltage and the initial voltage across the capacitor.

The current equation for Fig. 7-21A is:

$$i = [(E - E_o)/R]e^{-t/RC} \tag{7-33}$$

The voltage drop equations for the voltage drop across the resistor and the capacitor are:

$$v_R = (E - E_o)e^{-t/RC} \tag{7-34}$$
$$v_C = E - (E - E_o)e^{-t/RC} \tag{7-35}$$

The time for the voltage drop across the resistor to reach a given value can be found by using the following equation:

$$t = 2.3\ RC \log_{10}\ [(E - E_o)/v_R] \tag{7-36}$$

If the polarity of the initial voltage drop across the capacitor were reversed, then the Kirchhoff voltage equation would still be:

$$E = v_R + v_C \qquad (7\text{-}37)$$

The current and voltage drop equations for Fig. 7-21B would be the same as Eqs. (7-33), (7-34), and (7-35), except that there would be a positive sign in front of E_o. Also, the time equation, Eq. (7-36) will have a positive sign in front of E_o. The time constant equation for both cases will be

$$T = RC$$

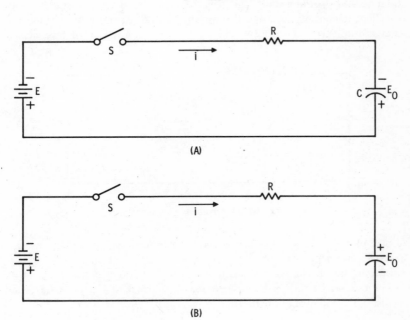

Fig. 7-21. Charging a capacitor that has an initial charge. (A) E_o has a negative voltage initially, and (B) E_o has a positive voltage initially.

As an example, assume that in Fig. 7-21A, R is 0.25 megohms, C is 0.06 μf, E_o is 50 volts, and E is 120 volts. Determine (a) the time constant, (b) the voltage drop across the resistor after one time constant, and (c) the voltage drop across the capacitor after one time constant.
Solution:

(a) $T = RC = (0.25)(10^6)(0.06)(10^{-6}) = 15$ msecs

(b) $v_R = (E - E_o)e^{-t/RC} = (70)(0.37) = 25.9$ volts

(c) $v_C = E - v_R = 120 - 25.9 = 94.1$ volts

7-12. Discharging a Capacitor

When a capacitor is charged, it stores energy in its dielectric field. The amount of energy that it stores can be found by multiplying the square of the voltage across the capacitor by the capacitance, and dividing this by 2.

Thus,

$$w = v_C{}^2\, C/2 \tag{7-38}$$

where w is the energy in joules or watts-seconds, v_C is the voltage drop across the capacitor, and C is the capacity of the capacitor. This energy will remain there until the capacitor is discharged.

Figure 7-22 shows a capacitor with an initial voltage of E_0 volts, a switch, and a resistor. At the instant when the switch is closed, $t = 0$, a current will flow. The amount of current at this instant is E_0/R. At this same instant, the voltage drop across the resistor will be E_0 volts. As a matter of fact, at any

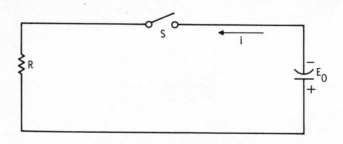

Fig. 7-22. Discharging a capacitor.

instant of time, the voltage across the resistor is the same voltage as that across the capacitor. However, the voltage across the capacitor will decrease with time, and it will reach almost 0 volts after five time constants.

The current flowing in the circuit for any instant of time can be found by using the following equation:

$$i = (E_0/R)e^{-t/RC} \tag{7-39}$$

The voltage drop across the resistor is the same as the voltage across the capacitor. This voltage drop is a function of time because the voltage drop across the capacitor decreases with time. To find the voltage drop across the resistor or the capacitor, the following equation can be used:

$$v_R = v_C = E_0 e^{-t/RC} \tag{7-40}$$

The time constant for this same circuit is still the product of resistance and capacitance, $T = RC$. After one time constant, the current flowing in the circuit will be 37% of E_0/R. The voltage drop across the resistor and the capacitor will be 37% of E_0. For all practical purposes, the current flowing in the circuit will be 0 after five times constants. Also, after five times constants, the capacitor is said to be fully discharged. The time that it takes for the capacitor to reach a given voltage can be found by using the following equation:

$$t = 2.3\, RC \log_{10} E_0/v_C \tag{7-41}$$

The curves of i, v_R, and v_C versus time are shown in Fig. 7-23.

As an example, assume a capacitor of 10 μf is charged to 200 volts, and

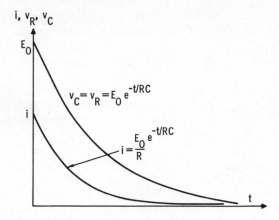

Fig. 7-23. The current and voltage curves for discharging a capacitor.

it is then discharged through a 1-megohm resistor. Determine the current, and the voltage drop across the resistor after five seconds.

Solution:

$RC = (10)(10^{-6})(10^6) = 10$ sec

$i = (E_o/R)e^{-t/RC} = (200/10^6)e^{-5/10} = 200/e^{0.5} = 200/\sqrt{2.72} = 121 \ \mu a$

$v_R = iR = (121)(10^{-6})(10^6) = 121$ volts

7-13. Problems

1. Define a series circuit. If four resistors are in series, what is the formula for the total resistance? What is the formula for the Kirchhoff's voltage equation?

2. State the voltage proportionality law. Can this law be applied in a series circuit containing three resistors? Explain your answer.

3. A series circuit containing three resistors whose values are 15, 25, and 60 ohms is placed across a 40-volt supply. The voltage drop across the 25-ohm resistor is 10 volts. Determine:
   (a) The voltage drops across the 15- and 60-ohm resistors.
   (b) The current flowing in the circuit.
   (c) The power taken by each resistor.
   (d) The total power taken by the circuit.

4. Define a parallel circuit. Give the equations for the current inverse proportionality law. Can you derive these equations? If you can't, refer to the Appendix for their derivation.

5. A combination circuit consists of a resistor of 18 ohms in series with a parallel circuit whose resistors are 20 and 30 ohms. The applied voltage to this circuit is 120 volts. Determine:
   (a) The current flowing through each resistor.
   (b) The voltage drop across each resistor.
   (c) The power dissipated by each resistor.

6. In Fig. 7-7, $R_1 = 5$ ohms, $R_2 = 10$ ohms, $R_3 = 15$ ohms, $R_4 = 20$ ohms, and $R_5 = 25$ ohms, $E_1 = 50$ volts, and $E_2 = 75$ volts. Using loop equations, determine:
   (a) The current flowing through each resistor.
   (b) The voltage drop across each resistor.

7. Using the same circuit and values given in **Problem 6**, determine the currents flowing in the circuit using the superposition theorem. Do you feel that this method is faster and simpler than the loop equation method?

8. Using the same circuit and values given in **Problem 6**, determine the current flowing through the 25-ohm resistor, R_5, using Thevenin's theorem.

9. Using the same circuit and values given in **Problem 6**, determine the current flowing through the 20-ohm resistor, R_4, using Norton's theorem.

10. Using the same circuit and values given in **Problem 6**, determine the current flowing through the 15-ohm resistor, R_3, using the node pair voltage theorem.

11. In Fig. 7-15, $R_1 = 10$ ohms, $R_2 = 20$ ohms, $R_L = 50$ ohms, $E_1 = 20$ volts, and $E_2 = 30$ volts. Determine the current flowing through R_L using Millman's theorem.

12. If the rate of change of voltage, $\Delta v_C / \Delta t$, that is applied to a capacitor is a constant (ramp voltage), what would be the equation for the current flowing in the circuit? Why?

13. A capacitor of 10 μf and one of 40 μf are placed in series across a 100-volt supply. How much voltage will there be across each capacitor?

14. A capacitor of 10 μf, and a resistor of 10 megohms are placed in series across a 100-volt d-c supply. What is the voltage across the capacitor after one time constant? What is the voltage across the resistor after one time constant? For this same time, what is the current flowing in the circuit?

15. When a capacitor is discharged across a resistor, the voltage across the resistor is the same as the voltage across the capacitor. Why?

8

Basic Concepts of Diodes and Transistors

In digital type computers, there are a large number of diode circuits which are used for either logic circuits or for pulse-forming circuits. Computers have been built that use thousands of diodes for logic circuits. It is expedient, therefore, to understand the basic concepts of diodes. In Chapter 9, the application of diodes to logic circuits will be shown. Here, we are interested primarily in giving some theory and facts about diodes.

Also, some of the modern digital computers use transistors for either logic circuits or amplifiers. In order to understand this application of transistors, it is necessary that the reader knows the basic concepts of transistors. For this reason, a qualitative discussion on transistors is included in this chapter. If the reader is familiar with diodes and transistors, he can pass over this chapter and proceed to Chapter 9.

8-1. Diodes

A diode is a unilateral, two-element electronic device. It is said to be unilateral because a perfect diode will conduct current in only one direction. In practice, all diodes conduct in both directions; the amount of conduction depends on the quality of the diode.

There are various types of diodes, such as tubes, metallic, and crystal, but basically they all have a cathode and an anode. The function of the cathode is to generate a current flow, and the function of the anode is to collect the current that the cathode generates. For the most part, tube- and crystal-type diodes are used, and these two will be discussed.

8-2. Vacuum-Tube Diodes

The tube diode consists of a filament, cathode, and plate or anode. These elements are housed in an evacuated enclosure to protect the filament. The filament is usually made of thoriated tungsten. Its function is to heat the cathode. In directly heated cathodes, the filament and the cathode are the same element. In indirectly heated types, the filament heats the cathode, and the latter emits electrons.

167

The function of the cathode is to emit electrons which constitute the plate current flowing in the tube. The cathode of indirectly heated tubes is made of oxide coated barium or strontium. These materials will emit electrons readily at a temperature lower than that of the filament.

The function of the plate or anode is to collect the electrons that are emitted by the cathode. Though there isn't any physical contact between the anode and the cathode, there is an electrical contact between them whenever the plate is made positive with respect to the cathode. The reason for this is that the electron, since it has a negative charge, will be attracted by a positive charge. Therefore, whenever the anode is made positive with respect to the cathode, it will attract electrons from the cathode's space charge region which is the region around the cathode where the electrons are accumulated.

Figure 8-1A shows the symbol for the vacuum type diode, and Fig. 8-1B shows the basic construction of the diode.

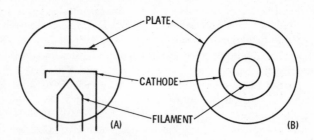

Fig. 8-1. (A) The most common symbol for the basic vacuum diode, and (B) the usual construction of a vacuum diode.

The diode conducts current whenever its plate is made positive with respect to its cathode. It does not conduct current whenever its anode is made negative with respect to its cathode because of the repelling action of the negative field to the electron. This action is what makes the diode a unilateral device. It is, however, a nonlinear device when it does conduct. This is represented in Fig. 8-2. The diode is especially nonlinear at the knee of the curve, which is the curved upper part of the curve. The saturation portion is the upper portion of the curve where an increase in plate-to-cathode voltage doesn't give any appreciable increase in plate current.

Whenever the plate is made positive with respect to the cathode, plate current flows, and the diode during this time has a relatively low resistance. This resistance is referred to as the forward resistance of the diode and is usually symbolized as R_f. However, when the plate is made negative with respect to the cathode, the diode does not conduct, and its resistance is now relatively high. This resistance is referred to as the back resistance of the diode, and it is usually symbolized as R_b. The *ideal* diode has a forward resistance of zero ohms, and a back resistance of infinite ohms. In practice,

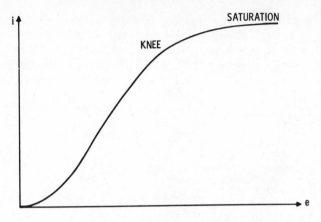

Fig. 8-2. A typical diode characteristic curve.

the diode's forward resistance is not zero, but could be as high as a thousand or more ohms, and its back resistance is not infinite. For a vacuum diode, it usually is in the order of megohms. This means that a diode is not a perfect unilateral devcie, and this should be remembered at all times. This is especially true for crystal diodes.

A simplified equivalent circuit for a diode is shown in Fig. 8-3. When the switch is in position 1, the diode is conducting, and it can be represented by its forward resistance. When the switch is in position 2, the diode is not conducting, and now it has a back resistance of R_b ohms. It should be

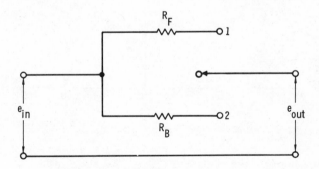

Fig. 8-3. A simplified circuit representation of a diode.

remembered that this is a simplified equivalent circuit because a diode is essentially a nonlinear device, and for this reason becomes somewhat complicated to represent.

When an alternating voltage is applied to a diode and a load resistor, as is shown in Fig. 8-4, the output voltage across R_L will be rectified. The reason for this is that the diode conducts only when its plate is positive with respect to its cathode. During this time, the diode acts like a small resistance, and if the load resistor is large compared with the diode's forward resistance, then most of the input voltage will be across the load resistor. On the other hand, when the input voltage is negative with respect to the cathode, the diode doesn't conduct, and it acts like a very high resistance. If the load

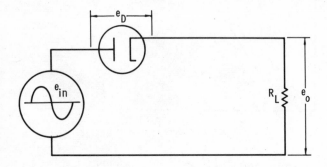

Fig. 8-4. A diode circuit that is used for rectification.

resistor is now very much less than the back resistance of the diode, then all of the input voltage is essentially across the tube. During this time, there is practically no current flowing in the circuit; therefore, there will be no voltage drop across the load resistor. The waveforms for these voltages are shown in Fig. 8-5.

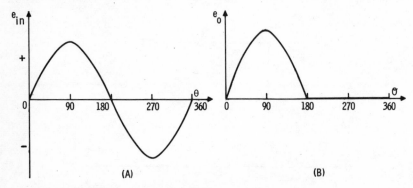

Fig. 8-5. (A) Input and (B) output voltages for a diode circuit.

8-3.   Basic Semiconductor Physics

In order to understand junction diodes and transistors, it is necessary that the reader has some idea of the physics of semiconductors.

The smallest subdivision of matter that retains its same form is a *molecule*. A molecule can in turn be further subdivided into *atoms*. The atom consists of a *nucleus* which consists essentially of positively charged *protons*, and negatively charged *electrons* which revolve about the nucleus. These electrons revolve about the nucleus in a definite elliptical pattern. In a two-dimensional plane, these layers are also referred to as shells or rings. Each shell or ring has a definite maximum number of electrons. The electrons in the outermost shell are referred to as *valence* electrons. This term is important to remember, for it is quite commonly used in semiconductors.

The two most commonly used elements for semiconductors are germanium and silicon. Germanium has 32 protons, 32 electrons. In its outermost shell, it has four electrons. Hence, there are four valence electrons in the germanium atom, and for this reason it is said to be *tetravalent*. Silicon has 14 protons, and 14 electrons. Silicon also has four valence electrons. Figure 8-6

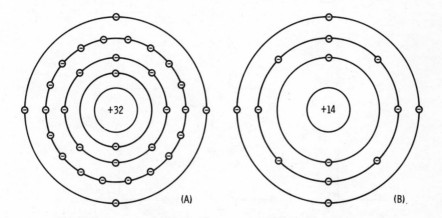

Fig. 8-6. (A) The germanium atom, and (B) the silicon atom.

shows the construction on a two-dimensional plane for the germanium and the silicon atoms. Notice that for the germanium atom as well as for the silicon atom, the number of protons is the same as the number of electrons. Whenever there are as many electrons as there are protons in an atom, the atom is said to be electrically neutral, i.e., it has a zero charge.

In a piece of germanium or silicon, there are an indeterminate number of atoms. In both of these atoms, the outermost shell would be complete if it had eight electrons. Since this is the case, the valence electrons of neighboring electrons are shared with one another to make the conjoined outermost shell completely full. This sharing of electrons causes what is referred to as *covalent electron bonds*. Thus, there are eight electrons in the covalent bond; see Fig. 8-7.

A piece of germanium or silicon that has no impurities is said to be intrinsic. An intrinsic piece of germanum or silicon has essentially no current carriers, and for this reason is of little use. In order to increase the current carrying capacity of germanium or silicon, impurities are purposely put into them. This injection of impurities into the intrinsic germanum is known as *doping*.

If a trivalent atom, one that has three valence electrons, is injected into germanium or silicon, there will be a deficiency of one electron in some of the covalent bonds. Since there is a deficiency of one electron in the covalent bond, the result is that the outermost shell has a positive charge. An atom with this deficiency is called a p-type material. This deficiency of

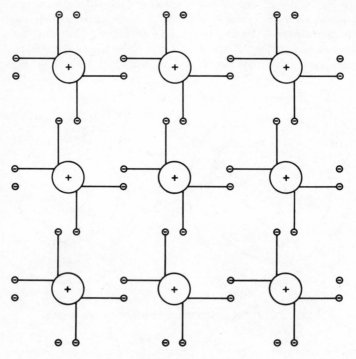

Fig. 8-7. A two-dimensional illustration that illustrates the idea of covalent bond of neighboring germanium atoms.

one electron causes a hole to exist which has a positive charge, and is capable of pulling an electron from a filled covalent bond. This captured electron fills the hole, and causes a hole to exist in the donor electron. Therefore, postive charges, or holes, flow in p-type material. In p-type material, hole carriers are the majority carriers.

If, on the other hand, a pentavalent atom, one that has five valence electrons, is injected into germanium or silicon, then there will be an excess or a donation of one electron. In this case, the covalent bond will be filled, but there will be a free electron which can freely travel from one atom to another. Since there will be an excess of electrons, this type of material will have a negative charge, and is referred to as n-type material. In n-type material, electrons are the majority carriers.

It is almost impossible to make germanium or silicon intrinsically pure. Invariably, there are always some impurities present. In p-doped material, therefore, there will be some impurities which will cause electrons to flow. In n-type material, there will be some impurities which will cause holes to flow. These carriers, electrons in p-type material and holes in n-type materials, are referred to as *minority carriers*. These minority carriers are important for they contribute to current flowing in germanium or silicon when there should not be flow.

8-4. P-N Junction Diode

A p-n junction diode consists of a section of p-type material joined to a section of n-type material. The area where they are joined is referred to as the *junction*. Figure 8-8 illustrates a p-n junction diode. On the left is a section of p-type material which has an excess of holes. On the right is a piece of n-type material which has an excess of electrons. Notice that at the junction there are negative charges in the p-type material, and positive charges in the n-type material. The reason for this is the following: Electrons

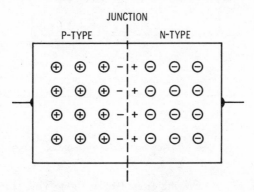

Fig. 8-8. A p-n junction diode.

from the n-type material diffuse through the junction to the p-type material because the p-type material is positively charged. Holes from the p-type material diffuse through the junction into the n-type material because it is negatively charged. This diffusion takes place until an equilibrium occurs. When this is reached, there is a sufficient negative charge on the left side of the junction to repel any further electrons from flowing into it, and there is a sufficient positive charge on the right side of the junction to repel any more positive charges from flowing into it. Usually, there is sufficient charge at the junction to cause 0.2 volts to be established across it. The left side of the junction will be negative with respect to the right side.

To cause a current to flow in a p-n junction diode, an external voltage must be applied. The polarity of this voltage, which is necessary to cause current flow, is referred to as the *forward bias*. The diode is forward biased when a positive potenial is applied to the p region, and a negative potential is applied to the n region. One of the reasons for this is that the positive potential on the p region will attract electrons from the left side of the junction. This will, in turn, cause electrons to flow from the n-type into the p-type. At the same time, the negative potential on the n section will attract holes from the right side of the junction which in turn will further cause holes to flow through the junction into the n-type material. This is represented in Fig. 8-9. Notice that hole current is flowing from left to right, and, at the same time, electrons are flowing from right to left. In the external wires,

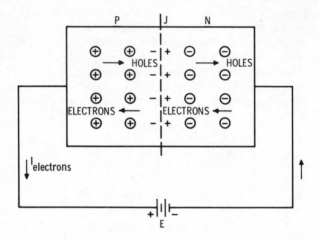

Fig. 8-9. Forward-biasing a p-n diode.

there will be a current flowing from left to right. This current is due to electron flow. It can also be said that hole current is flowing in the external circuit from right to left. Since the diode is now forward biased, there is a current flowing, and the diode represents a small resistance which is its forward resistance.

If the polarity of the voltage that is applied to the p-n junction is reversed, such that a negative voltage is now applied to the p section and a positive voltage to the n section, there will be no current flowing. The reason for this is that the charge at the junction will not be broken down as was the case when a forward bias was applied to the p-n junction. A probable cause is that the area of the junction will become greater, decreasing the probability of current flow.

From this discussion, we see that a p-n junction conducts current when the p section has a positive potential applied to it, and the n section has a negative voltage applied to it. It does not conduct when the p section has a negative voltage applied to it, and the n section has a positive voltage applied to it. Therefore, the p-n junction exhibits a diode action and is a

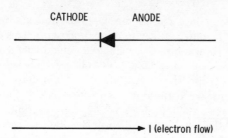

CATHODE   ANODE

I (electron flow)

Fig. 8-10. The symbol for a semiconductor diode showing the direction of current (electron) flow.

unilateral device. The symbol for semiconductor diodes is shown in Fig. 8-10. The arrow indicates electron current flow.

It has been mentioned that if a p-n junction is reverse biased, no current will flow. This is essentially true; however, if a sufficiently large reverse voltage is applied, then a breakdown point will be reached. This breakdown point voltage is referred to as the *Zener* voltage. When this Zener voltage is reached, a reverse current flows through the diode. There are special type Zener diodes which are used for voltage regulation, but these are not used for logic circuits.

A typical volt–ampere characteristic curve for a p-n junction is shown in Fig. 8-11. Notice that the diode needs a very small amount of forward

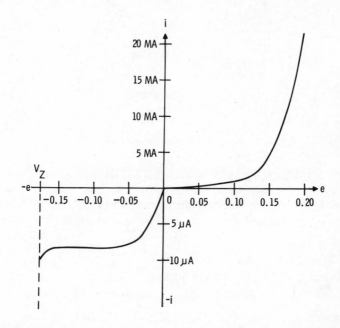

Fig. 8-11. A typical volt-ampere characteristic curve for a p-n junction diode.

voltage to conduct. Since this is the case, the forward resistance is very small, usually on the order of fifty to a hundred ohms. This curve also shows that if a sufficient reverse bias is placed across the diode, it will break down, and cause a reverse current to flow. This voltage is labeled as V_Z, the Zener voltage. The curve also shows that there is some current flowing, in the order of microamps, when the diode is reverse biased. For this reason, the diode does not have an infinite back resistance but a finite value, anywhere from a hundred thousand to megohms. Needless to say, the higher the reverse bias resistance, the better the diode because it will more nearly approach the ideal diode.

8-5.   Point Contact Diodes*

The first semiconductor diode was the point contact type. This diode consists of a pointed tungsten or gold wire which is in the form of a spring, and which presses against a wafer of n-type germanium or silicon of very small dimensions. A typical unit is the 1N34A which is a general purpose type, and which is shown in Fig. 8-12. The glass enclosure protects against contamination and humidity.

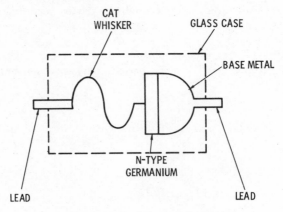

Fig. 8-12. A point-contact diode.

In the manufacturing process, a surge of current is passed through the diode, and a p-n junction of extremely small area is formed at the point contact. This makes the diode's capacitance very small, and hence, makes this diode very useful for pulse circuits because it will have fast recovery times.

8-6.   Basic Transistor Physics

A transistor consists of a p-n junction joined, once again, with either another p- or n-type element. Either a p-n-p or an n-p-n combination can

---

* Millman, Jacob, *Vacuum-Tube and Semiconductor Electronics*, New York: McGraw-Hill Book Company, 1958, pp. 124-125.

be formed. Figure 8-13A shows the configuration for a p-n-p type, and Fig. 8-13B shows the n-p-n type. Both are commonly available, and are used quite extensively today. In either type, the base region is very much smaller than either the emitter or the collector. Usually, the emitter is more heavily doped than the collector.

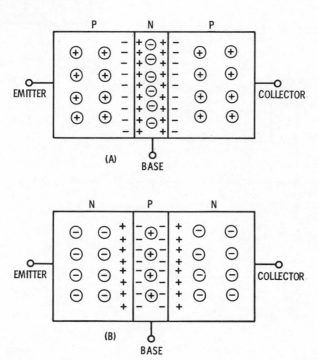

Fig. 8-13. (A) A p-n-p junction transistor, and (B) an n-p-n junction transistor.

Figure 8-14A shows the biasing of a p-n-p transistor. Notice that the emitter to base is forward biased. The reason for this is that the emitter is the element that causes the current to flow in a transistor. When a p-n junction is forward biased, current begins to flow. In a p-n-p transistor, since the emitter is made of p-type material, the majority carriers are holes. These majority carriers flow toward the base. Notice that the collector-to-base voltage is such that the collector is negative with respect to the base. This is true only for the p-n-p transistor because there are hole carriers in the emitter which are positively charged. In order to attract these positive charges, a negative field must be present. Since the collector is negative with respect to the base, the holes that come from the emitter will be attracted to the collector. Some of the holes will flow in the base region; however, the majority of the holes will flow to the collector. Since the collector current comes from the emitter, the collector current can never be greater than the emitter current. As a matter of fact, since some of the emitter current flows in the base, the collector current must always be less than the emitter current. This concept is true both for a p-n-p and n-p-n types.

There are three currents shown in Fig. 8-14A. These are for the emitter,

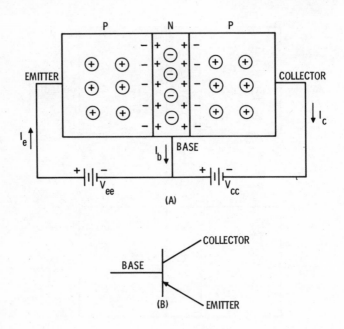

Fig. 8-14. (A) A basic p-n-p transistor, and (B) a p-n-p transistor symbol.

base, and collector, and are symbolized I_e, I_b, and I_c, respectively. The directions shown are for hole current. Since all of the current comes from the emitter, it must return to the emitter. Thus, the emitter current is the sum of the base and collector currents. Therefore,

$$I_e = I_b + I_c \qquad (8\text{-}1)$$

The symbol for a p-n-p transistor is shown in Fig. 8-14B.

In Fig. 8-15A is shown the correct bias polarities for an n-p-n transistor. Notice that the emitter has a negative voltage with respect to the base, and that the collector has a positive voltage with respect to the base. That this biasing is correct can be verified from the following: The emitter is now an n-type material, which has electrons as its majority carriers. In order to have these majority carriers flow, a negative voltage must be applied to the emitter with respect to the base. For the collector to attract the electrons, there must be a positive voltage on the collector with respect to the base.

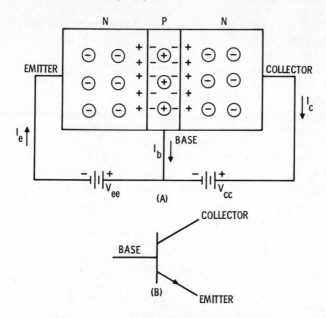

Fig. 8-15. (A) The correct bias polarities for an n-p-n transistor, and (B) a n-p-n transistor symbol.

The currents shown are, once again, I_e, I_b, and I_c. Again, the emitter current is the sum of the base and collector currents. However, the direction of the currents is for electron flow. The hole current flow is in the opposite direction to that shown. The fact that the conventional or hole current is flowing away from the emitter is the reason why, in the conventional n-p-n transistor, the arrow points away from the base. This is shown in Fig. 8-15B.

In both the p-n-p and the n-p-n transistors, the applied collector-to-base voltage is very much larger than the applied emitter-to-base voltage. This is necessary for the collector to collect holes or electrons that the emitter emits. The usual applied emitter-to-base voltage is on the order of one or two volts, whereas the applied collector-to-base voltage can be as high as 25 volts.

8-7. Basic Transistor Circuits

There are three basic transistor circuits: The common or grounded emitter, the common or grounded base, and the common or grounded collector. The most frequently used circuit is the common emitter because, as we shall see, it has a current gain, a power and voltage gain, and an output-to-input phase reversal which makes it useful as an inverter or NOT circuit.

8-8. Common-Base Circuit

As its name implies, the common-base circuit is one that uses the base as the common element between its input and its output. It has the following characteristics:

1. It has a current gain of less than one.
2. It generally has a voltage and power gain.
3. It does not have any phase reversal between its input voltage or current, and its output voltage or current.

The basic circuit for a p-n-p, common- or grounded-base circuit is shown in Fig. 8-16. The d-c voltage applied to the emitter is symbolized as V_{ee}, and the d-c voltage applied to the collector is symbolized as V_{cc}. Notice that the emitter is forward biased while the collector is reverse biased. In order to control the current flowing in the emitter circuit, an input resistor, R_1, is placed in series with the emitter base circuit. In order to develop an output voltage,

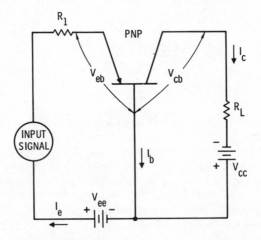

Fig. 8-16. The basic circuit for a common-base p-n-p transistor. The direction of current flow is for hole current.

a load resistor, R_L, is placed in the collector-to-base circuit. Notice that the input signal is placed in series with the emitter forward bias voltage. To fully understand the operation of this circuit, one must first understand how the volt–ampere characteristic curve for this circuit is developed. Therefore, let us discuss how this is done.

A typical, output, volt–ampere characteristic curve is shown in Fig. 8-17. To develop this curve, the emitter current is held constant, and the collector current is observed while varying the collector-to-base voltage. For example, in Fig. 8-17, for a 2-ma emitter current, the collector-to-base voltage is varied from 0 to a −20 volts, and the collector current is observed for each value of the collector-to-base voltage. Notice that the collector current is never greater than the emitter current. The emitter current is now set to some new value, and held constant. For this new emitter current, once again the collector-to-base voltage is varied, and the collector current is observed for each value of the collector-to-base voltage. This procedure is continued until the family of curves shown in Fig. 8-17 is generated.

If the emitter-to-base circuit is open-circuited, and if a reverse bias voltage is placed between the collector and base, there will be collector current. The reason for this is the impurities that are present in the collector region. In a p-n-p transistor, the collector region has holes as its majority carriers.

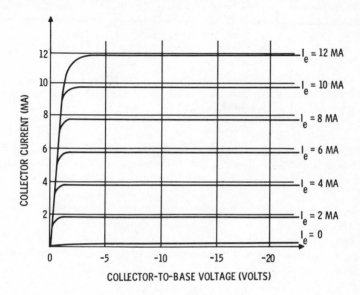

Fig. 8-17. A typical common-base characteristic curve for a p-n-p transistor.

Any impurities in this region are due to minority carriers or electrons. These minority carriers are attracted by the positive field on the base, and cause some collector current to exist. This current is referred to as the *collector leakage current*, and is symbolized as I_{co}. This leakage collector current is affected by heat. Experiments show that I_{co} doubles for each ten-degrees-centigrade change in temperature. As an example, assume that for a p-n-p transistor the value of I_{co} is 2 μa at 20 °C. If the transistor's temperature rose to 60 °C, it will be found that the value of I_{co} at this temperature will be approximately 32 μa. It is important, therefore, that a transistor should not be operated at too high a temperature. The maximum temperaure for most germanium transistors is 85 °C. For silicon transistors, the maximum temperature is approximately 150 °C. Most transistor manufacturers give the value of I_{co} at 20 °C, which is approximately room temperature, and the maximum temperature at which the transistor can be operated safely.

The reason for no current gain in a common-base circuit can be seen clearly from the characteristic curve. Notice that the collector current is never greater than the emitter current. Since the output current for this circuit is the collector current, and since the input current is the emitter current, there can not be a current gain greater than one in this circuit. The reason for this is that the collector current comes from the emitter. Since some of the emitter current must flow through the base circuit, the collector current must be less than the emitter current. The ratio of the change in collector current to the change in emitter current for a fixed collector-to-base voltage is referred to as alpha, α, or h_{fb}. This is mathematically represented as:

$$\alpha \text{ or } h_{fb} = \frac{\Delta I_c}{\Delta I_e} \bigg|_{V_{cb}} \tag{8-2}$$

The value of alpha is less than unity, ranging from 0.9 to 0.99 for most pulse transistors. The collector current can be found by multiplying the emitter current by alpha, and adding the value of I_{co}. Thus,

$$I_c = \alpha I_e + I_{co} \tag{8-3}$$

In Fig. 8-18, a typical input characteristic curve for a common-base circuit is shown. Notice that this curve is essentially a diode curve which is to be expected since the emitter and base form a p-n junction diode. This curve is developed by short-circuiting the collector-to-base circuit, and varying the emitter current while measuring the emitter-to-base voltage. From this curve, the input resistance, which is symbolized as h_{11} or h_{ib}, can be determined. This is done by taking a ratio of a change in emitter-to-base voltage to a change in emitter current for a constant collector-to-base voltage. Thus,

$$h_{ib} \text{ or } h_{11} = \frac{\Delta V_{eb}}{\Delta I_e} \bigg|_{V_{cb}} \tag{8-4}$$

The usual range of input resistance for pulse transistors is from 20 to 60 ohms.

It was briefly mentioned that the common-base circuit has a power gain. Let us see why this is true. In a common-base circuit, the output resistance is much larger than the input resistance. This can be verified by looking at the characteristic curves. The output resistance can be found from Fig. 8-17 by taking a change in collector-to-base voltage to a corresponding change in collector current for a constant base current. Thus,

$$R_{ob} = \frac{\Delta V_{cb}}{\Delta I_c} \bigg|_{I_b} \tag{8-5}$$

where R_{ob} is the output resistance for a common-base circuit. Since the collector current is approximately equal to the emitter current, and since the output resistance is much larger than the input resistance, the product of the collector current squared times the output resistance will be greater than the product of the emitter current squared times the input resistance. For this reason, the common-base circuit will have a power gain.

It was also briefly mentioned that the common-base circuit has a voltage gain. This voltage gain is the ratio of the output voltage that is developed across the load resistor to the voltage that is applied between the emitter and base. The input resistance of the transistor times the emitter current is the voltage between the emitter and the base. This is usually a very small voltage, on the order of tenths of a volt. The output voltage can be found by multiplying the collector current by the load resistor. Since the collector current is approximately equal to the emitter current, and since the load resistor

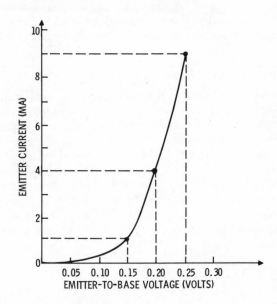

Fig. 8-18. A typical input curve for a p-n-p common-base transistor circuit.

is very much larger than the input resistance, it follows that there is a voltage gain in this circuit.

There is no phase reversal between the output voltage or current, and the input voltage or current in the common-base circuit because the collector current will increase and decrease as the emitter current increases and decreases. If the emitter current were to increase, the collector current will also increase. If the emitter current were to decrease, the collector current will also decrease. Thus, there cannot be any phase reversal between the input and output current. The same is true for the input and output voltages. If the polarity of the input signal voltage is assumed to be positive, i.e., the emitter is made more positive relative to the base, and assuming a p-n-p transistor is used, then the emitter current will increase. This increase in emitter current will give rise to an increase in the collector current. For a p-n-p transistor, this increase in collector current will cause the collector end of the load resistor to become more positive. The reason for this is that the collector current is hole current in a p-n-p transistor, and if the hole current that is flowing into a resistor increases, its voltage will become more positive. Conversely, if the emitter-to-base voltage becomes less positive, the emitter current will decrease which will cause a decrease in collector current. This decrease in collector current will cause the polarity of the voltage drop across the load resistor to be less positive. Thus, we see that there is no phase reversal between the input voltage or current, and the output voltage or current for a common-base transistor.

Because of its low input resistance, no phase reversal, and its current gain of less than unity, the common-base circuit is seldom used for a logic circuit. For most applications in logic circuits, the common-emitter circuit is used.

8-9. Common-Emitter Circuit

The common-emitter circuit is the most frequently used of all the types of transistor circuits because it has high current, voltage, and power gains as well as a phase reversal between its input voltage or current, and its output voltage or current. Before we examine these characteristics, let us see how the family of characteristic curves is generated for the common-emitter circuit.

The basic circuit that is used to generate the family of characteristic curves for a p-n-p common-emitter circuit is shown in Fig. 8-19. The base current can be adjusted by setting the potentiometer, R_1. The collector-to-emitter voltage can be varied by varying R_2. The base current is first set to zero by

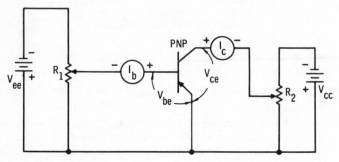

Fig. 8-19. A basic circuit for determining the family of characteristic curves for a p-n-p common-emitter circuit.

adjusting R_1 so that the voltage applied between the base and emitter is zero. With this zero base current, the voltage drop between the collector and the emitter is varied by varying R_2, and for each increment of collector-to-emitter voltage, the collector current is observed. It would appear that for a base current equal to zero, the collector current should also equal zero. This is not the case because there are some impurities in the collector which will cause a collector current to flow even for zero base current. As a matter of fact, it will be found that the collector current in this case will be greater than in the common-base circuit when its emitter current is zero. This will be explained further later in this section.

After this run has been done and recorded, the base current is set to some value, and maintained. Once again, the collector-to-emitter voltage is varied, and for each change in collector-to-emitter voltage, the collector current is observed and recorded. When this run is finished, the base current is set to some other value, and once again the collector-to-emitter voltage is varied, and the collector current is observed and recorded. This process continues until a family of curves is generated. A typical family of curves for the common-emitter circuit is shown in Fig. 8-20. Most transistor manufacturers provide these curves, and they can also be obtained from a transistor manual.

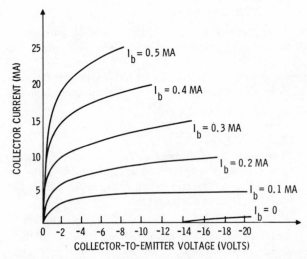

Fig. 8-20. A typical output family of curves for a common-emitter circuit.

It should be noted from Fig. 8-19 that the input current for a common-emitter circuit is the base current, and the output current is the collector current. Since the collector current is much greater than the base current, a current gain, which is referred to as beta (β), or h_{fe}, is obtained from this circuit. This current can be found from the characteristic curves by taking a change in collector current to a change in base current for a constant collector-to-emitter voltage. Thus,

$$\beta \text{ or } h_{fe} = \frac{\Delta I_c}{\Delta I_b} \bigg|_{V_{ce}} \tag{8-6}$$

The usual range of beta for logic transistors is from 30 to 100. Transistors having betas of greater than 300 can be obtained, but they are not in common use for logic circuits.

As a good approximation, it can be said that the collector current for a common-emitter circuit is equal to the product of the current gain times the base current. This approximation temporarily neglects the leakage current in a common-emitter circuit. Thus,

$$I_c = \beta I_b \tag{8-7}$$

Since the emitter current is equal to the sum of the collector current plus the base current, the emitter current can be found by multiplying the base current by the sum of the current gain plus one. This can be derived using the following steps:

Step 1: $I_e = I_c + I_b$ from Eq. (8-1).
Step 2: $I_c = \beta I_b$ from Eq. (8-7).
Step 3:   Substituting the value of I_c from Step 2 into Step 1.
            $I_e = \beta I_b + I_b$
Step 4: $I_e = I_b (\beta + 1)$ \hfill (8-8)

As a simple example of Eq. (8-8), let us assume a transistor that has a beta of 49 and a base current of 0.2 ma. Then the emitter current will be 10 ma.

The current gain for a common emitter circuit can be shown to be a function of alpha. The steps to derive this relation are as follows:

Step 1: $I_e = I_c + I_b$ from Eq. (8-1).
Step 2:   Divide through by I_e. Thus,
            $I_e/I_e = I_c/I_e + I_b/I_e$
Step 3: $1 = \alpha + 1/(\beta + 1)$ because $I_c/I_e = \alpha$, and $I_b/I_e = 1/(\beta + 1)$
Step 4: $\beta + 1 = \alpha (\beta + 1) + 1$. Multiply Step 3 by $(\beta + 1)$
Step 5: $\beta - \alpha\beta = \alpha$. Transposing all values of β.
Step 6: $\beta (1 - \alpha) = \alpha$. Factoring β.
Step 7: $\beta = \alpha/(1 - \alpha)$ \hfill (8-9)

As an example of Eq. (8-9), let us assume an alpha of 0.98. The beta for this transistor, using Eq. (8-9), will be 49, which is a typical value for logic, common-emitter circuits.

We have briefly mentioned that there will be some collector current even though the base current is zero. Let us now explain why this is so. If the base-to-emitter circuit is opened, and reverse bias is applied between the collector and the emitter, there will still be some collector current. This collector current is leakage current, and is due to the impurities that are present in the collector. To distinguish this leakage current of the common-emitter circuit from that of the common-base circuit, the symbol I_{ceo} will be used. This leakage current is more important in the common-emitter circuit than in the common-base circuit because, if care is not taken in the design of the common-emitter circuit, the transistor might destroy itself. The reason for this is that thermal runaway will occur in a common-emitter circuit because the leakage current of this circuit is much greater than that of the common-base circuit, and because leakage current is very temperature sensitive. Thermal runaway is due to the leakage current producing heat which in turn will produce more collector leakage current, and which in turn will produce more heat. This process continues until finally, the transistor has destroyed itself. This phenomenon can be prevented by proper circuit design, and a method will be discussed once we have proved that the collector leakage current for a common-emitter circuit is greater than that of a common-base circuit.

For this discussion, the symbol I_{co} will represent the collector leakage current for the common-base circuit, and the symbol I_{ceo} will represent the collector leakage current of the common emitter circuit. In order to relate these two leakage currents, substitute for I_e in Eq. (8-3) and that in Eq. (8-1). Once this has been done, algebraically manipulate this equation until an equation is developed that shows the collector current in terms of the base current, and the collector leakage current of the common base circuit. The steps that are necessary to develop this equation are:

Step 1: $I_c = \alpha I_e + I_{co}$ from Eq. (8-3).

Step 2: $I_e = I_c + I_b$ from Eq. (8-1).

Step 3: $I_c = \alpha (I_c + I_b) + I_{co}$

Step 4: $I_c - \alpha I_c = \alpha I_b + I_{co}$. Transposing all values of I_c.

Step 5: Factoring the I_c in the left-hand side of *Step 5*,
$I_c (1 - \alpha) = \alpha I_b + I_{co}$

Step 6: Dividing by $(1 - \alpha)$,
$$I_c = \alpha I_b/(1 - \alpha) + I_{co}/(1 - \alpha) \qquad (8\text{-}10\text{A})$$

Step 7: Since $\beta = \alpha/(1 - \alpha)$ from Eq. (8-9).
$I_c = \beta I_b + I_{co}/(1 - \alpha)$

Equations 8-10A and B clearly show the collector current in terms of the base current and the collector leakage current for the common-base circuit. Let us now proceed to analyze these equations. Notice that when I_b is zero, which is very likely to happen in logic transistor circuits, the collector current for the common-emitter circuit will be the leakage current of the common-base circuit divided by $(1 - \alpha)$. This quantity is usually a very small number because alpha is close to unity. Therefore, the ratio of $I_{co}/(1 - \alpha)$ will be a large number. As an example, assume that the leakage current for a common-base circuit is 4 μa at 20 °C, and that the alpha of this transistor is 0.98. The quantity $(1 - \alpha)$ will be 0.02. The collector leakage current for the common-emitter circuit will be 4 μa/0.02 which is equal to 200 μa or 0.2 ma. This is a rather large value of leakage current, and can easily cause thermal runaway.

Assuming that the transistor cannot be made any purer, the least value that the leakage current can obtain will be that for the common-base circuit. This can be done in transistor logic circuits by not letting the base current go to zero, but instead letting it be a $-I_{co}$. If this is the case, then the collector leakage current for the common-emitter circuit will be that for the common-base circuit. This can be proved by inserting the value $-I_{co}$ for I_b in Eq. (8-10A). Thus,

$$I_c = \alpha (-I_{co})/(1 - \alpha) + I_{co}/(1 - \alpha)$$
$$= (-\alpha I_{co} + I_{co})/(1 - \alpha)$$
$$= (1 - \alpha)(I_{co})/(1 - \alpha) = I_{co}$$

One method that is commonly used in transistor logic circuits to minimize the collector leakage current is shown in Fig. 8-21. Notice, in this figure, that V_{bb} is a positive voltage, the base is positive relative to the emitter, and it is applied to the base of a p-n-p transistor through a resistor, R_1. This positive voltage will cause the emitter to be slightly back-biased when the input

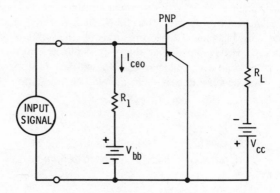

Fig. 8-21. Reverse biasing the base to emitter to decrease the value of I_{ceo}. This is done by inserting the battery, V_{bb}, and the resistor, R_1.

signal is zero. This positive voltage on the base will attract the minority carriers in the collector circuit, and in turn it will appreciably decrease the collector leakage current. The value of R_1 is chosen by dividing the value of V_{bb} by the $I_{c_e 0}$ at the highest temperature of operation.

Let us now develop the input characteristic curve for a common-emitter circuit. An input characteristic curve for the common-emitter circuit is shown

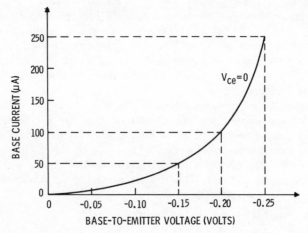

Fig. 8-22. A typical input curve for a p-n-p common-emitter circuit.

in Fig. 8-22. The circuit of Fig. 8-19 can be used to generate this curve. The procedure that is used to generate it is to first set the collector-to-emitter voltage to zero, and then the base-to-emitter voltage is measured while varying the base current. As for the common-base circuit, once again, this curve resembles a diode curve because the base-to-emitter is a diode. The input resistance, which is symbolized as h_{11} or h_{ie}, can be approximately obtained from this curve by taking a change in base-to-emitter voltage for a corresponding change in base current. Thus,

$$h_{11} = h_{ie} = \frac{\Delta V_{be}}{\Delta I_b} \bigg|_{V_{ce}} = 0 \qquad (8\text{-}11)$$

An input resistance of between 500 and 5000 ohms is common for a common-emitter circuit. Notice that the input resistance of a common-emitter-circuit is greater than that of the common-base circuit. This can be proved by substituting Eq. (8-8) into Eq. (8-11). Thus,

Step 1: $I_e = I_b \, (\beta + 1)$ from Eq. (8-8).

Step 2: $I_b = I_e/(\beta + 1)$ Solving for I_b in Eq. (8-8).

Step 3: $h_{ie} = \Delta V_{be}/\Delta I_b$ from Eq. (8-11).

Step 4: $h_{ie} = \dfrac{\Delta V_{be}}{\dfrac{\Delta I_e}{\beta + 1}} = \dfrac{\Delta V_{be}}{\Delta I_e} \, (\beta + 1)$

Step 5:   Since $h_{ib} = \Delta V_{be}/\Delta I_e$ from Eq. (8-4).

   $h_{ie} = h_{ib} \, (\beta + 1)$ \qquad\qquad\qquad\qquad (8-12)

From Eq. (8-12), it can be seen that the input resistance of the common-emitter circuit is $(\beta + 1)$ times greater than the common-base circuit. For pulse circuits, the input resistance of the common-emitter circuit is from 1000 to 2000 ohms.

A basic pulse, p-n-p common-emitter circuit is shown in Fig. 8-23. The function of R_1 and V_{bb} have been previously explained, and it should be

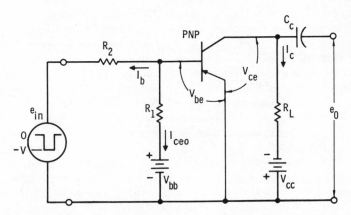

Fig. 8-23. A basic pulse type, p-n-p common-emitter circuit.

recalled that their function is to make I_{ceo} as small as possible. R_2 is a base current limiting resistor. The reason for it is that the input voltage in transistor pulse circuits is on the order of volts. From Fig. 8-22, it can be seen that in order to make the transistor conduct, approximately 0.1 volts is necessary. If five or six volts were applied between the base and the emitter, the base current would be excessive, and it might destroy the transistor. The value of R_2 can be determined once the base current, the drop from base to emitter, and the magnitude of the input voltage are known. The magnitude of the input voltage minus the drop from base to emitter will be the drop across R_2. The current flowing through it is I_b. Using Ohm's law, the value of R_2 can be computed. Thus,

$$R_2 = (V - V_{be})/I_b \qquad (8\text{-}13)$$

where V is the magnitude of the input voltage.

As an example, assume a base current of 0.1 ma is desired. Assume also that the magnitude of the input signal is 3 volts, and that the base-to-emitter voltage is 0.2 volts. The value of R_2 will be:

$$R_2 = (3 - 0.2)/(0.1)(10^{-3}) = 2.8/10^{-4} = 28\text{K ohms}$$

Referring once again to Fig. 8-23, R_L is the collector output resistor, which is necessary to develop an output voltage. For logic circuits, it has a value of between 1000 and 2000 ohms. Relative to the value of the output resistance for the common-emitter circuit, which is usually on the order of from 0.5 to 1 megohms, this collector load resistance is very small. The reason for this is that the lower the load resistance, the better the frequency response. Since pulses are fed into logic circuits, it is important that the output circuit responds without distortion. If a large value of collector load resistor is used, the frequency response of the circuit will decrease, which in turn will give rise to pulse distortion.

C_c of Fig. 8-23 is a coupling capacitor which is used to block the dc from going into the next stage, as well as to couple the varying signal from collector to emitter into the next stage.

Let us now show why the common-emitter circuit has a phase reversal between its input and output voltage. Referring to Fig. 8-23; when a negative-going signal is applied between base and emitter, the emitter will become forward biased. This will cause emitter current to flow, which in turn will cause base and collector currents to flow. For a p-n-p transistor, the collector current is hole current. This collector hole current makes the upper terminal of R_L become positive relative to the lower terminal. Since the input signal is a negative-going pulse, and since the drop across R_L is going in a positive direction, there is a phase reversal between the input and the output signals. In a similar manner, when the input signal returns to 0 volts, the base-to-emitter voltage, V_{be}, becomes slightly positive because of the V_{bb} and R_1 circuit. This positive voltage between the base and the emitter back-biases the emitter, making the collector current approximately zero. The instantaneous drop across R_L now is approximately 0 volts which means that it has gone in a negative direction, since it was positive. Notice that a positive-going input voltage caused a negative-going output voltage, which once again shows that there is a phase reversal between the input and the output voltages. Figure 8-24 shows this phase reversal between the input and the output voltages.

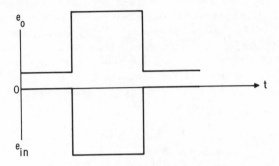

Fig. 8-24. Ideal input-output signals for a p-n-p common-emitter circuit.

Let us now discuss the voltage gain properties of a common-emitter circuit. At the beginning of the discussion on the common-emitter circuit, it was mentioned that it has a voltage gain. However, for most transistor logic circuits, the voltage gain is not large. The voltage gain now being referred to is the ratio of the output voltage to the *applied* input voltage. As a matter of fact, it is common to make this voltage gain equal to unity so as to maintain a common voltage signal throughout the computer. For example, if a 6-volt amplitude signal is fed into the base of the common-emitter circuit, it is quite desirable from the standpoint of having a constant amplitude signal to make the amplitude of the output signal also six volts. It should be realized that this is a unity voltage gain when the output voltage to the *applied* input signal is considered. If, on the other hand, the amplitude of the signal that is applied between the base and the emitter is considered, then there will be a voltage gain that is much greater than unity.

The common-emitter circuit will have a large power gain. This is true because the collector current is beta times the base current. The approximate output power at the collector circuit can be found by taking the square of the collector current, and multiplying it by the load resistor. Thus,

$$P_o = I_c^2 R_L \qquad (8\text{-}14)$$

The input power to the transistor is the square of the base current times the input resistance. Thus,

$$P_i = I_b^2 h_{ie} \qquad (8\text{-}15)$$

The power gain is the ratio of the output power to the input power. The symbol used for the power gain is P.G.

$$\text{P.G.} = P_o/P_i = I_c^2 R_L / I_b^2 h_{ie} \qquad (8\text{-}16)$$

Since $I_c = \beta I_b$, then the power gain will be:

$$\text{P.G.} = [(\beta)(I_b)]^2 R_L / I_b^2 h_{ie} = \beta^2 R_L / h_{ie} \qquad (8\text{-}17)$$

Since R_L and h_{ie} are usually the same value for logic circuits, then the power gain is approximately the square of beta. As an example, assume an $R_L = h_{ie} = 1K$ ohms. Assume further a beta of 50, which is a common value for a pulse transistor. The power gain in this case will be 2500. Power gains of 5000 and larger are quite common with transistors.

In Fig. 8-25 is shown a typical load line for a p-n-p common-emitter circuit. One end of the load line is shown as point A, and the other as point B. Point A is determined by assuming that the collector-to-emitter cir-

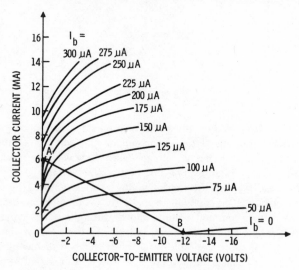

Fig. 8-25. A typical p-n-p common-emitter output characteristic curve that illustrates a load line.

cuit is short-circuited. For this assumption, the collector-to-emitter voltage will be zero, and the current flowing through the collector circuit can be found by dividing the magnitude of the collector applied voltage, V_{cc}, by R_L. The lower extreme point, point B, can be found by assuming the collector-to-emitter is open-circuited. For this assumption, there will be no collector current, and the voltage drop between the collector and emitter will be a $-V_{cc}$ volts. If, for example, in Fig. 8-23, the load resistor is 2000 ohms, and the applied voltage to the collector is a -12 volts, the maximum collector current that can flow is 6 ma. This is point A of Fig. 8-25. Point B of this same figure is at -12 volts and 0 collector current. For this case, all of the applied collector voltage is between the collector and the emitter.

It appears, from Fig. 8-25, that a base current of 200 μa will cause a collector-to-emitter voltage of approximately zero volts and a collector current of six ma. This is not the case. To verify this, an expanded curve of the low collector voltages needs to be obtained. Manufacturers provide these curves, and a typical one is shown in Fig. 8-26. This is the expanded curve for the low collector voltages in that of Fig. 8-25.

In Fig. 8-26, the load line is once again drawn. The point where the collector current is six ma is labeled A, and the point on the load line where the base current is 200 μa is labeled A'. The load line of Fig. 8-26 is con-

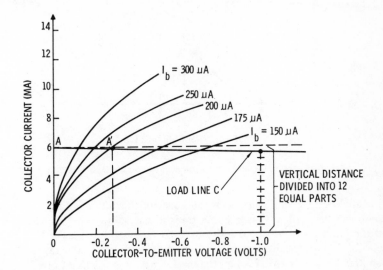

Fig. 8-26. Expanded low collector voltage of the common-emitter curve for Fig. 8-25.

structed by first drawing a vertical dashed line at a V_{ce} of −1 volt up to a horizontal dashed line drawn through the collector current of six ma. Since the magnitude of V_{ce} now being used is one-twelfth of that in Fig. 8-25, the vertical distance is divided into twelve parts, and the load line is drawn from A to point C on the vertical line, one-twelfth below the line drawn through the collector current.

From Fig. 8-26, it can be seen that a base current of 200 μa does not cause a collector current of six ma, but slightly less. The reason for this is that the collector-to-emitter voltage is not 0 volts which Fig. 8-25 seems to indicate. From Fig. 8-26, it can be seen that the collector-to-emitter voltage at a base current of 200 μa is approximately −0.25 volts. It might be argued that this voltage is insignificant when compared with −12 volts. As far as computing the maximum collector current is concerned, this is true. However, this voltage is very significant when it comes to determining if the transistor is saturated.

A transistor is saturated when its collector-to-base voltage is forward biased. In order to determine if a transistor is saturated, the expanded output curves as well as the input curves must be available. If these curves

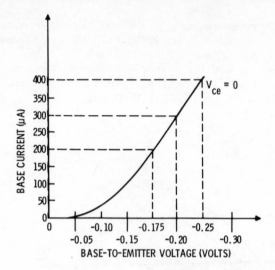

Fig. 8-27. An input curve for the common-emitter circuit of Fig. 8-19.

are available, then one can check the collector-to-emitter voltage, and the base-to-emitter voltage to see if the transistor is saturated. Let us assume that the input curve for the transistor we are discussing is that of Fig. 8-27. From this figure, it can be seen that for a base current of 200 μa, the base-to-emitter voltage is -0.175, i.e., the base is negative relative to the emitter by 0.175 volts. From Fig. 8-26, it can be seen that the collector-to-emitter voltage for a base current of 200 μa is a -0.25 volts. Figure 8-28A shows the voltages on the transistor, and it clearly shows that the collector is not forward biased, therefore, the transistor is not saturated.

On the other hand, let us assume that the base current is 300 μa. From Fig. 8-26, it can be seen that for a base current of 300 μa, the collector-to-

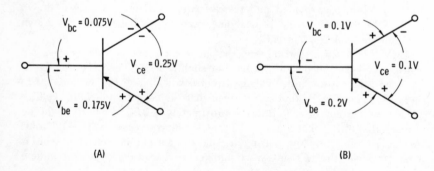

(A)   (B)

Fig. 8-28. (A) Voltages across a transistor which show that the transistor is not saturated. Notice that the collector-to-base voltage is reverse biased. (B) Voltages across a transistor that show the transistor is saturated. Notice that the collector-to-base voltage is forward biased.

emitter voltage will be −0.1 volts. From Fig. 8-27, it can be seen that the base-to-emitter voltage will be a −0.2 volts. Figure 8-28B shows these voltages on the transistor, and it clearly shows that the collector-to-base voltage is now forward biased. The transistor is now in saturation.

When a transistor is saturated, the collector behaves as an emitter, which means that the collector will inject holes into the base region. These holes will be trapped in the base region until the transistor is turned off by a zero base current. The effect of these holes that are injected into the base region is to increase the width of the output pulse. This is illustrated in Fig. 8-29.

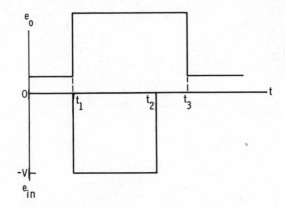

Fig. 8-29. Input and output pulses for a saturated transistor; $t_3 - t_2$ is the storage delay time.

At t_1, the base voltage relative to the emitter is negative, which will turn on the transistor. Let us assume for this discussion that the collector current reaches its maximum value in zero time, which is not the case in practice, but which will be discussed more fully later. At t_2, the base voltage goes to zero, which in turn means that the transistor should be off. However, if the transistor is in saturation, when the transistor is turned off there will still be time before the collector current is turned off, because the hole current that was injected into the base region must take time to diffuse from this region. The time from t_2 to t_3 is the time needed to make the collector current go to zero, and it is referred to as *storage time.*

There are many ways of decreasing the storage time, but the most common and practical is to let the base current, when it is going to turn the transistor off, become negative. A common way to do this to place a capacitor across R_2. This is shown in Fig. 8-30. Figure 8-31A shows the normal input base pulse without the capacitor. Figure 8-31B shows the input base pulse with the capacitor. Notice that at t_1 of Fig. 8-31B, the base goes a little positive because of the capacitor. This will in turn decrease the storage time as well as decrease the turn-on time. (The turn-on time is that time when the transistor is just turned on.)

It was assumed in the previous discussion that when the transistor is

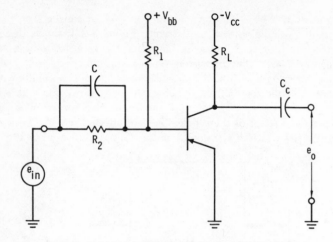

Fig. 8-30. A common-emitter pulse-type circuit that contains the speed-up capacitor, C.

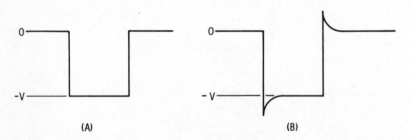

(A)   (B)

Fig. 8-31. (A) The input pulse when the speed-up capacitor is not in the circuit; (B) the resulting input pulse when the speed-up capacitor is in the circuit.

turned on, its collector current would reach a maximum value in zero time. This is not the case. The reason for this is that the transistor has an input capacitance as well as an input resistance. A simplified equivalent circuit of the input of the transistor is shown in Fig. 8-32. R_2 is the base-current limiting resistor, and C_i and R_i represent the input capacitance and resistance, respectively.

If a square wave of voltage were to be applied to this circuit, it would take some time for the capacitor to become fully charged. This is shown in Fig. 8-33. The input to the base will not be a square wave, but an exponentially rising wave. This, in turn, will cause the collector output voltage waveform to be an exponentially rising wave. When capacitor C is placed across R_2, such as is shown in Fig. 8-34, the output voltage will have the same waveform as in the input if the product of R_2C is equal to R_iC_i. Since C_i, R_i, and R_2 are fixed, one chooses a value of C that will make the product of R_2C equal to R_iC_i. Unfortunately, R_i and C_i are not the same for all transistors of the same type, and since they do differ, C must be hand-picked for each transistor.

Still another method to decrease the turn-on time is to overdrive the transistor. This is also commonly done in practice. This is illustrated in Fig.

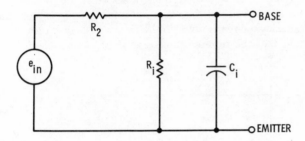

Fig. 8-32. An equivalent circuit for the input circuit of a common-emitter circuit.

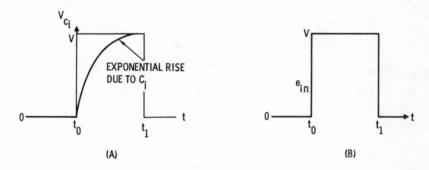

Fig. 8-33. An effect of the input capacity of a transistor.

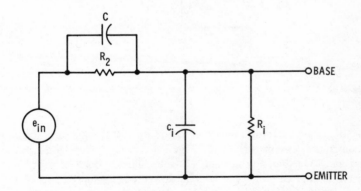

Fig. 8-34. The equivalent input circuit with a capacitor placed across R_2. If e_{in} is a square wave and $R_2C = R_1C_i$, then the output voltage will also be a square wave.

8-35. The pulse labeled A is the normal collector current without overdrive. Notice that the collector current will reach its maximum value at t_2. On the other hand, if the transistor were overdriven by feeding in a larger-than-normal base voltage, the collector current will reach its maximum value at t_1. Since t_1 is less than t_2, the turn-on time, which for this case refers to the time that it will take for the collector to reach its maximum value, will decrease. Since logic circuits must do their work in as fast a time as possible, it is important that the turn-on time be as short as possible.

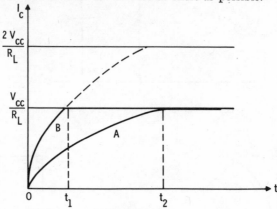

Fig. 8-35. (A) Collector current output without base overdrive; (B) collector current output with base overdrive.

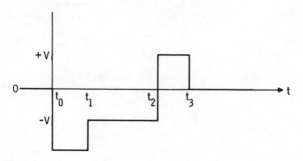

Fig. 8-36. The ideal input waveform to decrease turn-on, turn-off, and storage times.

The ideal base waveform to decrease turn-on and storage time for a p-n-p common-emitter circuit is shown in Fig. 8-36. From t_0 to t_1, the input wave is more negative than the normal $-V$ volts. This is done to overdrive the transistor so that turn-on time will be decreased. From t_1 to t_2, the input signal is at its normal value, at $-V$ volts. At t_2, turn-off time begins. In order to decrease storage and turn-off time, the base is driven slightly positive from t_2 to t_3. This ideal waveform can be accomplished by using the capacitor C across R_2.

8-10. Common-Collector or Emitter Follower Circuit

The common-collector or emitter follower, Fig. 8-37, uses the collector as its common point. The collector is at a-c ground because of the bypass capacitor, C. However, it is not at d-c ground. The bypass capacitor has a very low reactance to the lowest frequency of operation, and, for this reason, will make the collector the common element in the circuit. This circuit has a current and power gain, but no voltage gain and phase reversal.

Since the input is, once again, the base current, and since the output is the emitter current, there must be a current gain in this circuit. The ratio

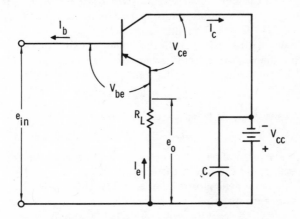

Fig. 8-37. Basic circuit for a common-collector or emitter follower circuit.

of the emitter current to the base current is the current gain of this circuit. From Eq. (8-8), the emitter current is $(\beta + 1)$ times the base current. Therefore, the current gain for this circuit is $(\beta + 1)$.

There will be a power gain in this circuit because of the current gain, and because the load resistor for this circuit is usually larger than the input resistance. Therefore, the square of the emitter current times the load resistor will be greater than the square of the base current times the input resistance.

There can not be a voltage gain in this circuit because of the negative feedback that exists across R_L. In order to understand this, we must first realize that in this circuit there is no phase reversal between the input and output voltage. To prove this, assume a negative input signal. This signal will now make the base negative relative to the emitter. Since the emitter is now forward-biased, it will cause an emitter current to flow in resistor R_L. Since we are assuming a p-n-p transistor, the emitter current will be hole or conventional current. This current will, in turn, make the lower side of R_L positive relative to the emitter. Therefore, the voltage from the emitter to collector is going in a negative direction which is the same direction that the input signal is going. It is for this reason that this circuit is also referred to as an emitter follower.

Once you understand that there is no phase reversal in this circuit, we can proceed to determine why there is a negative feedback occurring here. First, let us define negative feedback. A circuit is said to have negative feedback if a voltage fed back to its input will cause the resulting input signal to be less than its applied input signal. If, in Fig. 8-37, we assume that R_L is not in the circuit, then the input signal between the base and the emitter will be the applied signal, e_{in}. If we now consider R_L as being in the circuit, and if we recall that the voltage drop across it is of the same polarity as the input voltage, then we can see that the resulting base-to-emitter voltage will be the input voltage minus the drop across R_L. Since further, the resulting base-to-emitter voltage is less than the applied input voltage, there is negative feedback in this circuit.

This circuit has the characteristics of having a high input impedance, and a low output impedance. For this reason it is used as an impedance matching device. The input resistance can be found by using the following equation:

$$R_{in} = R_L(\beta + 1) \tag{8-18}$$

The output resistance is given by the following equation:

$$R_o = R_g/(\beta + 1) \tag{8-19}$$

where R_g is the internal resistance of the generator that is driving this circuit.

As an example of the use of these equations, assume an R_L of 1K ohms, a beta of 50, and a generator resistance of 510 ohms. From Eq. (8-19), the input resistance is:

$$R_{in} = (10^3)(50 + 1) = 51,000 \text{ ohms}$$

From Eq. (8-19), the output resistance is:

$$R_o = 510/51 = 10 \text{ ohms}$$

Thus, we see that this circuit will have a large input resistance and a very small output resistance.

8-11. Problems

1. Why is a diode a unilateral device? Are resistors unilateral devices? Are capacitors or inductors bilateral or unilateral devices? Why?
2. Define the following: molecule, element, atom, electron, proton, and nucleus.
3. What are the two most commonly used elements for semiconductors? How many electrons does the germanium atom have? How many does silicon have?
4. Explain the following terms: valence electrons, covalent bond, tetravalent, trivalent, and pentavalent.
5. What does doping mean? How is an n-type material doped? Why? How is a p-type material doped? Why?
6. What does the word "hole" mean when applied to a semiconductor? What relative polarity of charge does it have? Explain hole current flow in a p-type semiconductor.

7. What is a p-n junction? Why does current flow in a p-n junction when it is forward biased? Why doesn't current flow in it when it is reversed biased?

8. Explain why a p-n-p transistor conducts when the emitter is forward biased and the collector is reversed biased? Draw the symbol for a p-n-p transistor, showing the correct voltages that are necessary to forward-bias the emitter, and reverse-bias the collector.

9. Explain the difference between a p-n-p and an n-p-n transistor. Draw the symbol for an n-p-n transistor, showing the correct voltages that are necessary to make the transistor conduct.

10. Draw the circuit for an n-p-n common-base circuit. Explain how it works.

11. Why doesn't the common-base circuit have a current gain greater than one? Why does it have a voltage and a power gain? Why doesn't it have a phase reversal between its output and input voltage or current?

12. Define the following terms: alpha, collector leakage current, input resistance, and output resistance as they are applied to a common-base circuit.

13. A manufacturer states that the collector leakage current for a common-base circuit is 2 μa at 20 °C. What is the collector leakage current at 80 °C?

14. Why is the common-emitter circuit more frequently used than a common-base or a common-collector circuit?

15. Assume that you desire to verify the curves for a common-emitter circuit. Explain how you would obtain the collector or output curves. How would you obtain the input curve?

16. Why does a common-emitter circuit have a current gain that is greater than one? Why does it have a voltage and power gain? Explain why there is a phase reversal between the output and input voltage or current in a common-emitter circuit.

17. Explain how you would determine the beta or h_{fe} of a common-emitter circuit if you were given the transistor's collector or output characteristic curve.

18. The beta of a transistor when it is being used in a common-emitter circuit is 49, and the base current is 0.2 ma. Assuming leakage current equal to zero, what is the emitter current? What is the collector current?

19. A transistor has an alpha of 0.98. What is its beta? What is the alpha of a transistor if its beta is 100? If alpha is equal to 1, what is the value of beta? For this value of beta, what would the base current have to be?

20. Why is the collector leakage current of a common-emitter circuit greater than that of a common-base circuit?

21. Explain thermal runway. Show a circuit that will prevent it. Explain how this circuit works.

22. A transistor, when used in a common-base circuit, has an input resistance of 30 ohms. If the beta of this transistor is 49, what is its input resistance for a common-emitter circuit?

23. Explain when a transistor is saturated. What is the main disadvantage of saturating a transistor? How can this be overcome?

24. Why does overdriving a transistor reduce its turn-on time? Why does it increase its storage time?

25. Explain why a common-collector or emitter follower has a current gain. Why doesn't it have a voltage gain greater than one? Why is the common-collector circuit also referred to as an emitter follower?

9

Diode Logic Circuits

In analyzing any circuit, there are, basically, three parts in which we are mostly interested: the input or inputs, the output, and the circuit configuration. When the circuit input and output are the most important considerations, the black-box method of circuit analysis is usually used to determine the circuit requirements. Often, as in the case of logic circuits, a certain output is desired when certain known conditions exist at the input. The problem then is to find the circuit configuration inside the black box that will produce the desired output for the given input. Until now, our discussion of logic circuits has been confined to this type of black-box investigation. In this chapter, we shall investigate the input and output signals more closely, and study the circuit configurations inside the logic blocks.

9-1. Logic Circuit Inputs and Outputs

In general, logic circuits have one or more inputs, and each input may assume either of two given voltage levels. Because the logic circuits inside the black boxes must respond to or "recognize" only two distinct voltage levels, a convenient type of input signal is a pulse input. The input to a logic circuit is usually continuous, i.e., rather than consisting of a single pulse, the input is usually a series of pulses appearing at different intervals of time. For this reason, the input to a logic circuit may be more accurately described as a *train of pulses*. A typical pulse train is shown in Fig. 9-1A. As you can see, the pulse train has only two voltage levels: 0 volts and 10 volts. Between t_0 and t_1, the voltage level is 10 volts; during this time interval, a pulse *exists*. Between t_1 and t_2, however, the voltage level is 0 volts; during this time interval, a pulse *does not exist*. A pulse exists between t_2 and t_3, and between t_3 and t_4; a pulse does not exist between t_4 and t_5 or between t_5 and t_6. Finally, the last pulse in this train exists between t_6 and t_7. From this example of a train of pulses, you can see that, at any time, the input signal to a logical black box is at one of only two possible voltage levels. Realize that the significant factor is the existence of the two voltage levels, and not the amplitudes of the voltage levels. The amplitudes of 10 volts and 0 volts have been chosen quite arbitrarily; actually, there is no reason why amplitudes such as those in Fig. 9-1B could not be used. In this illustration, the pulses have a maximum amplitude of ±10 volts, and a peak-to-peak amplitude of 20 volts. Nevertheless, the voltage level at any time is either +10 or −10 volts. Again, you see, there are only two possible voltage

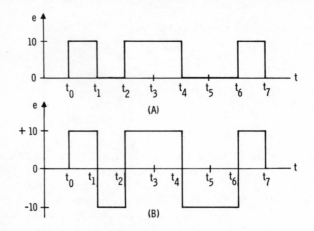

Fig. 9-1. The input to a diode logic circuit is usually a train of pulses. (A) The peak-to-peak amplitude of the pulses is 10 volts, and (B) the peak-to-peak amplitude of the pulses is 20 volts.

levels. During the time intervals between t_0 and t_1, t_2 and t_3, t_3 and t_4, and t_6 and t_7, the voltage level is +10 volts; during these intervals a pulse is said to exist. Between t_1 and t_2, t_4 and t_5, and t_5 and t_6, the voltages level is at −10 volts; during these time intervals, a pulse is said not to exist. A close observation of the pulse trains in Fig. 9-1A and B reveals that, although different amplitudes are used, pulses exist and do not exist during the same respective time intervals in both instances. Because it is somewhat easier to work with, the pulse train in Fig. 9-1A will be used in all future discussions involving waveforms.

Having examined the properties of the typical input signal used with logic circuits in general, let us now consider the voltage waveforms associated with the specific logic circuits.

A truth table is a great aid in studying logic circuit waveforms because it

TABLE 9-1.   INPUT AND OUTPUT CONDITIONS FOR AN "AND" GATE

	$t_0 - t_1$	$t_1 - t_2$	$t_2 - t_3$	$t_3 - t_4$
e_1	0	0	1	1
e_2	0	1	0	1
e_0	0	0	0	1

shows immediately all the input and output conditions that are possible for a particular circuit. For instance, the truth table in Table 9-1A gives all the input and output conditions possible for the AND gate of Fig. 9-2A. Notice that each of the four possible conditions has been assigned a time. By assigning a specific time to each condition, we can construct a voltage diagram for a logic circuit, as shown in Fig. 9-2A. Recall that a zero in the truth table means that the voltage does not exist. For the purpose of our

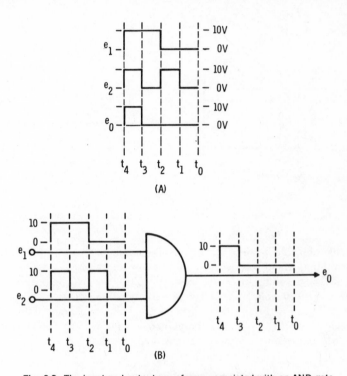

Fig. 9-2. The input and output waveforms associated with an AND gate.

voltage diagram, this means that the level of the voltage is 0 volts. Similarly, a 1 in the truth tables means that the voltage exists, and, for our voltage diagram, this indicates a voltage level of 10 volts. Translating the information in the truth table to the voltage diagram, we have the voltage waveform for the input voltages, e_1 and e_2, and the output voltage, e_0. At t_0, e_1 is 0 volts, e_2 is 0 volts, and e_0 is 0. At t_1, e_1 is 0 volts, e_2 is 10 volts, and e_0 is 0 volts. At t_2, e_1 is 10 volts, e_2 is 0 volts, and e_0 remains at 0 volts. Finally, at t_3, both e_1 and e_2 are 10 volts. As you would expect from an AND circuit, the output voltage is present (10 volts) under the last input conditions. In Fig. 9-2B, the same voltage waveforms are shown along with the logic block with which they are associated.

A similar series of illustrations is shown in Fig. 9-3 for an OR gate. The

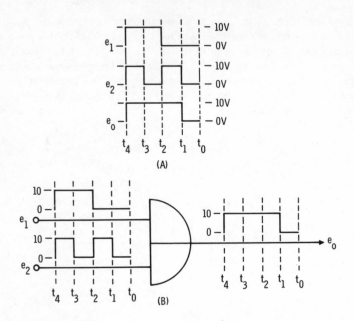

Fig. 9-3. The input and output waveforms associated with an OR gate.

truth table of Table 9-2 lists all the possible combinations of input voltages (for two inputs), and the resultant outputs for an OR circuit. Again, a zero indicates that a voltage does not exist (0 volts), and a 1 indicates that a voltage exists (10 volts). Each voltage combination occurs at a specified time: t_0, t_1, t_2, or t_3. From the truth table, the voltage diagram of Fig. 9-3A is developed. In Fig. 9-3B, the input and output voltage waveforms are shown in conjunction with the OR circuit logic block.

TABLE 9-2. INPUT AND OUTPUT CONDITIONS FOR AN "OR" GATE

	$t_0 - t_1$	$t_1 - t_2$	$t_2 - t_3$	$t_3 - t_4$
e_1	0	0	1	1
e_2	0	1	0	1
e_0	0	1	1	1

9-2. Basic Diode AND Gates

The basic diode AND gate, shown in Fig. 9-4, consists simply of diodes and resistors. Because of the relationship between the bias voltage, E, and the input voltages, e_1 and e_2, and of the way in which the diodes are placed in the circuit with respect to these voltages, this circuit produces an output

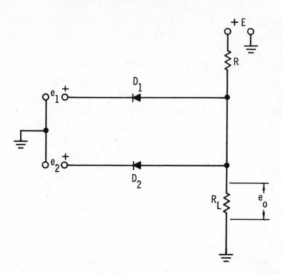

Fig. 9-4. A basic diode AND gate circuit.

only when all of the input voltages are present. For all possible input combinations, the circuit in Fig. 9-4 generates the outputs described by the truth table values for an AND gate logic block. Consequently, the diode circuit may replace the logic blocks that were previously used to generate AND statements. Although only two inputs are shown in Fig. 9-4, the diode AND gate is not restricted to having only two inputs. For each addition input, however, another diode must be added to the circuit. In view of this fact, you may have already realized that the electronic components considered in the discussions of logic blocks are the diodes in the actual circuit, and by using a Boolean statement in its simplest form, we reduce the number of electronic components, or diodes, needed to generate the statement.

To analyze the basic AND gate, we will use the circuit as it is redrawn in Fig. 9-5. Except for a slight rearrangement, this circuit is the same as

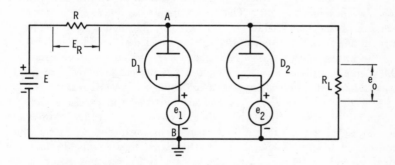

Fig. 9-5. Another arrangement of the AND gate circuit.

that shown in Fig. 9-4. To show that the waveforms in Fig. 9-2A apply to this circuit, we shall determine the output, e_0, for the given inputs, e_1 and e_2, at times t_0, t_1, t_2, and t_3.

For proper circuit operation, the bias voltage, E, must be more positive than any of the input voltages. Let us assume that E is approximately 30 volts, and that the maximum values of e_1 and e_2 is 10 volts. Let us also assume that R is 10 kilohms, and R_L is 50 kilohms. At t_0, both e_1 and e_2 are at 0 volts; the cathodes of D_1 and D_2 are, therefore, at ground potential. Because of the bias voltage, E, the anodes are at a positive potential with respect to ground; therefore, the diodes both conduct. With respect to R and R_L, the forward resistances of D_1 and D_2 are negligible, and the diodes act like short circuits across the load R_L. The current path in the circuit at t_0 exists through R, D_1, and D_2. Consequently, practically all of the circuit voltage is dropped across R, and e_0 is zero. Using Millman's theorem, we can obtain the same result analytically. But first, we have to assume forward, and reverse resistances for the diodes. For convenience, let's say that the diodes are electrically identical, that their forward resistances R_f, are 50 ohms each, and that their reverse resistances, R_b, are 500 kilohms each. Recall Millman's theorem (Section 7-2, ff.)

$$E_0 = \frac{E_1/R_1 + E_2/R_2 + E_3/R_3 + E_4/R_4}{1/R_1 + 1/R_2 + 1/R_3 + 1/R_4}$$

Referring to the circuit in Fig. 9-5, we can make the following substitutions: E_1 is the bias voltage, E; R_1 is R; E_2 is e_1, R_2 is R_{f1} or R_{b1}; E_3 is e_2; R_3 is R_{f2} or R_{b2}; E_4, which is the voltage in the circuit branch containing R_4, is zero; R_4 is R_L; and E_0 is e_0. At t_0, both e_1 and e_2 are zero, and E is 30 volts. In the previous discussion, we saw that both diodes would conduct under these conditions; therefore, we shall use their forward resistances in the equation to calculate e_0. Substituting the circuit parameter values at t_0:

$$e_0 \Big|_{t_0} = \frac{30/10(10^3) + 0/50 + 0/50 + 0/50(10^3)}{1/10(10^3) + 1/50 + 1/50 + 1/50(10^3)}$$
$$= 30(10^{-1})/40.12 = 0.0748 \text{ volts}$$

This calculated voltage is less than 0.1 volts, and, for all practical purposes, may be considered as zero. The reason for its existence is the forward resistance of the diodes. Had we assumed that the diodes were ideal diodes having no forward resistance, the voltage calculated would then be 0 volts. As the forward resistance of the diodes increases, the voltage drop across AB increases; this is also the voltage that is present across R_L. In practice, it is desirable to use diodes with a minimum of forward resistance.

Now that we have shown by two methods that the AND gate circuit has an output of, essentially, 0 volts when e_1 and e_2 are 0 volts, let us examine the output of the circuit under the conditions existing at t_1. At t_1, input e_1 remains at 0 volts; however, e_2 has increased to 10 volts. Initially, both diodes conduct because both anodes are still more positive than their cathodes. Looking at Fig. 9-5, you can see that e_2, which is 10 volts, causes the cathode of D_2 to be 10 volts above ground potential. But, the plate of D_2 is initially at 30 volts; hence D_2 is still forward biased. Since e_1 is 0 volts, D_1 conducts very heavily, and is effectively a short circuit to ground. This means that the anode of D_1 is at the same potential as its cathode, or 0 volts with respect to ground. The action of D_1 causes the voltage at point A in Fig. 9-5 to remain at 0 volts. Consequently, the plate of D_2, which is also point A, remains at 0 volts, and D_2 becomes reversed biased. In effect, because e_1 is zero volts, D_1 short-circuits D_2, causing it to stop conducting. Now the current path is through R and D_1 alone, and, since R_{f1} is negligible, approximately all of the circuit voltage is dropped across the resistor, R. From this analysis, we can conclude that, when only one of the two input voltages is present, the output, e_0, of the AND gate circuit is 0 volts. Let us now check our conclusion using Millman's theorem. Because of the input conditions at t_1, there are two changes to be made in substituting the circuit parameter values into the equation. Since D_2 conducts only momentarily and then cuts off, we must consider its reverse resistance, R_{b2}, rather than its forward resistance. We have already assumed that R_{b2} is approximately 500 kilohms. The second change is in e_2, which is now 10 volts instead of the 0 volts used in the previous calculation. Substituting the circuit parameter values at t_1 into the equation gives:

$$e_0 \Big|_{t_1} = \frac{30/10(10^3) + 0/50 + 10/500(10^3) + 0/50(10^3)}{1/10(10^3) + 1/50 + 1/500(10^3) + 1/50(10^3)}$$
$$= 30.2(10^{-1})/20.1 = 0.15 \text{ volts}$$

This calculated voltage is on the order of 0.1 volts, and, for all practical purposes, may be considered as zero. Again, the reason that this negligible voltage appears in the calculation is the forward resistance of D_1. We assumed a forward resistance of 50 ohms for each diode; it is across this resistance that the voltage drop of 0.15 volts develops.

We have now shown by two methods that the AND gate circuit has an output of approximately 0 volts when e_1 is 0 volts and e_2 is 10 volts. Thus far, the circuit has produced outputs as predicted by the truth table in Table 9-1. For the input voltages that are present at t_2, the analysis of the circuit is almost the same as that at t_1. The only difference is that D_2 conducts heavily, and acts as a short circuit across D_1 and R_L. Since the analysis and the calculation are almost identical to those at t_1, they will be left as an exercise.

The last possible combination of input voltages occurs at t_3: e_1 and e_2 are both equal to 10 volts. Since both of the input voltages exist, the cathodes of D_1 and D_2 are both at a potential of 10 volts with respect to ground. However, the plates of the diodes remain at 30 volts because of the bias voltage, E. Both diodes are forward biased because their anodes are more positive than their cathodes. When D_1 and D_2 conduct, their plate-to-cathode resistances (R_f) are so small that the plate and cathode of each tube are essentially at the same potential, 10 volts. Point A, which is common to both plates, remains therefore, at 10 volts. Under these conditions, a potential difference of approximately 10 volts exists across points A and B, and significantly, across R_L. This tells us that the current path is through R, D_1, D_2, and R_L, and that e_0 is approximately 10 volts. Because both diodes conduct at t_3, their forward resistances, rather than their reverse resistances, are present in the circuit. So, to find e_0 using Millman's theorem, we shall use R_{f1} and R_{f2} in the equation. Substituting the circuit parameter values at t_3 into the equation gives:

$$e_0 \Big|_{t_3} = \frac{30/10(10^3) + 10/50 + 10/50 + 0/50(10^3)}{1/10(10^3) + 1/50 + 1/50 + 1/50(10^3)}$$
$$= 403/40.12 = 10.04 \text{ volts}$$

The calculated output voltage is slightly *more* than 10 volts because of the voltage drop across the diodes' forward resistance. If the forward resistance were zero, e_0 would be exactly 10 volts. The voltage across AB, which is equal to e_0, is 10 volts plus the voltage across R_f. The electrons flowing from the cathode to the anode cause a voltage drop across R_f that is positive with respect to ground. This positive voltage increases the voltage across AB, making e_0 equal to 10.04 volts. Nevertheless, the difference is so small that, for all practical purposes, we may consider e_0 to be 10 volts.

We have now completed the analysis of the basic, two-input AND gate circuit, and found that for each combination's output was what we expected according to the truth table. That is, the circuit generates an output only when both of the input voltages are present. A similar analysis can be made for an AND gate having three or more inputs; the solution of the three-input AND gate shown in Fig. 9-6 is left as an exercise. As shown in the accompanying truth table, Table 9-3, there are eight input combinations for this circuit; however, it will be necessary to determine the state of conduction of the diodes only four times because of similar combinations. Then, the

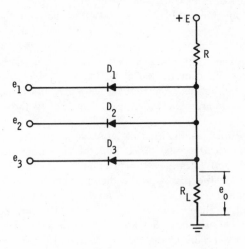

Fig. 9-6. A three-input AND gate.

TABLE 9-3. INPUT AND OUTPUT CONDITIONS
FOR A THREE-INPUT "AND" GATE

	1	2	3	4	5	6	7	8
e_1	0	1	0	1	0	1	0	1
e_2	0	0	1	1	0	0	1	1
e_3	0	0	0	0	1	1	1	1
e_0	0	0	0	0	0	0	0	1

proper value of diode resistances must be substituted into Millman's equation each time to determine the calculated output voltage. According to the truth table, e_0 for the first seven input combinations should be approximately zero, and e_0 when all the input voltages are present should be approximately 10 volts. The same resistance and voltage values used in the analysis of the two-input AND gate may be used in this exercise.

9-3. Basic Diode OR Gates

The basic diode OR gate, shown in Fig. 9-7, consists simply of diodes and resistors. The output of this circuit depends on the relationship between the bias voltage, $-E$, the input voltages e_1 and e_2, and the way in which the diodes are placed in the circuit with respect to the voltages. As you will

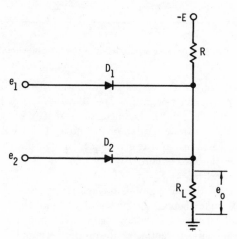

Fig. 9-7. A basic diode OR gate circuit.

see, this circuit is an OR gate because it generates an output voltage when either one or both of the input voltages are present. In general, for all possible combinations of input voltages, the circuit in Fig. 9-7 generates the outputs described by the truth table values for an OR gate logic block. Consequently, the diode circuit may replace the logic blocks previously used to generate OR statements. Although two inputs are shown in the figure, the diode OR gate is not restricted to having only two inputs; however, for each additional input, another diode must be added to the circuit.

We shall use the same approach to analyze the diode OR circuit as we used to analyze the AND circuit in the preceding section. To facilitate the analysis, the OR circuit has been redrawn as shown in Fig. 9-8; except for a slight rearrangement, this circuit is the same as that of Fig. 9-7. To show that the waveforms in Fig. 9-3A apply to our diode OR circuit, we shall now determine the output, e_0, for the given inputs, e_1 and e_2, at times t_0, t_1, t_2, and t_3. You can see that the diode OR gate looks very similar to the diode AND gate. Actually, there are only two differences in the circuit: (1) In the OR circuit, the polarity of the bias voltage is negative with respect to ground

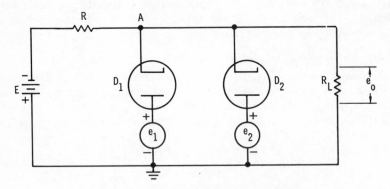

Fig. 9-8. Another arrangement of the OR gate circuit.

and, (2) the positions of the plates and cathodes of the diodes are opposite to those of the AND gate. For proper operation, $-E$ must be more negative than any of the input voltages. Let us assume that it is approximately -30 volts, and that the maximum value of e_1 and e_2 is 10 volts. The polarities are indicated in the figure. For convenience, we can use the same resistance values as used in the AND circuit: $R = 10$ kilohms, $R_L = 50$ kilohms, $R_{f1} = R_{f2} = 50$ ohms, and $R_{b1} = R_{b2} = 500$ kilohms.

The first combination of input voltages occurs at t_0. At this time, both e_1 and e_2 are 0 volts; hence, the plates of D_1 and D_2 are both at ground potential. Initially, before the diodes begin to conduct, the cathodes of both diodes are at the same potential as the upper terminal of the bias source. Since this potential is -30 volts with respect to ground, the cathodes are biased more negatively than the plates. Conversely, the plates are more positive than the cathodes; therefore, both diodes begin to conduct. With respect to R and R_L, the forward resistances of D_1 and D_2 are negligible; the diodes, therefore, act like short circuits across R_L. The current path in the circuit at t_0 is through R, D_1, and D_2. Practically all of the circuit voltage is dropped across the resistor, R, and e_0 is effectively 0 volts. At t_0, then, we've established that both of the diodes conduct. This means that their forward resistances, however small, are present in the circuit. These resistances and the given input voltages can now be substituted into Millman's equation to find e_0:

$$e_0 \bigg|_{t_0} = \frac{-30/10(10^3) + 0/50 + 0/50 + 0/50(10^3)}{1/10(10^3) + 1/50 + 1/50 + 1/50(10^3)}$$
$$= -30(10^{-1})/40.12 = -0.0748 \text{ volts}$$

This calculated voltage is less than 0.1 volt, and may be considered zero for all practical purposes. It is a negative voltage because of the way the current is flowing in the circuit. Electrons leave the cathodes (point A) and flow to the anodes, which are at ground potential, causing whatever voltage that exists at point A to be negative with respect to ground. The results of our examination and calculation indicate that the OR gate circuit has an output of essentially 0 volts when e_1 and e_2 are 0 volts. Therefore, as predicted by the truth table of Table 9-2, the OR gate output does not exist at t_0.

Let us now find the output of the circuit under the input conditions existing at t_1. At this time, input e_1 remains at 0 volts, and e_2 rises to 10 volts. Momentarily, both diodes conduct because both plates are more positive than the cathodes. This initial condition quickly changes because of the presence of e_2, which is a plus 10 volts, in the circuit. D_2, which is more positively biased than D_1, begins to conduct very heavily. Ignoring the small voltage drop across R_{f2}, we can see that the plate and cathode of D_2 are approximately at the same potential, +10 volts with respect to ground. The action of D_2 causes the voltage at point A in Fig. 9-8 to be +10 volts; consequently, the cathode of D_1 is also at +10 volts. Now, the cathode of D_1 is more positive than the plate. It is evident that because of e_2, D_1 becomes reverse biased, and stops conducting. The current path now is through R, D_2, and R_L. Current must flow through R_L because the +10 volts that exists from point A to ground is also the voltage across the terminals of R_L. The rest of the circuit voltage is dropped across the resistor, R. From this examination, we can conclude that the OR gate circuit generates an output of approximately +10 volts when e_1 is 0 volts and e_2 is 10 volts. We can check this conclusion using Millman's theorem. Because of the input conditions at t_1, two different circuit parameter values must be used in the equation. Because D_1 conducts only momentarily and then cuts off, we must consider its reverse resistance, R_{b1}, instead of its forward resistance. We've already assumed that R_b is 500 kilohms. The second change in circuit values is in e_2, which is now 10 volts rather than the 0 volts used in the previous calculation. Substituting the circuit parameter values at t_1 into the equation gives:

$$e_0 \bigg|_{t_1} = \frac{-30/10(10^3) + 0/500(10^3) + 10/50 + 0/50(10^3)}{1/10(10^3) + 1/500(10^3) + 1/50 + 1/50(10^3)}$$
$$= 197/20.1 = +9.8 \text{ volts}$$

The loss of 0.2 volts in this calculated value of e_0 can be attributed to the voltage drop across the forward resistance of D_2. However, this voltage drop is negligible, and the output voltage is considered to be 10 volts. We have now shown that the OR gate circuit generates an output voltage of approximately 10 volts when only one of the input voltages exist. So far, the action of the circuit has conformed to the truth table of Table 9-2. To analyze the circuit for the input conditions existing at t_2, the same procedure is used. Since the analysis and the calculation are almost identical to those at t_1, they will be left as an exercise. Upon performing the exercise, you will find that the OR gate circuit also generates an output voltage when e_1 is 10 volts and e_2 is 0 volts.

The last possible combination of input voltages occurs at t_3: e_1 and e_2 are both 10 volts at this time. Since both inputs exist, the plates of D_1, and D_2 are at +10 volts with respect to ground; hence, both diodes are equally biased in the positive direction. The diodes conduct equally, causing the cathodes to be at approximately the same potential as the plates with respect to ground. Since the voltage drops across the forward resistances of the diodes are negligible, point A is also at a potential of 10 volts. Because of this potential difference between point A and ground, current flows through R_L and produces a voltage drop, e_0, which is measured across R_L. The complete current path is through R, D_1, D_2, and R_L; and the remainder of the circuit voltage is dropped across the resistor, R. Our examination of the circuit at t_3 indicates that e_0 is approximately 10 volts when e_1 and e_2 are 10 volts. Using Millman's theorem, we can arrive at essentially the same conclusion.

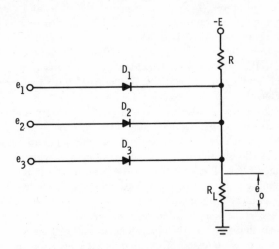

Fig. 9-9. A three-input OR gate.

It is, of course, necessary to use the correct circuit parameter values: e_1 and e_2 are both +10 volts; and D_1 and D_2 both conduct, so their forward resistances of 50 ohms must be used.

$$e_0 \bigg|_{t_3} = \frac{-30/10(10^3) + 10/50 + 10/50 + 0/50(10^3)}{1/10(10^3) + 1/50 + 1/50 + 1/50(10^3)}$$

$$= (400 - 3)/40.12 = +9.9 \text{ volts}$$

The slight loss of voltage in this calculated value of e_0 occurs because of the forward resistances of the diodes. For all practical purposes, however, this drop is negligible, and e_0 is essentially 10 volts.

We have now completed the analysis of the basic, two-input OR gate circuit, and have established that the output generated for each input combination of voltages is as predicted by the truth table of Table 9-2, i.e., the OR gate circuit generates an output when either, or both, of the input voltages exist. A similar analysis can be made for an OR gate circuit having three or more inputs. The solution of the three-input OR gate shown in Fig. 9-9 is left as an exercise. As shown in the truth table of Table 9-4,

TABLE 9-4. INPUT AND OUTPUT CONDITIONS
FOR A THREE-INPUT "OR" GATE

	1	2	3	4	5	6	7	8
e_1	0	1	0	1	0	1	0	1
e_2	0	0	1	1	0	0	1	1
e_3	0	0	0	0	1	1	1	1
e_0	0	1	1	1	1	1	1	1

there are eight input combinations for this circuit. However, it is necessary to find the state of conduction of the diodes only four times since there are only four different combinations. Then, the proper values of diode resistances must be substituted into Millman's equation each time to determine the calculated output voltage. The same voltage and resistance values used for the two-input OR gate analysis may be used in this exercise.

9-4. Mixed AND and OR Gates

To generate most of the Boolean statements you encountered in earlier chapters, a simple AND or OR gate alone is inadequate. Rather, combinations of AND and OR gates are needed, as you shall now see. Suppose we want a circuit that will generate an output voltage in accordance with the statement: $e_0 = e_1e_2 + e_3e_4$. We can see immediately that three logic circuits are needed. An AND gate is needed to generate e_1e_2, a second AND gate is needed to generate e_3e_4, and an OR gate is needed to generate the complete statement, $e_1e_2 + e_3e_4$. Altogether, there are six inputs (two inputs to each logic circuit); so we know that the mixed AND and OR circuit will contain six diodes. The logic block diagram that will generate this statement is shown in Fig. 9-10. Now that we know what kind of circuit configurations are contained inside the black boxes, we can draw the corresponding diode logic

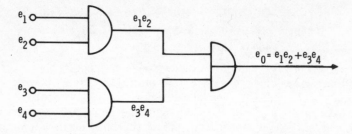

Fig. 9-10. A logic block diagram containing AND and OR gates.

circuits. Figure 9-11 shows the schematic diagram of this mixed AND and OR gate circuit. One AND gate consists of diodes D_1 and D_2, and resistor R_1. The inputs to this gate are e_1 and e_2; and E is the positive bias voltage. The output of this gate exists from point A to ground. Since the OR gate is connected from point A to ground, it acts as the load for the first AND gate. The second AND gate consists of diodes D_3 and D_4, and resistor R_2. The inputs to this gate are e_3 and e_4, and E is the positive bias voltage. The

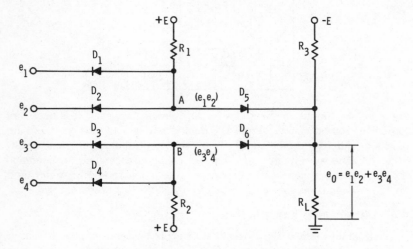

Fig. 9-11. A diode logic circuit consisting of AND and OR gates.

output of this AND gate exists from point B to ground. Since the OR gate is connected from point B to ground, it also acts as the load for the second AND gate; hence, no separate R_L is shown in the schematic. The OR gate consists of diodes D_5 and D_6, and resistors R_3 and R_L. Notice that the positions of D_5 and D_6 are reversed in the circuit (as compared to the AND gate diodes), and that the bias voltage, E, for the OR gate is negative. The inputs to the OR gate are the voltages that exist at points A and B, and the output, e_0, is taken across R_L as shown in the figure.

From the previous discussions, you know that a voltage will exist at point A only if both e_1 and e_2 exist simultaneously. Similarly, a voltage will exist at point B only if both e_3 and e_4 exist simultaneously. In the OR circuit, there will be an output if either or both of its inputs exist. This final output, e_0, is what we are mostly interested in because it is a function of the logic Boolean statement with which we began. This is just one example of how

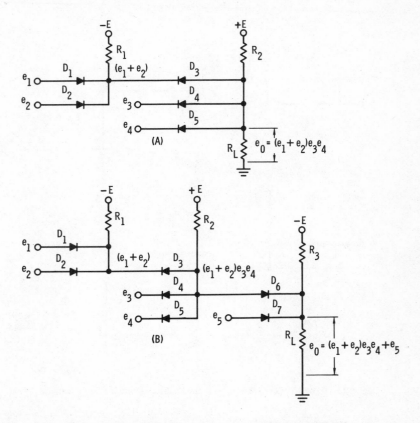

Fig. 9-12. Other diode logic circuits using both AND and OR gates.

it is possible to design diode circuits to behave logically, according to given Boolean statements. Examples of other diode logic circuits using AND and OR gates are shown in Fig. 9-12. For practice, trace both circuits through, locating each AND and OR gate, until you have ascertained the Boolean statement that represents the logic output of each circuit. Then, check your statements with those given in the figure.

9-5. Diode-Transistor Gates

Because of loading effects, there is a practical limit to the number of diodes that can be used in a logic circuit. When it is necessary to have numerous inputs, or to have more output power to drive succeeding stages, transistors are often used in conjunction with the basic diode gates to provide current amplification. The circuits in Fig. 9-13A and B illustrate the use of transistors with AND and OR gates to obtain current amplification without affecting the logic operations of the circuits.

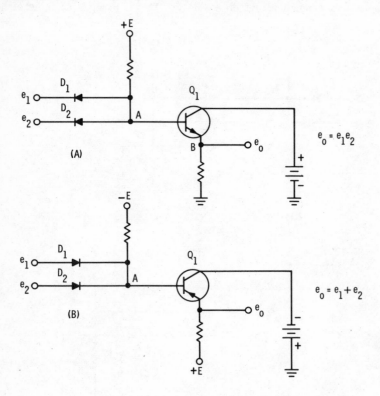

Fig. 9-13. Transistors are often used in diode gates to provide amplification.

The circuit of Fig. 9-13A is an ordinary AND gate with an emitter follower (common-collector circuit) connected at point A. When either e_1 or e_2 is 0 volts, the AND gate has no output; hence, the voltage at point A is zero. Because the voltage at A is zero, the transistor is reversed biased (the base-emitter resistance is very large), and does not conduct. Under these conditions, e_0 is also 0 volts. When both e_1 and e_2 exist, however, the AND gate generates an output which is applied to the base of Q_1 at point A. This positive voltage causes the transistor to be forward biased, and conduction occurs. When Q_1 conducts, the base-to-emitter resistance is so small that it is almost a "dead" short. Consequently, the voltage, e_0, at point B is essentially the same as that at point A, which is the output of the AND gate. Although the addition of the emitter follower does not significantly alter the output voltage of the basic diode AND gate, or effect its logic operation, it increases the power output needed to drive the succeeding stage by providing current amplification.

The circuit in Fig. 9-13B is an ordinary OR gate with an emitter follower connected at point A. When e_1 and e_2 are both 0 volts, the OR gate has no output. Since the voltage at point A is 0 volts with respect to ground, the emitter follower remains forward biased. When Q_1 conducts, the base-emitter resistance is so small that the voltage at the emitter is approximately the same as the voltage at point A, or 0 volts. Because the output of Q_1 is taken directly from the emitter, e_0 is also approximately 0 volts. This shows that the output of the entire circuit does not exist when e_1 and e_2 do not exist. The situation changes, however, when either e_1 or e_2 both exist. Under these conditions, the output of the gate (at point A) is a positive voltage. This positive voltage is applied to the base of the transistor, upsetting the forward bias in the base-emitter circuit. The base-emitter resistance now becomes very large, and conduction ceases. When this occurs, e_0 becomes a positive voltage; hence, the output of the entire circuit exists when e_1 or e_2 exists. The logic OR operation is not affected by and does not depend on the addition of the emitter follower to the basic diode circuit. As in the AND circuit, however, the power output needed to drive succeeding stages is increased as a result of the current gain provided by the transistor circuit.

9-6. Binary Addition Using Diode Logic Circuits

Until now, the diode circuits introduced were designed to perform some logic (Boolean) operation. As examples, the diode AND gate performs logic multiplication, and the OR gate performs logic addition. In the following sections of this chapter, you will see how we use the concepts of Boolean algebra to combine these logic circuits so that they'll perform arithmetic operations such as binary addition. Before delving into the circuitry, some important points must be considered. As you know from the explanation of binary addition in Chapter 1, there are only two binary digits or bits, 0 and 1. You also know that Boolean variables have only two truth values: 0 means that the variable (voltage) does not exist, and 1 means that the variable (voltage) exists. In adding circuits, voltage levels are used to represent the bits. The 0 bit is represented by the absence of a voltage, or the truth value 0; and the 1 bit is represented by the presence of a voltage, or the truth value 1.

The simplest form of binary addition is that which deals with only single-digit numbers, that is, the augend and addend each consist of one bit. As shown below, there are only four instances in which this type of addition can occur. The column headed X contains the augend bits, and the column headed Y contains the addend bits. The sum and carry bits resulting from

X	Y	S	C	
0	0	0	0	X = Augend
0	1	1	0	Y = Addend
1	0	1	0	S = Sum
1	1	0	1	C = Carry

each binary addition are shown in their respective columns. Using this table, we can set up our circuit requirements, and design a logic circuit that can add the combination of X and Y, and generate the proper outputs, S and C, for each input condition. But first, let us write the Boolean statements for S and C. For S, an output is generated for two input combinations: when X exists, but when Y does not exist; and when X does not exist, but Y exists. The Boolean statement for S, then, is:

$$S = \bar{X}Y + X\bar{Y}$$

Observe that this is an exclusive OR statement; hence, S can be generated by an exclusive OR logic circuit. Looking again at the table, you can see that a carry bit is generated only when X and Y exist simultaneously. The Boolean statement for C, then, is the simple AND statement:

$$C = XY$$

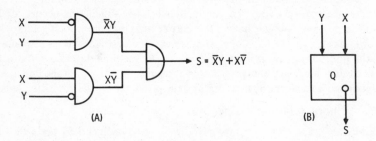

Fig. 9-14. A quarter adder consists of two AND gates and one OR gate.

A simple logic circuit that can be used to generate S, but that does not accommodate carries is called a *quarter adder*, or an exclusive OR. The logic block diagram for this circuit is shown in Fig. 9-14A. Although this circuit is not, in itself, capable of generating both S and C for a simple binary addition, it is often used as a component in more complex adding circuits, as you shall see later. The logic symbol for a quarter adder, when used as a component of another circuit, is shown in Fig. 9-14B. The diode logic circuits capable of generating S and C for a simple binary addition, among other things, are the *half adder* and the *full adder*. These circuits shall be developed in the following sections.

9-7.   Diode Half Adders

A half adder is a logic circuit designed to generate the sum and carry bits resulting from the binary addition of two numbers. A basic half-adder circuit may be obtained by simply using the Boolean statements for S and C determined in the preceding section. This circuit is shown in Fig. 9-15A. This half adder is made up of a quarter adder, which generates S, and an AND gate, which generates C. If the actual circuit, shown in Fig. 9-15B, were constructed as indicated in the block diagram, eight diodes, and two

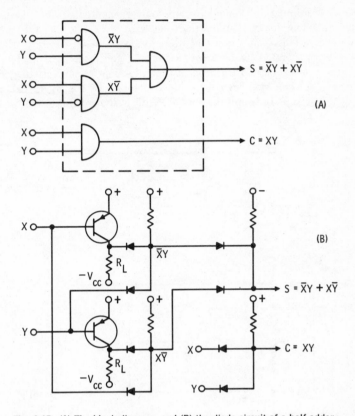

Fig. 9-15. (A) The block diagram, and (B) the diode circuit of a half adder.

inverters (transistors) would be needed. However, it is possible to simplify the circuit by applying the rules of Boolean algebra to the original statements for S and C. Recall that:

$$S = \overline{X}Y + X\overline{Y}$$

To simplify this statement, we first negate both sides, and then use De Morgan's theorem. This gives:

$$\overline{S} = \overline{\overline{X}Y + X\overline{Y}} = (X + \overline{Y})(\overline{X} + Y)$$

Using the distributive law, we obtain:

$$\overline{S} = X\overline{X} + XY + Y\overline{Y} + \overline{X}\overline{Y} = XY + \overline{X}\overline{Y}$$

As it stands, this statement is true for $\overline{S}$; to make the statement true for S; we must again negate both sides, and apply De Morgan's theorem:

$$\overline{\overline{S}} = \overline{XY + \overline{X}\overline{Y}} = S = (\overline{XY})\,(X + Y)$$

At first glance, a saving of only one inverter is apparent; however, there is still the carry to consider. The statement, $C = XY$, is in its simplest form;

algebraic manipulation cannot save any logic elements here. But, look again at the statement for S, and see that one term, $(\overline{XY})$, is also the negation of the carry. This is an important observation because it tells us that the carry bit is generated in the logic circuit that generates the sum bit. It is, therefore, unnecessary to construct a separate logic circuit just to generate the carry bit. The simplified logic block diagram of the diode half adder is shown in Fig. 9-16A, and the actual circuit is shown in Fig. 9-16B. Look-

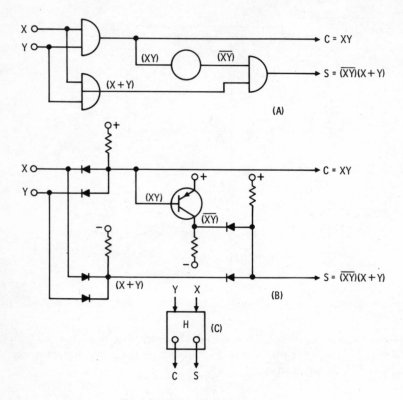

Fig. 9-16. A simplified diode half adder.

ing at the circuit, you can see that it uses only six diodes, and one inverter (transistor). This is a saving of two diodes, and one transistor over the original circuit in Fig. 9-15. The logic symbol used to designate a half adder is shown in Fig. 9-16C.

Although the half adder can add two digits, generating a sum bit and a carry bit, it cannot add numbers containing more than one digit each. The reason for this is that a half adder has provisions for only two inputs: one representing the augend digit, and the other representing the addend digit. In practice, however, numbers being added usually contain more than one digit each. Furthermore, the addition of two digits may produce a carry which must be added to the augend and addend of the next higher order column. This operation requires that the adding circuit have provisions for three inputs, the extra input accommodating the carry bit from the lower order. While the half adder cannot add multidigit numbers, you shall now see that it can be used as a component of the full adder which can perform this operation.

9-8. Diode Full Adders

Suppose we wanted to add two four-digit binary numbers such as 1101 and 1001. On paper, this numerical example would appear as:

$$
\begin{array}{ccccc}
 & 1 & 1 & 0 & 1 \\
 & 1 & 0 & 0 & 1 \\
\hline
 & 0 & 1 & 0 & 0 \\
1 & & 1 & & \\
\hline
1 & 0 & 1 & 1 & 0 \\
\end{array}
$$

If we represent the augend, 1101, as $X_4X_3X_2X_1$, and the addend, 1001, as $Y_4Y_3Y_2Y_1$, we can rewrite the problem in the general form:

$$
\begin{array}{ll}
X_4\,X_3\,X_2\,X_1 & \textit{Augend} \\
\underline{Y_4\,Y_3\,Y_2\,Y_1} & \textit{Addend} \\
S_{t4}\,S_{t3}\,S_{t2}\,S_{t1} & \textit{Temporary Sums} \\
\underline{C_4\,C_3\,C_2\,C_1} & \textit{Carry Bits} \\
C_4\,S_4\,S_3\,S_2\,S_1 & \textit{Complete Sum}
\end{array}
$$

Adding X_1 and Y_1 presents no problem so far as the half adder is concerned because there is no carry bit from a lower order to consider. But, by adding X_1 and Y_1, a carry C_1, may result as it does in this numerical example. This carry bit must be added to the digits of the next higher order as shown. The addition of X_2 and Y_2 yields a temporary sum, S_{t2}. This temporary sum is added to C_1, and the result is S_2. Since a half adder cannot add X_2, Y_2, and C_1 by itself, another circuit arrangement must be devised; and this is the full adder. A closer look at the addition of X_2, Y_2, and C_1 reveals that there are really two separate additions involved. The first is $X_2 + Y_2$; it may be accomplished by a half adder, H_1, as shown in Figure 9-17A. If both X_2 and Y_2 were 1, this addition would produce a carry bit, C_2', which is one output of H_1. The second output of H_1 is S_{t2}, the temporary sum. To add S_{t2} to C_1, we could use another half adder, H_2, as shown in Fig. 9-17B. The outputs of H_2 are the complete sum, S_2, and C_t. Since it is possible for both S_{t2} and C_1 to be 1, the addition of these quantities may produce a carry bit, C_t. So far, using two half adders, we have been able to generate the complete sum of X_2, Y_2, and C_1. Now, however, we have two carry outputs, C_2', and C_t, to accommodate. These carry outputs must somehow be combined so that we have a single carry, C_2, to add to the digits of the next higher order. A means for combining C_2' and C_t becomes more apparent after setting up a truth table, and examining all the possible combination of carry bits that can exist.

X_2	Y_2	C_1	S_{t2}	C_2'	S	C_t	C_2
0	0	0	0	0	0	0	0
0	0	1	0	0	1	0	0
0	1	0	1	0	1	0	0
0	1	1	1	0	0	1	1
1	0	0	1	0	1	0	0
1	0	1	1	0	0	1	1
1	1	0	0	1	0	0	1
1	1	1	0	1	1	0	1

By binary addition, we obtain S_{t2} and C_2' for all combinations of X_2 and Y_2. Then, we add all the combinations of S_{t2} and C_1 to obtain the values of S and C_t. If you compare the digits in the C_2' and C_t columns, you will see

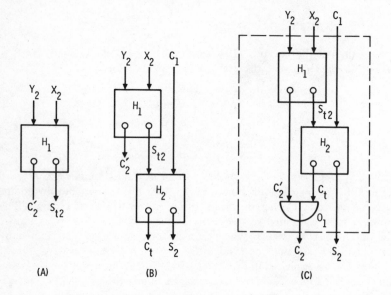

(A)   (B)   (C)

Fig. 9-17. The development of a full adder.

that, for any combination of inputs, these two carries never exist simultaneously. We already know that C_2' and C_t are related to C_2. From the truth table, we can glean the exact relationship: C_2 exists when either C_2' or C_t exists. By using a logic OR circuit to combine the carry outputs of H_1 and H_2, we have generated a single carry bit, C_2, which is added to the next order.

The addition of X_2, Y_2, and C_1 has been completely performed by two half adders, and an OR circuit. These components constitute a full adder, and are shown in Fig. 9-17C. The symbol for the full adder is shown in Fig. 9-18A. As you can see, it has three inputs: X represents the augend digit, Y the addend digit, and C_L the carry bit from the lower order. The two outputs of the full adder are S, the complete sum, and C_H the carry bit to the higher order. The diode circuit for the full adder is shown in Fig. 9-18B. It consists simply of two half adders, and an OR gate; each of these components is indicated by dashed lines for easy identification.

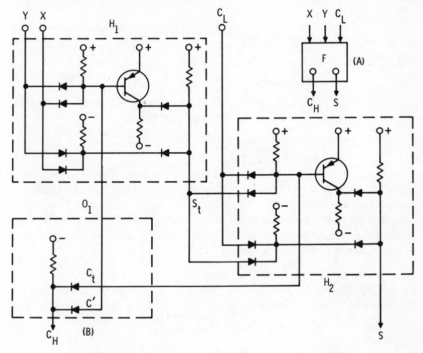

Fig. 9-18. (A) The symbol, and (B) the diode circuit of a full adder.

The full adder circuit we have just developed is by no means the only circuit capable of adding X, Y, and C_L, and producing S and C_H. Indeed, there are many other variations. To illustrate another possible circuit arrangement, let us proceed along more analytical lines, using a truth table and Boolean simplification. In the truth table, we need not consider S_t, C' and C_t because we shall not necessarily be using half adders. All we are concerned with are the three inputs, the sum, and the carry bit.

X	Y	C_L	S	C_H
0	0	0	0	0
0	0	1	1	0
0	1	0	1	0
0	1	1	0	1
1	0	0	1	0
1	0	1	0	1
1	1	0	0	1
1	1	1	1	1

To obtain the truth table values for S and C_H, we add each combination of X, Y, and C_L by binary addition. Having done this, we shall now write the Boolean statements for S and C_H. In the truth table, we see that S exists for four combinations of the inputs. This means that the statement for S will have four terms:

$$S = \bar{X}\bar{Y}C_L + \bar{X}Y\bar{C}_L + X\bar{Y}\bar{C}_L + XYC_L$$

In the truth table, we see that C_H exists for four combinations of the inputs; hence, the Boolean statement for C_H will also contain four terms:

$$C_H = \bar{X}YC_L + X\bar{Y}C_L + XY\bar{C}_L + XYC_L$$

Leaving the algebra for you as an exercise, we shall merely state that the statements for S and C_H may be simplified to:

$$S = (X + Y + C_L) \cdot \overline{(X + Y)(XY + C_L)} + XYC_L$$
$$C_H = (X + Y)(XY + C_L)$$

Notice that there are two terms common to both S and C_H. These are $(X + Y)$, and $(X + Y)(XY + C_L)$. This is an important observation because it will help us to avoid the use of unnecessary logic circuits in the full adder. If we construct the adder so that it will generate C_H first, we can use some of the outputs generated for C_H as inputs to the logic circuits generating S. The statement for S can be rewritten:

$$S = (X + Y + C_L)\,\bar{C}_H + XYC_L$$

Having obtained and examined the Boolean statements for S and C_H, we can proceed to set up the logic block diagram from the statements. The

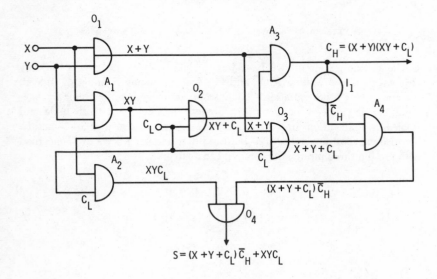

Fig. 9-19. The block diagram of a full adder variation.

block diagram for the full adder is shown in Fig. 9-19. Trace the inputs through the logic blocks and notice how the outputs of blocks O_1 and A_3 are used in the generation of both C_H and S. Using this approach to develop a full adder requires 16 diodes, and one transistor; whereas the full adder circuit of Fig. 9-18 uses 14 diodes, and two transistors. Although the two circuits are quite different, they produce identical results.

The diode circuit corresponding to the block diagram in Fig. 9-19 is shown in Fig. 9-20. Because of the large number of diode logic circuits used in this and other variations of the full adder, they are rather unwieldy.

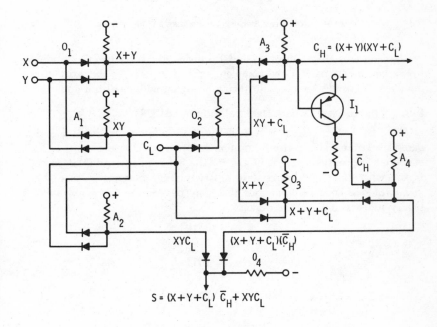

Fig. 9-20. The diode circuit of the full adder variation.

Rather than drawing the circuit each time, the general symbol for a full adder is more conveniently used. For example, let us return to the problem in addition that was introduced at the beginning of this section:

$$X_4\,X_3\,X_2\,X_1$$
$$Y_4\,Y_3\,Y_2\,Y_1$$
$$\overline{C_4\,S_4\,S_3\,S_2\,S_1}$$

To perform this binary addition, a series of adders arranged as in Fig. 9-21 is needed. Since the addition of X_1 AND Y_1 does not include a carry bit from a lower order, we may use a half adder as shown in the figure. However, the three succeeding binary additions must be accomplished by full adders because of the possibility of a carry from the lower orders. There

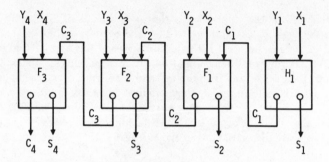

Fig. 9-21. A binary adder using full adders and half adders.

are no additions after that of X_4 and Y_4; hence, the carry bit, C_4, produced by F_3, becomes a part of the complete sum. If X_5 and Y_5 did exist in our numbers, C_4 would be added to their sum by an additional full adder.

9-9. The Binary Coded Decimal Adder (BCDA)

The BCDA is a system in which the basic adding circuits and logical gates are arranged to perform addition in codes such as the 8-4-2-1, XS3, etc. We shall consider here a BCDA for the 8-4-2-1 code. Addition in code is somewhat different from straight binary addition because we cannot use any forbidden code combinations that may be generated. For example, a binary adder would add the digits:

$$
\begin{array}{rl}
6 & 0110 \\
5 & 0101 \\
\hline
11 & 1011
\end{array}
$$

$$X_8\,X_4\,X_2\,X_1 \quad \text{AUGENDS}$$
$$\underline{Y_8\,Y_4\,Y_2\,Y_1} \quad \text{ADDENDS}$$
$$C_b\,/\,\overline{U_8\,U_4\,U_2\,U_1} \quad \text{UNCORRECTED SUMS}$$

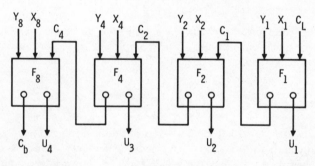

Fig. 9-22. When a binary adder is used for the 8-4-2-1 code, it generates uncorrected sums.

and generate a sum, 1011, as shown. Although this is correct as far as binary addition is concerned, the combination, 1011, does not exist in the 8-4-2-1 code. In the code, the decimal number 11 would be represented as 0001 0001, where the group of bits at the right represents the unit 1 in code, and the group at the left represents the decimal carry (having a decimal weight of 10). By making certain logic corrections, we can proceed to modify the binary adder in Fig. 9-22 so that it adds correctly in the 8-4-2-1 code. In the figure, the augend bits are represented by X and the addend bits by Y. The numerical subscripts indicate the code weight of the bit. We know that this adder will generate forbidden code combinations for certain inputs; therefore, we shall represent the sum bit generated by the full adders by U for uncorrected sum. We can now proceed to determine the necessary corrections.

Thus far, we have determined that no correction is needed if the sum of the binary coded decimal numbers is equal to or less than 9; any time the sum exceeds decimal 9, some correction is needed. Furthermore, sums equal to or greater than decimal 10 will have a decimal carry bit, C_d, but sums less than 10 can only have a binary carry bit, C_b. To find the necessary correction, we must examine every addition of the binary coded numbers that yields a sum equal to or greater than 10.

Example 9-1. $X = 7, Y = 8$:

$$
\begin{array}{r}
0111 \\
+\ 1000 \\
\hline
\end{array}
$$

1111	*Uncorrected Sum*
0110	*Add 6 to Correct*
1 /0101	*True Sum in 8-4-2-1 Code*

In this initial examination, we see that the addition of 7 and 8 in the code results in an uncorrected sum of 1111, or decimal 15. This combination of digits, as you know, is part of the forbidden code. In the 8-4-2-1 code, the decimal 15 is represented as 0001 0101, where 0001 is decimal 10 and 0101 is decimal 5. By adding 6 to the uncorrected sum, we obtain the true sum in the 8-4-2-1 code. As you can see in the example, the decimal carry of 1 at the left of the slash is the same as the 0001 that has the decimal weight of 10, and the 0101 represents the 5 in the code. In this example, then, the addition of 6 to the uncorrected binary sum gives us the correct answer.

Example 9-2. $X = 5, Y = 9$:

$$
\begin{array}{r}
0101 \\
1001 \\
\hline
\end{array}
$$

1110	*Uncorrected Sum*
0110	*Add 6 to Correct*
1 /0100	*True Sum in 8-4-2-1 Code*

Again we find that the addition of 6 to the uncorrected binary sum gives us the correct answer in the 8-4-2-1 code. In this example, the sum of decimal 5 and decimal 9 is 14. The decimal carry of 1 at the left of the slash represents the 1 in the sum, and the 0100 represents the 4.

Example 9-3. $X = 8, Y = 9, C = 1$ (a carry from a lower order).

$$
\begin{array}{l}
1000 \\
1001 \\
0001 \\
\end{array}
$$

1 /$\overline{0010}$	*Uncorrected Sum Containing a Binary Carry Bit*
0110	*Add 6 to Correct*
1 /$\overline{1000}$	*True Sum in the 8-4-2-1 Code*

In this example, we have included the possibility of having a carry bit from a lower order. As you can see, the addition of 6 to the uncorrected sum again gives us the true sum in the 8-4-2-1 code. In addition, you can see that the uncorrected sum also contained a binary carry bit which would be applied to the next higher order addition.

To avoid needless repetition, we shall not attempt to examine every possible addition resulting in a sum equal to or greater than decimal 10. If, however, you wish to examine a few more, you will find that in every instance, the addition of 6 to the uncorrected sum will result in the correct sum in the code. Having ascertained the correction required, we can now try to develop a logic recognition circuit that will make the correction, and recognize the decimal carry. Since the binary adder in Fig. 9-22 is an integral part of the BCDA, let us set up a table showing its outputs. In Table 9-5, five variables are presented: the four uncorrected sums, and the binary carry. Because there are five variables, there is a total of 32

TABLE 9-5. PARTIAL LIST OF OUTPUT COMBINATIONS OF THE BINARY ADDER*

COMBINATION	0	1	2	3	4	5	6	7	8	9	10	11	12	13	14	15	16	17	18	19	20
U_1	0	1	0	1	0	1	0	1	0	1	0	1	0	1	0	1	0	1	0	1	0
U_2	0	0	1	1	0	0	1	1	0	0	1	1	0	0	1	1	0	0	1	1	0
U_4	0	0	0	0	1	1	1	1	0	0	0	0	1	1	1	1	0	0	0	0	1
U_8	0	0	0	0	0	0	0	0	1	1	1	1	1	1	1	1	0	0	0	0	0
C_b	0	0	0	0	0	0	0	0	0	0	0	0	0	0	0	0	1	1	1	1	1

$\overline{C}_d$ ◄ C_d ►

*THE UNIQUE COMBINATIONS IN THE TABLE SHALL BE USED TO DESIGN A CORRECTION CIRCUIT FOR A BINARY CODED DECIMAL ADDER.

possible combinations that can exist. After the fifteenth combination, the values of the uncorrected sums repeat themselves, and the value of the binary carry becomes 1. Because of the repetition, the table in the figure is abbreviated to only 20 combinations; however, the elimination of the last 12 combinations will not affect the validity of our discussions.

Examining the table for unique combinations, we see first that C_b does not exist before the sixteenth combination, but that it does exist for every combination from 16 to 32. The heavy line between the ninth and tenth combinations indicates the point at which the 8-4-2-1 code departs from the binary count. The significance of this is that beginning with the tenth combination, a decimal carry must be generated. By using certain unique combinations of uncorrected sums, we can develop a circuit that will recognize the combinations following the tenth, and generate a decimal carry. Because the binary carry exists for all the combinations following and including the sixteenth, it is unique, and can be used for recognition. This leaves us with only the combinations from 10 to 15 to recognize. For combinations 10, 11, 14 and 15, both U_8 and U_2 exist simultaneously. This does not happen for any combination before 10, so we may use U_8 and U_2 for recognition. For combinations 12 and 13, U_8 and U_4 exist simultaneously. Since this does not happen for any combination before 10, we may use these uncorrected sums for recognition. Now, we can write:

$$C_d = C_b + U_8 U_2 + U_8 U_4$$

which can be simplified to:

$$C_d = C_b + U_8 (U_2 + U_4)$$

From this Boolean statement, we can arrange a logic circuit that will gen-

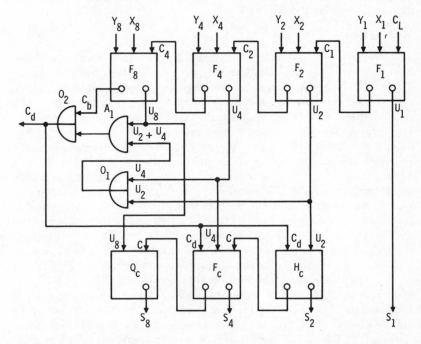

Fig. 9-23. A binary coded decimal adder consisting of a binary adder and a correction circuit.

erate C_d for every sum greater than decimal 9. Only one problem remains now, and, that is, how to add 6 to the uncorrected sum. Realize that 6 is added each time a decimal carry is generated. We can, therefore, use the decimal carry to accomplish the correction. This procedure is shown in Fig. 9-23.

As shown in the figure, the recognition circuit consists of A_1, O_1, and O_2. The inputs to O_1 are U_2 and U_4; and the output, $U_2 + U_4$, is fed to A_1 along with U_8. The output of A_1 is one term of the Boolean statement for C_d, or $U_8 (U_2 + U_4)$. This output is fed to O_2 along with the binary carry, C_b, from F_8. The output of O_2 is the decimal carry, $C_d = C_b + U_8(U_2 + U_4)$. In order to add 6 to the uncorrected sum of the BCDA, the decimal carry is fed to F_c and H_c in the correction circuit. This is the same as adding 0110 to the uncorrected sum. When U_2 and C_d are added in H_c, the result is the correct sum, S_2, and a possible carry, which is fed to F_c. In F_c, the lower order carry is added to U_4 and C_d, resulting in the correct sum, S_4, and a possible carry. Because of this possible carry, it is necessary to include the quarter adder, Q_c, in which the addition of U_8 and the carry is accomplished. The final output of the BCDA is $S_8 S_4 S_2 S_1$ in the 8-4-2-1 code.

Binary coded decimal adders can be designed to operate in codes other than the 8-4-2-1. All that is necessary to develop such adders is to determine the necessary correction or corrections, and to design the appropriate recognition circuit for each different code. The procedure is similar to that used here for the 8-4-2-1 code.

9-10. Diode Matrixing

In computers, it is frequently desirable to select a particular condition from a given set of conditions. One way of doing this is by diode matrixing. Perhaps the best way to explain matrixing is to show an example. Assume that we have two variables, X and Y, and that we want to select individually each of the conditions or combinations that exist for these two variables. The variables are represented by the *states of the flip-flops* shown in Fig. 9-24. A flip-flop is a circuit that has two outputs, 1 and 0, as shown in the figure. At any time, a flip-flop can be in one of two possible states: 1 or 0. Using positive logic, the following conditions are defined: When a flip-flop is in the 1 state, its 1 terminal is at a high potential, and its 0 terminal is at a low potential. When a flip-flop is in the 0 state, its 1 terminal is low and its 0 terminal is high. (Do not confuse the states and outputs of the flip-flops, for they are both designated by 1's and 0's.) Flip-flops, and the logic of flip-flops are discussed in greater detail in Chapter 11; for the purpose of this discussion the definitions given will suffice.

As shown in Fig. 9-24, one flip-flop is designated as FFX, and the other as FFY. Since there are two variables, X and Y, there will be four possible combinations that can exist. The first combination exists when both FFX and FFY are in the 0 state; the second combination is when FFX is in the 0 state, and FFY is in the 1 state; the third combination is when FFX is in the 1 state, and FFY is in the 0 state; and the fourth combination exists when both FFX and FFY are in the 1 state. In the matrix circuit, there is an output line for each of these combinations; the lines are labeled 00, 01, 10 and 11. Actually, each line is the output of an AND gate. This shall become more obvious to you as we analyze the circuit.

The first combination is selected when there is an output on the 00 line. To obtain an output here, the AND gate made up of D_1, D_2, and R_1 must have both of its inputs present. When FFX and FFY are both in the 0

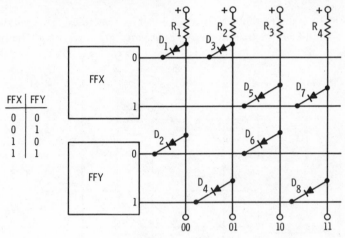

FFX	FFY
0	0
0	1
1	0
1	1

NOTE: CONNECTIONS ARE INDICATED
BY THE DOTS. ALL OTHERS ARE
CROSSOVERS.

Fig. 9-24. Diode matrixing for two variables.

state, their 0 terminals are at a high potential; therefore, as shown in the figure, D_1 is connected to the 0 output terminal of FFX, and D_2 is connected to the 0 terminal of FFY. Thus, when both flip-flops are in the 0 state, there is an output on the 00 line, and the first of the four combinations is selected.

The second combination is selected when there is an output on the 01 line. This line is the output line of the AND gate that is made up of D_3, D_4, and R_2; hence, the inputs to D_3 and D_4 must be present for an output to exist. When FFX is in the 0 state, its 0 terminal is high; so we connect the 0 terminal to D_3. When FFY is in the 1 state, its 1 terminal is high; therefore, we connect the 1 terminal to D_4. Thus, when the second combination, 01, exists, there is an output on the 01 line.

The AND gate used to select the third combination, 10, is made up of D_5, D_6, and R_3. To obtain an output on the 10 line, both of the inputs to the gate must be high. When FFX is in the 1 state, its 1 terminal is high, and is, therefore, connected to D_5. When FFY is in the 0 state, its 0 terminal is high, and is connected to D_6. Thus, when 10 exists, there is an output on the 10 line, and the third combination has been selected.

Finally, for the fourth combination, or condition, both FFX and FFY are in the 1 state. The AND gate used to select this combination is made up of D_7, D_8, and R_4. To obtain both inputs to the gate, the diodes are connected to the 1 terminals of the flip-flops. In connecting the diodes this way, we obtain an output on the 11 line, and the fourth combination is selected.

Figure 9-25 shows diode matrixing for three variables. To select each of the 8 combinations that can exist, AND gates are again used; however,

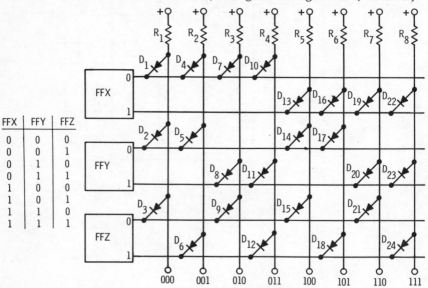

FFX	FFY	FFZ
0	0	0
0	0	1
0	1	0
0	1	1
1	0	0
1	0	1
1	1	0
1	1	1

NOTE: CONNECTIONS ARE INDICATED
BY THE DOTS. ALL OTHERS
ARE CROSSOVERS.

Fig. 9-25. Diode matrixing for three variables.

each AND gate is now comprised of three diodes. Notice the pattern that exists: There are four consecutive connections to the 0 output of FFX, and then, four consecutive connections to the 1 output of the same flip-flop; there are also two consecutive connections to the 0 terminal of FFY, and then, to the 1 terminal of FFY. This pattern continues insofar as the connections to the flip-flops are concerned. Finally, for FFZ, the diodes are connected in an alternating fashion, beginning with a connection at the 0 output of FFZ, then at its 1 output, then at its 0 output, etc. This pattern is sometimes helpful in constructing a three-variable matrix circuit, but it is most important to remember that each AND gate must have all of its inputs present before an output can exist on its output line.

9-11. Problems

1. How many inputs may a logic circuit have? How would you describe the input to a logic circuit? When is an input said to exist, and when is it said not to exist?

2. Draw the waveforms describing the input and output conditions for an exclusive OR logic circuit.

3. How does the circuit configuration of the diode AND gate differ from that of the diode OR gate?

4. Why must the bias voltage, E, in an AND gate be more positive than any of the inputs to the gate?

5. Explain the operation of a three-input AND gate for each of the eight possible input combinations without using Millman's theorem.

6. What must be done before an additional input can be added to a logic circuit?

7. In Fig. 9-8, what is the function of the resistor, R? What is the function of R_L?

8. Because there is no such thing as an ideal diode, the forward resistances of the diodes used in the AND and OR gates are not 0, and the reverse resistances are not infinite. What effect, if any, does this have on the circuit voltages?

9. Without the use of Millman's theorem, explain the operation of a three-input OR gate for each of the eight input combinations.

10. Draw the diode logic circuits that will generate the following statements:

   (a) $e_1 e_2 + e_1 \overline{e}_3 + e_2 e_3$ (b) $e_1 (\overline{e_2 + e_3}) + e_1 \overline{e}_3$
   (c) $(e_1 + e_2 e_3)(e_1 e_2)$ (d) $e_1 + \overline{e_1 e_2}(e_2 + \overline{e}_3)$

11. When are transistors used in diode logic circuits? What is their effect on diode logic circuits?

12. What type of fundamental Boolean statement does a quarter adder generate?

13. In your own words, explain the difference between a quarter adder, a half adder, and a full adder in terms of their outputs.

14. What is the difference between the binary carry and the decimal carry?

15. What does a full adder consists of? How many inputs can it accommodate.

16. Why does the diagram in Fig. 9-21 differ from the diagram in Fig. 9-23? What must be done to the diagram in Fig. 9-22 to make it perform addition in other codes?

17. Design an adder that can add two four-bit numbers in the XS3 code. Use the procedure followed in the text for designing the Binary Coded Decimal Adder.

18. What is the potential at the output terminals of a flip-flop that is in the 1 state? In the 0 state?

19. A diode matrix circuit consists primarily of a series of AND gates. Draw a block diagram of the matrix circuit in Fig. 9-24.

20. Explain how the first four combinations of variables are selected in Fig. 9-25.

10

Transistor Logic Circuits

The first digital computers used gears and other mechanical devices as logic circuits; later, relays were used. Still later electron tubes replaced relays as logic circuits. Tubes had the advantage over relays because they provided much faster operation, and they were somewhat more reliable. They were more reliable in the sense that they were not electromechanical devices, and did not require considerable maintenance. Electron tubes were faster because they were capable of performing in microseconds instead of milliseconds, which was the average time for a relay to perform an operation.

The modern digital computer no longer uses tubes to perform logic operations; instead, it uses transistors. There are many reasons for this. For one, the transistor requires much less power because it does not have any filaments. Consider a system that contains five thousand diodes, each having a filament voltage of 6.3 volts and a current rating of 0.15 amperes. In such a system, the filament power alone would be approximately 5000 watts. You can imagine that this power would give rise to considerable heat which, in turn, presents an elaborate air-conditioning problem. Digital computers that use transistors are air conditioned because, as explained in Chapter 8, transistors are temperature-sensitive devices. However, because they have no filaments, much less heat is generated in the computer itself and the amount of air conditioning that is necessary is reduced. Still another advantage of the transistor when compared to the electron tube is its smaller size. A direct consequence of the smaller component is that less space is required; hence, the overall dimension of the digital computer is reduced.

When compared to diode logic circuits, transistor logic circuits have current, voltage, and power gains. This is true assuming that a common-emitter circuit, which is the most frequently used circuit, is being employed.

For these and other reasons, the majority of the digital computers designed in the past five years use transistor logic circuits. In this chapter, you will see some of the most commonly used transistor logic circuits, and how they are used to perform Boolean operations.

10-1. The Transistor Inverter

One of the most fundamental operations in Boolean algebra is inversion or negation. Although this was explained in Chapter 3, we shall review it briefly here. If a variable, X, can either exist or not exist, then $\overline{X}$ is the negation of the variable X. This means that if X exists, $\overline{X}$ does not exist; and when X does not exist, $\overline{X}$ exists. If we use a 1 to signify existence, and a 0 to signify nonexistence, then the truth table for X and $\overline{X}$ is that shown in Table 10-1. Notice that when X is 1, $\overline{X}$ is 0; and when X is 0, $\overline{X}$ is 1. This corresponds to what we have just explained. As you know, there are

TABLE 10-1. THE NEGATION
(INVERSION) OF X

X	0	1
$\overline{X}$	1	0

many logic symbols that are used to represent a logic inverter; but perhaps the simplest to remember, and the one used in this text, is the symbol shown in Fig. 10-1. As shown in this figure, the input to the inverter is X, and the output of the inverter is $\overline{X}$. This simply means that the output of an inverter is the negation or the inversion of the input. In Fig. 10-2A, a voltage that can be represented by X is shown. During the interval of the time from t_0 to t_1 the voltage level is 0 volts. During the interval from t_1 to t_2, the voltage level is $-V$ volts. From t_2 and afterward, the voltage level is again 0 volts. In Fig. 10-2B, the corresponding voltage waveform for $\overline{X}$ is shown.

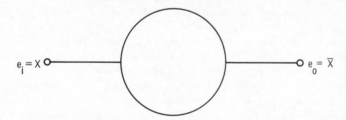

Fig. 10-1. A logic symbol used to represent the logic operation of inversion.

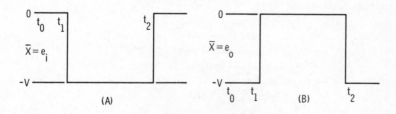

Fig. 10-2. Voltage representation of X and $\overline{X}$: (A) represents X, and (B) represents $\overline{X}$.

Compare this waveform with that of Fig. 10-2A and you will see that when X is 0 volts, $\overline{X}$ is $-V$ volts. Similarly, when X is $-V$ volts, $\overline{X}$ is 0 volts. If we define a voltage as existing when it is zero volts, and not existing when it is $-V$ volts, then we have interpreted the Boolean operation of inversion in terms of voltages. This is shown in Tables 10-2 and 10-3. In Table 10-2, the voltage representation of X and $\overline{X}$ is presented; in Table 10-3, the logic interpretation of these voltages is tabulated. Having done this, we must now find a circuit that will perform in accordance with the tabulation of Table 10-2. Here is where the transistor inverter comes into the picture.

TABLE 10-2.   VOLTAGE REPRESENTATION
OF X AND $\overline{X}$

$X = e_i$	0	-V
$\overline{X} = e_0$	-V	0

TABLE 10-3.   LOGIC INTERPRETATION
OF THE VOLTAGES

e_i	1	0
e_0	0	1

The basic transistor inverter circuit was described in Chapter 8. For convenience and reference, it is once again drawn in Fig. 10-3. The function of the components and the voltages were fully explained in Chapter 8, but notice that there is an additional component in this figure, and that is the diode D_1. The function of this diode is to clamp the output voltage to $-V$ volts when the transistor is not conducting. The cathode of the diode is placed at the collector end of the transistor while the anode is placed at $-V$ volts. If the magnitude of V is much less than the magnitude V_{cc}, the diode will conduct whenever the transistor is not conducting. As an example, assume that V is at 6 volts, and that V_{cc} is 20 volts. When the input voltage to the transistor is zero volts, the base-to-emitter voltage will be back-biased because of the action of V_{bb} and R_1. This voltage will cut the transistor off. Once the transistor is cut off, D_1 will conduct. Why D_1 conducts can be seen from Fig. 10-4. In this figure, you can see that the anode of D_1 is at a positive 14 volts with respect to the negative side of the V_{cc} supply. Since this is so, D_1 is forward-biased, and it will conduct. When a diode conducts, its forward resistance is so small that the diode can be considered as a short circuit. This means that the applied 14 volts will be dropped across R_L. Furthermore, if the diode is considered to be a short circuit, the voltage from the collector to the emitter of the transistor is -6 volts; or, the collector is negative with respect to the emitter. Hence, we see that when the transistor is cut off, its output voltage is clamped to -6 volts by the action

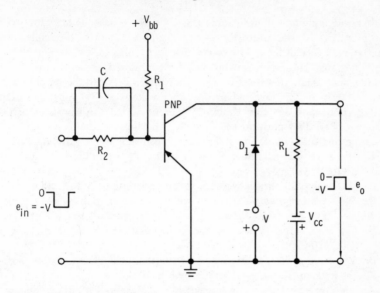

Fig. 10-3. A basic p-n-p transistor inverter that can be used to perform Boolean inversion or negation.

of D_1, and the -6-volt supply. This clearly shows the inversion action for the interval of time from t_0 to t_1 in Fig. 10-2 because when 0 volts is applied between the base and emitter, the output voltage is $-V$ volts.

Let us now analyze the output of the transistor inverter when $-V$ volts is applied to its input. During the interval of time when $-V$ volts is applied at the input, the base is negative with respect to the emitter. Under this condition, the emitter-to-base circuit is forward-biased, and the transistor conducts. Once the transistor conducts, collector current flows. This current, for the p-n-p transistor, is *hole* current. It flows down through R_L, causing the upper terminal of R_L to be more positive than the lower terminal.

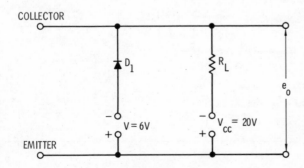

Fig. 10-4. A simplified schematic of the output circuit of the transistor inverter.

This positive-going voltage causes the collector-to-base voltage to become less negative. If the transistor is in or near saturation, the collector-to-emitter voltage will be on the order of a few tenths of a volt. For all practical purposes, this small voltage can be considered as zero volts. Hence, we see, once again, that there will be an inversion between the input and output voltages. In this case, when the input voltage is $-V$ volts, the output voltage is 0 volts. We can conclude, therefore, that the transistor inverter just described does perform the operation of logic inversion.

From this discussion, the following points should be fully understood:

1. We have defined, in a Boolean sense, the operation we desired to perform; i.e., negation.
2. We have symbolically represented this operation; see Fig. 10-1.
3. We have assigned polarities of voltages to the variables; see Fig. 10-2.
4. We have tabulated these voltages for the variables; see Table 10-2.
5. We have presented the logic interpretation of these voltages; see Table 10-3.
6. We have chosen a transistor circuit that will electronically perform the logic operation we desired; see Fig. 10-3.

An inverter using an n-p-n transistor is shown in Fig. 10-5. The input

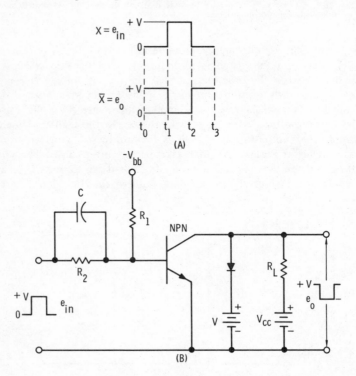

Fig. 10-5. A possible n-p-n inverter: (A) The input and output voltages, and (B) the n-p-n inverter circuit.

and output voltages representing X and $\overline{X}$, respectively, are shown in Fig. 10-5A. Notice that the input voltage goes from 0 volts to $+V$ volts. This is necessary because an n-p-n transistor will not conduct unless its input voltage causes the emitter to be negative with respect to the base. To do this, a positive voltage must be fed into the base circuit. During the time that the input voltage is 0 volts, the base will be at some negative voltage with respect to the emitter, and this means that the transistor will be cut off. What causes the base to be negative with respect to the emitter when the input voltage is zero is the $-V_{bb}$ supply. This, however, is not the main function of the $-V_{bb}$ supply. You should remember from Chapter 8 that the primary function of $-V_{bb}$ is to prevent thermal runaway. Nevertheless, $-V_{bb}$ does back-bias the transistor when the input voltage is zero. A tabulation of the input and output voltages represented by X and $\overline{X}$, respectively, is shown in Table 10-4. We shall define the positive voltage as an existing voltage and

TABLE 10-4. VOLTAGE REPRESENTATION
OF N-P-N TRANSISTOR

$X = e_{in}$	0 VOLTS	$+$ V VOLTS
$\overline{X} = e_o$	$+$ V VOLTS	0 VOLTS

represent it symbolically by 1, and the *relatively* negative voltage as non-existing and represent it by 0. (0 volts is more negative than $+V$ volts; hence, it is a relatively negative voltage.) We can now symbolically tabulate the input and output voltages as shown in Table 10-5.

TABLE 10-5. LOGIC INTERPRETATION
OF THE VOLTAGES

$X = e_{in}$	0	1
$\overline{X} = e_o$	1	0

The circuit of an n-p-n transistor inverter is shown in Fig. 10-5B. When we compare this circuit to that of Fig. 10-3, we notice the following differences: the base bias voltage is now negative, the diode and the clamping voltage are now oppositely polarized, and the V_{cc} supply is now positive. Why these changes are necessary was explained in Chapter 8.

It is frequently desirable for a digital computer to be capable of performing the Boolean operation of double negation or inversion. In Chapter 3, you learned that $X = \overline{\overline{X}}$. Now that you know the basic concepts of Boolean algebra as well as how a transistor inverter functions, you will be able to understand how it is possible to perform double negation using transistors. First, let us draw the logic block diagram for this operation. This is shown in Fig. 10-6A. Next, we must define voltages that are represented by these

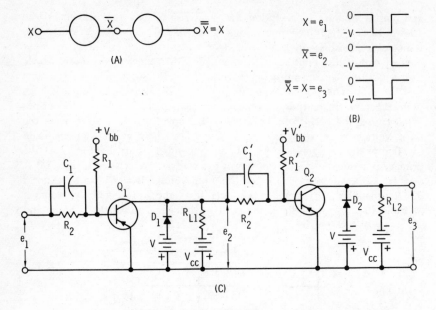

Fig. 10-6. (A) A logic block diagram showing double negation, (B) the voltages that represent the Boolean variables, and (C) a pair of similar transistor inverters that can perform double negation.

Boolean variables. These voltages are shown in Fig. 10-6B. In Table 10-6, the voltages have been tabulated. The table showing the symbolic representation of these voltages is Table 10-7. The transistor circuit that performs the Boolean operation of double negation is shown in Fig. 10-6C. By studying this figure and the tables carefully, you should be able to see why the circuit performs double negation.

TABLE 10-6. VOLTAGE REPRESENTATION
OF A DOUBLE INVERTER

$X = e_1$	0	-V
$\overline{X} = e_2$	-V	0
$\overline{\overline{X}} = X = e_3$	0	-V

TABLE 10-7. LOGIC INTERPRETATION OF THE VOLTAGES

$X = e_1$	1	0
$\overline{X} = e_2$	0	1
$\overline{\overline{X}} = X = e_3$	1	0

10-2. Transistor NOR Circuits

Before we examine the transistor NOR circuit, let us define the Boolean NOR operation. The NOR operation is simply the negation of an OR a NOT OR. You can see how the NOR operation derived its name. As you learned in Chapter 3, the OR function is defined as existing when either one or the other or both of two variables exist. (Actually, any number of variables may be used.) If we let X represent one variable, and Y the other, then the third row of Table 10-8 shows that the OR function exists for three combinations of the two variables. Since the NOR function is a negation of the OR function, all that is necessary to develop the NOR function is to negate the third row.

TABLE 10-8. THE DEVELOPMENT OF THE "NOR"
FUNCTION FOR TWO VARIABLES

X	0	1	0	1
Y	0	0	1	1
X + Y	0	1	1	1
$\overline{X+Y}$	1	0	0	0

The negation is shown in the fourth row. In this row, you can see that the NOR exists when the quantity X OR Y does not exist. You can also observe that the NOR function exists when $\overline{X}$ AND $\overline{Y}$ exists. The reason for this is that in column 3, a zero appears when X and Y are both 0; since X AND Y do not exist, the NOR function exists. This can be proved by recalling De Morgan's theorem which states: $\overline{X + Y} = \overline{X}\overline{Y}$. This suggests that we can represent the NOR function in two ways: $\overline{X + Y}$ or $\overline{X}\overline{Y}$.

In Fig. 10-7A, the logic block diagram for the first form of the NOR function is developed. The circular portion at the output of the OR symbol represents the inverter needed to negate the expression. The figure consists

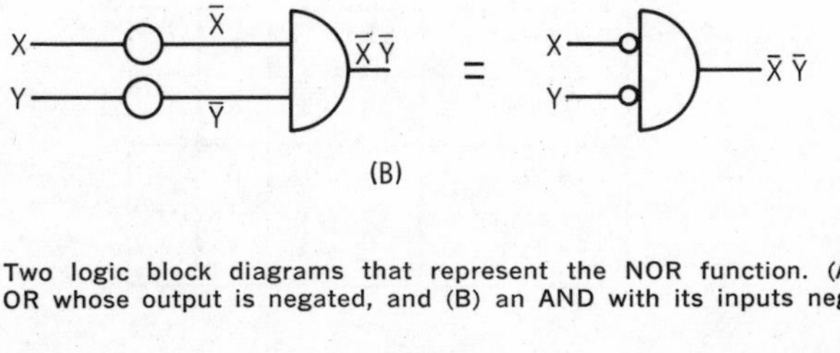

(A)

(B)

Fig. 10-7. Two logic block diagrams that represent the NOR function. (A) An OR whose output is negated, and (B) an AND with its inputs negated.

simply of an OR circuit followed by an inverter. In Fig. 10-7B, the second form, $\overline{X}\overline{Y}$, of the NOR function is shown. Observe that the inverter symbols are shown at the input of the AND circuit. By inverting X and Y before they are ANDed together, the output of the AND gate is $\overline{X}\overline{Y}$.

From Fig. 10-7A, we can see one method how to construct an electronic circuit that can generate the NOR function. We must invert the output of an OR gate, as shown in Fig. 10-8. The circuit in this figure consists of diode OR gate, and a transistor inverter. The OR gate is composed of diodes

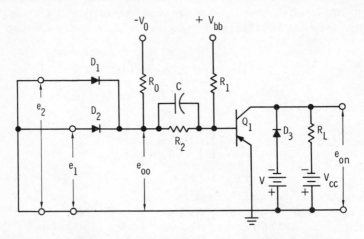

Fig. 10-8. One possible circuit that can be used for generating the NOR function.

D_1 and D_2, as well as the $-V_0$ supply and R_0. The output of the OR gate is represented by e_{oo}. The remainder of the NOR circuit is the inverter, whose input is the OR gate output.

To show that this circuit will electronically fulfill the requisites for the NOR function, let us assign voltages for X and Y. Assume that the magnitudes of X and Y are either 0 or $-V$ volts. Further, let us represent X or Y symbolically as 1 when they are 0 volts, and 0 when they are $-V$ volts. Now, we can transform the truth table, Table 10-8, into the voltage tabulation of Table 10-9. All we have to do now is to show that the circuit

TABLE 10-9.   VOLTAGE REPRESENTATION FOR
THE "NOR" FUNCTION

$X = e_1$	-V	0	-V	0
$Y = e_2$	-V	-V	0	0
$X + Y = e_{oo}$	-V	0	0	0
$\overline{X + Y} = e_{on}$	0	-V	V	-V

in Fig. 10-8 will adhere to the tabulation of Table 10-9. For the first condition, both e_1 and e_2 are $-V$ volts. With the assumption that $-V_0$ is more negative than $-V$ volts, we know that D_1 and D_2 will both conduct, and the output of the OR gate will be $-V$ volts. When $-V$ volts is fed into the transistor inverter, causing the emitter-to-base circuit to be forward-biased, the transistor conducts, and its output is essentially 0 volts. For the second condition, e_1 is 0 volts and e_2 is $-V$ volts. For this condition, D_1 conducts and D_2 does not conduct and the output of the OR gate is 0 volts. When 0 volts is fed into the transistor inverter, the transistor will not conduct, and its output will be clamped to $-V$ volts because of the $-V$ supply between the collector and emitter. For the third condition, e_1 is $-V$ volts and e_2 is 0 volts. Since the input to D_2 is 0 volts, this diode will conduct; D_1, whose input is $-V$ volts, does not conduct. The output of the OR gate, then, is 0 volts. Once again, the transistor inverter will not conduct, and its output will be clamped to $-V$ volts. For the fourth and last condition, both e_1 and e_2 are 0 volts. Both of the diodes in the OR gate will conduct, and the output of the OR gate will be 0 volts. Since 0 volts is again being fed into the inverter, the output of the inverter will again be clamped to $-V$ volts. We have shown, then, that the circuit in Fig. 10-8 performs the operation of the NOR function. A synchrogram which shows the waveforms for the various voltages of Fig. 10-8 is given in Fig. 10-9.

Another popularly used NOR transistor circuit is shown in Fig. 10-10. The difference between this circuit and the circuit in Fig. 10-8 is in the input circuit. The circuit in Fig. 10-8 uses a diode OR gate in the input of the NOR circuit, whereas the circuit in Fig. 10-10 uses resistors and capacitors. The capacitors are used for speed-up purposes as explained in Chapter 8. Resistors R_2 and R_3 are chosen so that the transistor will conduct only when both of the input voltages are $-V$ volts. For any other combination of input voltages, the transistor will not conduct, and the output of the NOR circuit will be clamped to $-V$ volts.

To explain this circuit more fully, we shall assign values to the voltages and resistors in the input circuit of Fig. 10-10. Let us assume the following: $V_{bb} = 14$ volts, $R_1 = 12K$ ohms, $R_2 = R_3 = 6K$ ohms, $e_1 = e_2 =$ either 0 volts or -6 volts, and h_{ie} is 1 kilohm when the transistor conducts and 1 megohm when the transistor does not conduct. The equation for the base-to-emitter voltage by Millman's theorem is:

$$V_{be} = \frac{V_{bb}/R_1 + e_2/R_2 + e_1/R_3 + 0/h_{ie}}{1/R_1 + 1/R_2 + 1/R_3 + 1/h_{ie}} \qquad (10\text{-}1)$$

The four possible conditions of the input voltages are listed in Table 10-10. Let us determine the base-to-emitter voltage for each condition. Keep in mind that if V_{be} is calculated to be a positive voltage, it means that the base-to-emitter voltage is positive, and that the transistor will not conduct. On the other hand, if the base-to-emitter voltage is calculated to be a negative quantity, the base is negative with respect to the emitter, and the transistor will conduct.

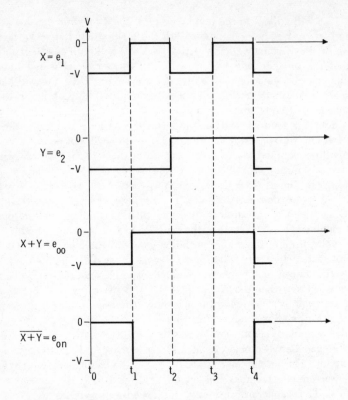

Fig. 10-9. Ideal waveforms for the circuit of Fig. 10-8.

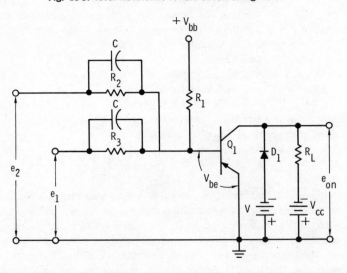

Fig. 10-10. A NOR circuit that uses a Kirchhoff's adder in its input to perform the OR operation.

TABLE 10-10. POSSIBLE CONDITIONS FOR INPUT
VOLTAGES OF FIG. 10-10

e_1	-6	-6	0	0
e_2	-6	0	-6	0
V_{be}	-0.6V	+0.4V	+0.4V	+2.8V
e_{on}	0	-6	-6	-6

For the first condition, e_1 and e_2 are both -6 volts. Therefore,

$$V_{be} = \frac{14/12K - 6/6K - 6/6K}{1/12K + 1/6K + 1/6K + 1/1K}$$
$$= \frac{14 - 12 - 12}{1 + 2 + 2 + 12}$$
$$= -10/17 \approx -0.6 \text{ volts}$$

For the second condition, $e_1 = -6$ volts and $e_2 = 0$ volts. Therefore,

$$V_{be} = \frac{14/12K - 0/6K + 6/6K}{1/12K + 1/6K + 1/6K + 1/1 \text{ meg}}$$
$$= (14 - 12)/(1 + 2 + 2) = 2/5 \approx +0.4 \text{ volts}$$

Note that $1/1$ meg is a negligible amount, and it was ignored in the calculation.

For the third condition, $e_1 = 0$ volts and $e_2 = -6$ volts. These values will yield mathematically the same results as those obtained for the second condition; hence, we know that V_{be} is approximately 0.4 volts for the third condition.

For the fourth condition, $e_1 = e_2 = 0$ volts. Therefore,

$$V_{be} = \frac{14/12K + 0/6K + 0/6K}{1/12K + 1/6K + 1/6K + 1/1 \text{ meg}}$$
$$= \frac{14/12K}{5/12K} \approx +2.8 \text{ volts}$$

Again, $1/1$ meg is a negligible quantity, and can be ignored in the calculation.

The tabulation of the base-to-emitter voltages is also shown in Table 10-10. Since for three conditions, the base-to-emitter voltage is positive, the transistor cannot conduct, and the output voltage for these three conditions is -6 volts. For the first condition, however, the base-to-emitter voltage is -0.6 volts. This means that the base is negative with respect to the emitter, and the transistor will conduct. For this condition, the output voltage of the NOR circuit is 0 volts. Thus, we see that this circuit also performs the NOR operation.

Now that we have explained the NOR operation in both a logic and electronic sense, let us see how we can apply it to Boolean algebra. For this discussion, we shall assume that we have available both the variable and the negation of the variable. This is usually true in digital computers because most of them employ flip-flops which have as their outputs both the variable, and the negation of the variable. We shall also assume that we have available the NOR element, and the inverter alone. This is usually true in digital computers that use NOR logic, for the NOR element is nothing more than an OR circuit followed by an inverter. In practice, these two circuits usually come as packaged units, and they, in turn, can be used to make other packaged units.

You shall now see how the OR function can be developed using NOR logic, and an inverter. Since the NOR is the negation of the OR, all we need do to

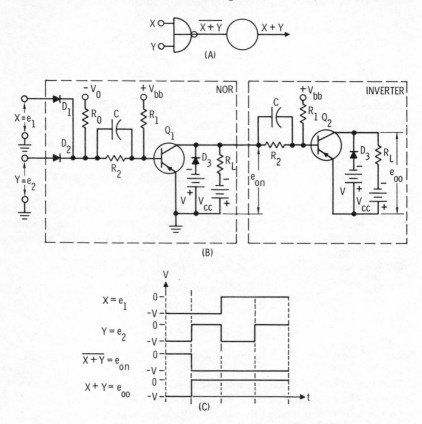

Fig. 10-11. (A) The logic development of the OR using a NOR element, and an inverter; (B) the schematic for the development of the OR; and (C) the waveforms of the various circuit voltages.

obtain the OR function is to negate the output of the NOR element. Using logic symbols, we have shown this process in Fig. 10-11A. The voltages tabulated in Table 10-11 are the input voltages to the NOR element, the

TABLE 10-11. VOLTAGE REPRESENTATION
FOR THE"OR"STATEMENT

$e_1 = X$	-V	-V	0,	0
$e_2 = Y$	-V	0	-V	0
$e_{on} = \overline{X+Y}$	0	-V	-V	-V
$e_{oo} = X+Y$	-V	0	0	0

output voltage of the NOR element, and the output of the inverter element. Table 10-12 consists of the symbolic representations of the voltage tabulated in Table 10-11. The logic used here is this: a voltage exists when it is relatively positive; an existing voltage is symbolized by 1; a voltage does not exist when it is relatively negative; this voltage is symbolized by 0. Notice that in Table 10-12, the tabulation for $X + Y$ does adhere to the basic Boolean function of the OR. A schematic of the circuit that electronically generates the OR function is shown in Fig. 10-11B. As you can see, this circuit is nothing more than the NOR circuit followed by an inverter. The various waveforms that are associated with the circuit are shown in Fig. 10-11C.

TABLE 10-12. LOGIC INTERPRETATION
OF THE VOLTAGES

X	0	0	1	1
Y	0	1	0	1
$\overline{X+Y}$	1	0	0	0
$X+Y$	0	1	1	1

At this point, you might be asking yourself: "Why is it necessary to go through all of this trouble when a simple diode circuit will perform the same operation?" The answer is simple: By using this technique to develop the OR function, we obtain a current and power gain. This means we can take the output of this OR circuit and feed it to the various parts of the computer where the OR function is to be used as an input. Depending on the particular type of transistor and components used in the design of this OR circuit, we can use its output to feed approximately 250 loads. If we used only ordinary diode logic, and assuming we desired the OR operation 250 times, we would need 250 separate diode logic OR gates. You can see now that by using the NOR logic circuit shown in Fig. 10-11B, we can save both space and money. These are two very important factors in the design of digital computers.

The development of the AND function using NOR logic is shown in Fig. 10-12, and Tables 10-13 and 10-14. The NOR symbols are shown in Fig. 10-12A and B. In both cases, the inputs are $\overline{X}$ and $\overline{Y}$. To show why it is

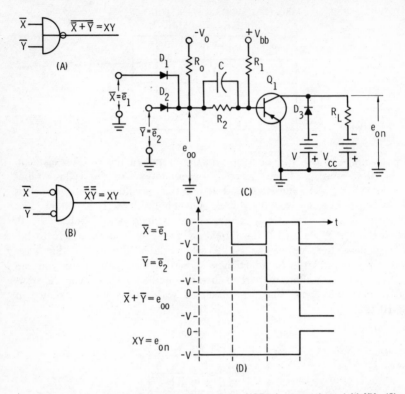

Fig. 10-12. (A and B) Representations of the NOR elements that yield XY; (C) the circuit of the NOR element; and (D) the waveforms of the circuit voltages.

TABLE 10-13. VOLTAGE REPRESENTATION FOR THE "AND"
FUNCTION USING "NOR" LOGIC

$X = e_1$	-V	0	-V	0
$Y = e_2$	-V	-V	0	0
$\bar{X} = \bar{e}_1$	0	-V	0	-V
$\bar{Y} = \bar{e}_2$	0	0	-V	-V
$\bar{X}+\bar{Y} = e_{00}$	0	0	0	-V
$\overline{\bar{X}+\bar{Y}} = \overline{\bar{X}\bar{Y}} = XY = e_{on}$	-V	-V	-V	0

necessary to use the negation of the variables, let us do some Boolean algebra:

Step 1: $XY = \overline{\overline{XY}}$ (Double Negation)

Step 2: $\overline{\overline{XY}} = \overline{\bar{X} + \bar{Y}} = \overline{\bar{X}\bar{Y}}$ (De Morgan's Theorem)

If we can obtain the output, XY from the NOR element, we will have developed the AND function using NOR logic. As shown in *Step 1*, XY can be changed to $\overline{\overline{XY}}$ which, in turn, can be changed to $\overline{X} + \overline{Y}$ by De Morgan's theorem. The term, $\overline{X} + \overline{Y}$ is the negation of the OR statement $\overline{X} + \overline{Y}$. Since the NOR function is also the negation of an OR statement, we can obtain $\overline{X} + \overline{Y}$ by feeding $\overline{X}$ and $\overline{Y}$ into the NOR element. The output, $\overline{X} + \overline{Y}$, of the NOR element, is equal to XY, as shown in *Steps 1* and *2*. Table 10-13 lists the voltages that are represented by $X, Y, \overline{X}, \overline{Y}, \overline{X} + \overline{Y}$, and XY. Table 10-14

TABLE 10-14. LOGIC INTERPRETATION OF THE VOLTAGES

X	0	1	0	1
Y	0	0	1	1
$\overline{X}$	1	0	1	0
$\overline{Y}$	1	1	0	0
$\overline{X} + \overline{Y}$	1	1	1	0
$\overline{\overline{X} + \overline{Y}} = \overline{\overline{X}\,\overline{Y}} = XY$	0	0	0	1

lists the symbolic representation using 0 and 1 for the voltages that are tabulated in Table 10-13. Notice that the tabulation for XY will yield the correct designation number for the AND statement, XY. The schematic of the NOR element that generates the correct output for XY is shown in Fig. 10-12C. The only difference between this circuit and the basic NOR circuit is that, here, the input voltages are negated. Figure 10-12D shows the waveforms of the voltages that are associated with the circuit. These waveforms are taken from the voltage tabulation of Table 10-13. It is important to understand and recognize these waveforms because they are often examined with the aid of an oscilloscope in checking out and maintaining computers. A technician must be able to interpret waveforms correctly to troubleshoot computer circuitry.

Before we show how NOR logic can be used for generating more complex Boolean functions, let us examine the various outputs from the two NOR symbols for two variable inputs. The NOR logic outputs for the four combinations of inputs are shown in Fig. 10-13. In Fig. 10-13A, the inputs are X and Y, and the outputs are either $\overline{X} + \overline{Y}$ or $\overline{XY}$. As you know, these two Boolean statements are identical. The purpose for showing both of these symbols, and their outputs is to simplify the interpretation of Boolean functions into NOR logic. For example, if in a Boolean function we saw $\overline{XY}$, we would know that the NOR element to use to generate this function is the one that has as its output, $\overline{XY}$. If, on the other hand, we had a Boolean function that contained $\overline{X} + \overline{Y}$, we could use the NOR symbol that has $\overline{X} + \overline{Y}$ as its output.

The remaining three combinations that are possible as inputs to the NOR element are shown in Fig. 10-13B, C, and D. In Fig. 10-13B, the inputs are X and $\overline{Y}$. For this combination of inputs, the output from one NOR symbol is $\overline{X} + \overline{Y}$; and from the other, the output is $\overline{XY}$. If we had a Boolean statement that contained the term $\overline{X}Y$, we could easily generate the term by using the NOR symbol that has $\overline{X}Y$ as its output. Similarly, we can obtain the term $\overline{X} + \overline{Y}$ by using the NOR symbol that has this term as its output. This analysis is true for the remaining two possible input combinations.

	NOR INPUTS	NOR LOGIC OUTPUTS FOR THE VARIOUS INPUTS	
		Negated OR Symbol	AND Symbol
(A)	X, Y	$\overline{X+Y}$	$\overline{X}\,\overline{Y}$
(B)	X, $\overline{Y}$	$\overline{X+\overline{Y}}$	$\overline{X}Y$
(C)	$\overline{X}$, Y	$\overline{\overline{X}+Y}$	$X\overline{Y}$
(D)	$\overline{X}$, $\overline{Y}$	$\overline{\overline{X}+\overline{Y}}$	XY

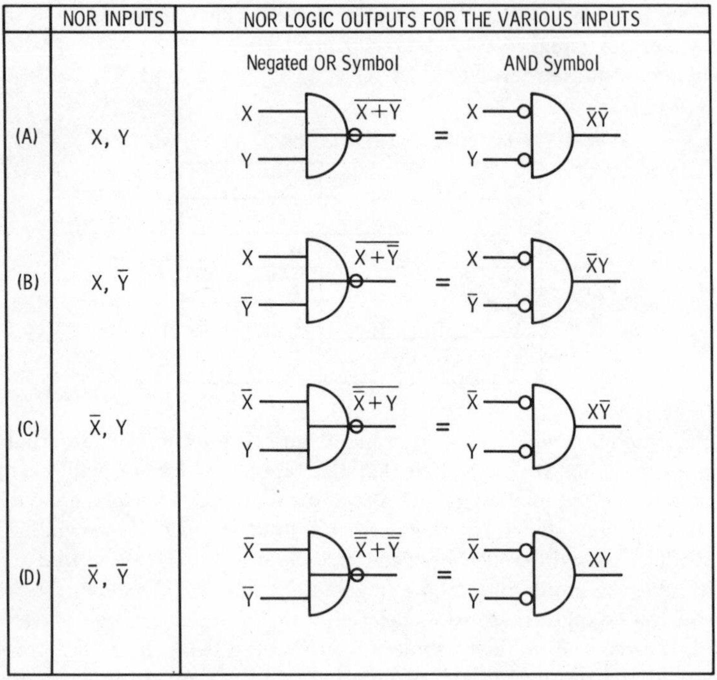

Fig. 10-13. NOR logic outputs for the two NOR symbols, and the four possible input combinations.

Let us now apply the preceding observations about NOR logic to combine NOR elements to produce Boolean functions. The first function we shall consider is, $\overline{X}Y + X\overline{Y}$. Two solutions shall be given. The first solution shall be straight forward, but it will not be the simplest one. The second solution will be simpler as far as circuitry is concerned, but it will involve some Boolean manipulation of the original function. In this discussion, only NOR circuitry (including inverters) will be used.

Notice that the function we are considering is in its simplest form, i.e., it cannot be further simplified because it contains no redundant terms. The first step in implementing NOR logic is to make sure that the statement is in its simplest form. Once this point has been confirmed, the next step is to draw the logic diagram using NOR elements taken directly from the function. For example, the first expression of the function is $\overline{X}Y$. We can implement this expression by using the AND symbol of the NOR element.

To get $\overline{X}Y$ as an output, we have to feed X and $\overline{Y}$ into the element. When this is done, the output of the NOR element is $\overline{\overline{X}\overline{Y}}$, which is equal to $\overline{X}Y$. To implement the term, $X\overline{Y}$, we will again use the AND symbol of the NOR element. To obtain $X\overline{Y}$ as an output, we must feed into the element, $\overline{X}$ and Y. When this is done, the output of the NOR element is $\overline{\overline{X}\,\overline{Y}}$, which is equal to $X\overline{Y}$. You can see then, that we need two NOR elements to implement the two expressions $\overline{X}Y$ and $X\overline{Y}$. Since we are using NOR circuitry only, we have to use a NOR element followed by an inverter to OR the two terms together. The NOR element symbol we shall use for this is the negated OR because, when we use this symbol, we know that the output of the NOR element will be the negated ORing of the inputs.

Figure 10-14A shows the logic block diagram for the function $\overline{X}Y + X\overline{Y}$. The input to the NOR logic block labeled 1 is X and $\overline{Y}$, and the output is

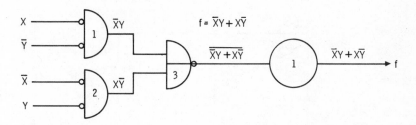

Fig. 10-14A. The logic block diagram that generates the function $\overline{X}Y + X\overline{Y}$ using NOR logic.

$\overline{X}Y$. The input to the NOR logic block labeled 2 is $\overline{X}$ and Y, and the output is $X\overline{Y}$. Observe that the outputs of blocks 1 and 2 are fed into the NOR logic block labeled 3. The NOR logic blocks labeled 1 and 2 use the symbol which will give as its output the individually negated ANDing of its inputs. This is done to make the implementing of the function simpler. The symbol used for NOR logic block 3 is the one that gives as its output the negated ORing of its inputs. Again, this is done to make the implementation of the function simpler (it is desired that the output function be an OR statement). The output of NOR logic block 3 is fed into an inverter whose output is the function we desire.

Now that we have the logic block for the function, let us assign voltages to the variables so that we can obtain the proper output from the electronic circuits for the function. We shall use the NOR gates that we have previously discussed in this section. The voltages assigned are tabulated in Table 10-15. The symbolic representations of the voltages are tabulated in Table 10-16. As you can see, $-V$ volts is represented by 0, and 0 volts is represented by 1. Notice that the designation number for the function is 0110. This should be the case because the function we are working with is an exclusive OR. It was shown in Chapter 5 that the designation number for an exclusive OR is 0110.

The next step is to convert the logic block diagram of Fig. 10-14A into

TABLE 10-15. SIGNIFICANT CIRCUIT VOLTAGES

$X = e_1$	-V	0	-V	0
$Y = e_2$	-V	-V	0	0
$\bar{X} = \bar{e}_1$	0	-V	0	-V
$\bar{Y} = \bar{e}_2$	0	0	-V	-V
$\bar{X}Y = e_{on1}$	-V	-V	0	-V
$X\bar{Y} = e_{on2}$	-V	0	-V	-V
$\overline{\bar{X}Y + X\bar{Y}} = e_{on3}$	0	-V	-V	0
$\bar{X}Y + X\bar{Y} = e_{of}$	-V	0	0	-V

TABLE 10-16. LOGIC INTERPRETATION OF THE VOLTAGES

$X = e_1$	0	1	0	1
$Y = e_2$	0	0	1	1
$\bar{X} = \bar{e}_1$	1	0	1	0
$\bar{Y} = \bar{e}_2$	1	1	0	0
$\bar{X}Y = e_{on1}$	0	0	1	0
$X\bar{Y} = e_{on2}$	0	1	0	0
$\overline{\bar{X}Y + X\bar{Y}} = e_{on3}$	1	0	0	1
$\bar{X}Y + X\bar{Y} = e_{of}$	0	1	1	0

an electronic circuit. This is accomplished by connecting three NOR gates, and an inverter as shown in Fig. 10-14B. The inputs to NOR gate 1 are e_1 and $\bar{e}_2$. These voltages correspond to X and $\bar{Y}$, respectively. The output of this NOR gate is e_{on1}, which corresponds to $\bar{X}Y$. This output voltage is fed into NOR gate 3. The inputs to NOR gate 2 are $\bar{e}_1$ and e_2 which correspond to $\bar{X}$ and Y, respectively. The output of this NOR gate is e_{on2}, which corresponds to $X\bar{Y}$. This output is also fed to NOR gate 3. The output of NOR gate 3 is e_{on3}, which corresponds to $\overline{\bar{X}Y + X\bar{Y}}$. This output is then fed into the inverter whose output is e_{of}. This output voltage corresponds to the function $\bar{X}Y + X\bar{Y}$. The waveforms of the voltages at the various inputs and outputs are shown in Fig. 10-14C. These waveforms are taken from the tabulation of the voltages in Table 10-15.

When we began the discussion on the development of the exclusive OR function, we mentioned that the final circuit would not be in its simplest form. As a matter of fact, you shall now see that we can omit the inverter.

We shall now develop the simplest electronic circuit that can generate the function, $\overline{X}Y + X\overline{Y}$, using NOR logic.

The first thing we must do is to change the function into a form that requires no inverters. We know, for instance, that if we can get the function into the form of the negated OR alone, we would not need to use an inverter. Once we change the function into this form, we can then determine what we need as inputs to a NOR circuit to obtain this function. The inputs to this NOR circuit will be the outputs of two other NOR circuits. Knowing the outputs of these two NOR circuits, we can then determine their inputs. We shall effectively work backwards to find the simplest circuit.

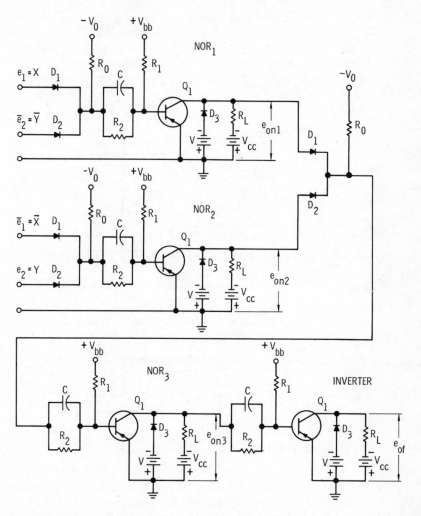

Fig. 10-14B. The schematic of the circuit for the logic block diagram of Fig. 10-14A.

To change the function so that it is in the form of a negated OR, we shall first apply some Boolean algebra.

Step 1: $\overline{X}Y + X\overline{Y} = \overline{\overline{\overline{X}Y + X\overline{Y}}}$ (Double Negation)

Step 2: $\overline{\overline{\overline{X}Y + X\overline{Y}}} = \overline{(\overline{\overline{X}Y})\,(\overline{X\overline{Y}})}$ (De Morgan's Theorem)

Step 3: $(\overline{\overline{X}Y})\,(\overline{X\overline{Y}}) = (X + \overline{Y})\,(\overline{X} + Y)$ (De Morgan's Theorem)

Step 4: $(X + \overline{Y})\,(\overline{X} + Y) = XY + \overline{X}\overline{Y}$ (Law of Distribution)

Step 5: $f = \overline{XY + \overline{X}\overline{Y}}$

In *Step 5,* we have accomplished what we desired, i.e., we have taken the exclusive OR statement, and have changed it into an equivalent statement that is in the negated OR form. Because we were able to accomplish this, we shall be able to eliminate the inverter in the electronic circuit.

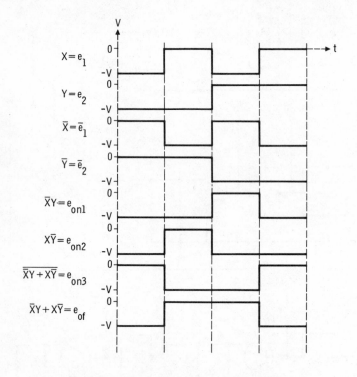

Fig. 10-14C. The waveforms of the circuit voltages.

Now that we have determined that $f = \overline{XY + \overline{X}\overline{Y}}$, let us proceed to develop the NOR logic block diagram for this function. Since the function is in the form of the negated OR, we can use the NOR logic symbol that has as its output the negated OR. To have this output from this NOR logic symbol, we must feed XY and $\overline{X}\overline{Y}$ into it. Remember that these inputs are the outputs of two other NOR logic symbols. Since these inputs are in the form of AND statements, we shall use the NOR logic symbol that yields as its output an AND statement. Furthermore, because these AND statements are the outputs of NOR elements, we will have to feed $\overline{X}$ and $\overline{Y}$ into one of the NOR elements, so that we will obtain XY at its output; and we will have to feed X and Y into the other NOR element, so that we will obtain $\overline{X}\overline{Y}$ at its output. This development is shown in Fig. 10-15A. When you compare this logic block diagram with that in Fig. 10-14A, you will notice that we have eliminated one inverter.

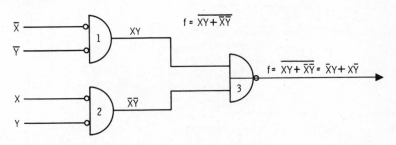

Fig. 10-15A. The logic block diagrams for generating the function $\overline{XY + \overline{X}\overline{Y}}$.

The voltages that represent the inputs and outputs of the three NOR elements are listed in Table 10-17. Observe that the output voltages of NOR element 3 are identical to the output voltages in Table 10-15. Of course, they should be identical since both circuits generate equivalent functions.

TABLE 10-17. SIGNIFICANT CIRCUIT VOLTAGES

$e_1 = X$	-V	0	-V	0
$e_2 = Y$	-V	-V	0	0
$\overline{e}_1 = \overline{X}$	0	-V	0	-V
$\overline{e}_2 = \overline{Y}$	0·	0	-V	-V
$e_{on1} = XY$	-V	-V	-V	0
$e_{on2} = \overline{X}\overline{Y}$	0	-V	-V	-V
$e_{on3} = \overline{XY + \overline{X}\overline{Y}}$	-V	0	0	-V

The symbolic representations of the voltages are listed in Table 10-18. Notice that the designation number of the function is 0110, which is the same as the designation number for the exclusive OR function. Figure 10-15B shows the electronic circuit that will generate this function. The develop-

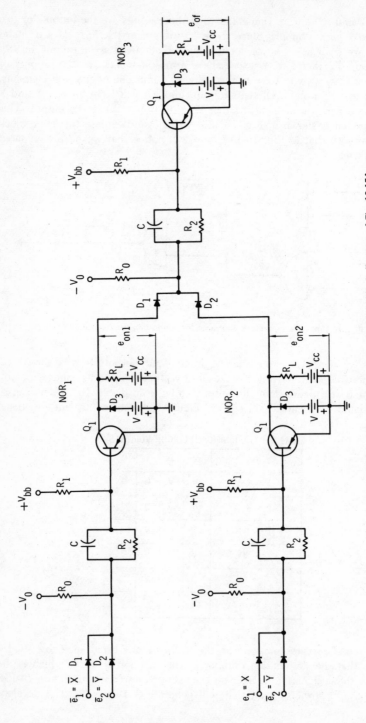

Fig. 10-15B. The schematic of the circuit for the logic block diagram of Fig. 10-15A.

TABLE 10-18. LOGIC INTERPRETATION OF THE VOLTAGES

$e_1 = X$	0	1	0	1
$e_2 = Y$	0	0	1	1
$\bar{e}_1 = \bar{X}$	1	0	1	0
$\bar{e}_2 = \bar{Y}$	1	1	0	0
$e_{on1} = XY$	0	0	0	1
$e_{on2} = \bar{X}\bar{Y}$	1	0	0	0
$e_{on3} = \overline{XY + \bar{X}\bar{Y}}$	0	1	1	0

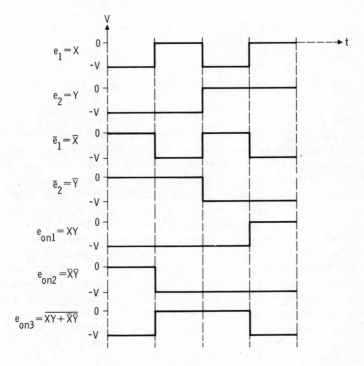

Fig. 10-15C. The waveforms of the circuit voltages.

ment of this circuit involves nothing more than transforming the logic block diagram into an electronic circuit. In Fig. 10-15C, the waveforms of the voltages associated with the circuit are shown.

Now that we have simplified the circuit that generates the exclusive OR statement, we shall show how to convert this circuit into a half adder. Recall that the half adder has as its carry the Boolean function XY, and as its sum the Boolean function $\overline{X}Y + X\overline{Y}$. We have already shown that $\overline{X}Y + X\overline{Y}$ is equal to $\overline{XY} + \overline{\overline{X}\overline{Y}}$, and we have shown how to generate the latter function. All we have to do now is to develop the circuit that will generate XY, which is the carry for the half adder. In Fig. 10-15A, it is interesting to note that the output of NOR element 1 is XY. Because of this, all we have to do to develop the half adder is to take an output from this NOR element. In doing so, we have obtained a half adder that uses NOR logic. The NOR logic block diagram from the half adder is shown in Fig. 10-16. The only difference

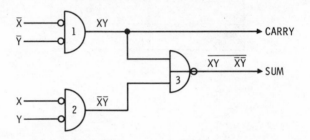

Fig. 10-16. The logic block diagram of a half adder using NOR logic.

between this diagram and that of Fig. 10-15A is the carry output. With the exception of the output lead from NOR gate 1, the schematic of the half adder is identical to the schematic in Fig. 10-15B. The voltages at the various inputs and outputs of the half adder are the same as those shown in Tables 10-17 and 10-18.

Though we have shown so far how to implement NOR logic circuits using only two inputs, it is possible to use more than two inputs. In fact, some of the modern digital computers do make use of NOR logic circuits with more than two inputs. Some NOR logic circuits can even accommodate as many as ten inputs. With this in mind, you should understand that the implementation of NOR logic depends upon the basic NOR element. If a digital computer is designed around a two-input NOR element, all of the Boolean functions must be put into expressions that can be implemented with two-input NOR logic. On the other hand, if a digital computer is designed around a NOR element that can accommodate ten inputs, the Boolean functions need not be rigorously manipulated until they are in two-input NOR logic.

Let us now implement the following three-variable Boolean function using only two-input NOR logic: $f = XYZ + \overline{X}Y\overline{Z}$. Because we are using two-input NOR logic, we must put the function in a form that is readily adaptable to this type of logic. The steps involved in changing the function to this form are:

Step 1: $f = XYZ + \overline{X}Y\overline{Z}$ (Law of Distribution)

$= Y(XZ + X\overline{Z})$

Step 2: $Y(XZ + \overline{X}\overline{Z})$ (Double Negation)

$= \overline{\overline{Y(XZ + \overline{X}\overline{Z})}}$

Step 3: $Y\overline{(XZ + \overline{X}\overline{Z})}$ (De Morgan's Theorem)

$= \overline{\overline{Y} + \overline{(XZ + \overline{X}\overline{Z})}}$

Step 4: $f = \overline{\overline{Y} + \overline{(XZ + \overline{X}\overline{Z})}}$

In *Step 4*, the function is in the form that can be implemented using two-input NOR logic. To implement this function, we shall again work backwards. To obtain the function as an output of a NOR element, the inputs to the element must be $\overline{Y}$ and $\overline{XZ + \overline{X}\overline{Z}}$. Let us assume that we have available $\overline{Y}$. Then we will have to generate $\overline{XZ + \overline{X}\overline{Z}}$. To generate this function, we must feed XZ and $\overline{X}\overline{Z}$ into a NOR element. To generate XZ, we shall have to feed $\overline{X}$ and $\overline{Z}$ into a NOR element; and to generate $\overline{X}\overline{Z}$, we shall have to feed X and Z into a NOR element. From this analysis, we can see that four NOR elements will be required. Figure 10-17A shows the logic block diagram that will generate this function. Notice that the outputs of the NOR elements 1 and 2 are XZ and $\overline{X}\overline{Z}$, respectively. These outputs are fed into NOR element 3, and the output of this element is $\overline{XZ + \overline{X}\overline{Z}}$. This output, along with $\overline{Y}$, is used as the input to the NOR element 4. The output of NOR element 4 is the function in which we are interested.

Assuming that we shall use the same electronic NOR gate that we have used thus far, the voltages at the inputs and outputs of the various NOR elements in Fig. 10-17A are listed in Table 10-19. The symbolic representa-

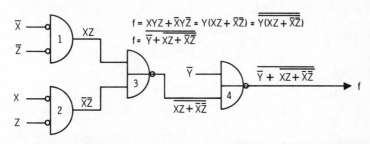

Fig. 10-17A. The logic block diagram that generates the function $\overline{Y} + \overline{\overline{XZ} + \overline{X}\overline{Z}}$.

tion of these voltages is listed in Table 10-20. Here again, 0 volts is symbolized by 1, and $-V$ volts is symbolized by 0. Notice that the designation number of the function is 0010 0001. This can be checked by using a truth table or by designation numbers. The designation number of XYZ is 0000 0001. The designation number of $\overline{X}Y\overline{Z}$ is 0010 0000. Logically summing these two designation numbers will yield the designation number of the function; hence, our result is correct.

The schematic for the logic block diagram of Fig. 10-17A is shown in Fig. 10-17B. To test your knowledge of how this circuit operates, and to

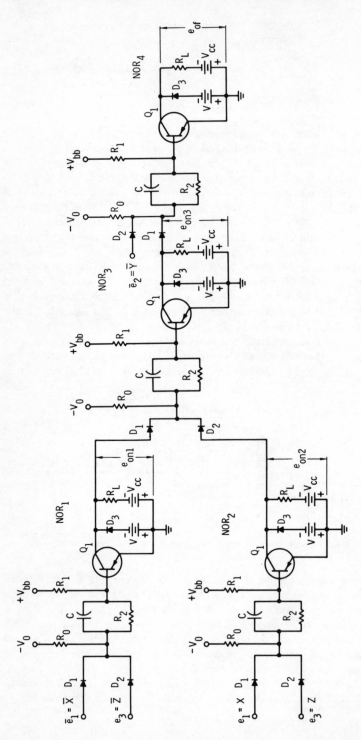

Fig. 10-17B. The schematic of the circuit for the logic block diagram of Fig. 10-17A.

prove that this circuit will generate the function, it is suggested that the reader take various combinations of the inputs, and see what outputs he obtains. Needless to say, he should obtain the voltages tabulated in Table 10-19. Figure 10-17C shows the voltage waveforms at the various inputs, and outputs of the NOR gates. These waveforms are reproduced from the voltage table, Table 10-19.

If a three-input NOR element were used to implement the original function

TABLE 10-19. SIGNIFICANT CIRCUIT VOLTAGES

$X = e_1$	-V	0	-V	0	-V	0	-V	0
$Y = e_2$	-V	-V	0	0	-V	-V	0	0
$Z = e_3$	-V	-V	-V	-V	0	0	0	0
$\overline{X} = \overline{e}_1$	0	-V	0	-V	0	-V	0	-V
$\overline{Y} = \overline{e}_2$	0	0	-V	-V	0	0	-V	-V
$\overline{Z} = \overline{e}_3$	0	0	0	0	-V	-V	-V	-V
$XZ = e_{on1}$	-V	-V	-V	-V	-V	0	-V	0
$\overline{X}\overline{Z} = e_{on2}$	0	-V	0	-V	-V	-V	-V	-V
$\overline{XZ + \overline{X}\overline{Z}} = e_{on3}$	-V	0	-V	0	0	-V	0	-V
$\overline{\overline{Y} + \overline{XZ + \overline{X}\overline{Z}}} = e_{on4}$	-V	-V	0	-V	-V	-V	-V	0

TABLE 10-20. LOGIC INTERPRETATION OF THE VOLTAGES

$X = e_1$	0	1	0	1	0	1	0	1
$Y = e_2$	0	0	1	1	0	0	1	1
$Z = e_3$	0	0	0	0	1	1	1	1
$\overline{X} = \overline{e}_1$	1	0	1	0	1	0	1	0
$\overline{Y} = \overline{e}_2$	1	1	0	0	1	1	0	0
$\overline{Z} = \overline{e}_3$	1	1	1	1	0	0	0	0
$XZ = e_{on1}$	0	0	0	0	0	1	0	1
$\overline{X}\overline{Z} = e_{on2}$	1	0	1	0	0	0	0	0
$\overline{XZ + \overline{X}\overline{Z}} = e_{on3}$	0	1	0	1	1	0	1	0
$\overline{\overline{Y} + \overline{XZ + \overline{X}\overline{Z}}} = e_{on4}$	0	0	1	0	0	0	0	1

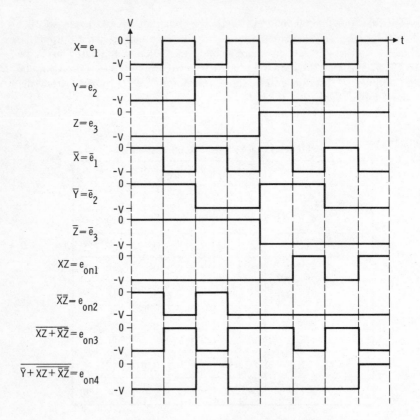

Fig. 10-17C. The waveforms of the circuit voltages.

$XYZ + \overline{X}Y\overline{Z}$, the NOR logic block of Fig. 10-18A could be used. Notice that NOR elements 1 and 2 have three inputs, and that their outputs are XYZ and $\overline{X}Y\overline{Z}$, respectively. These outputs are fed into a two-input NOR element whose output is the negation of the function that we desire. Therefore, an inverter is needed to give us the original function.

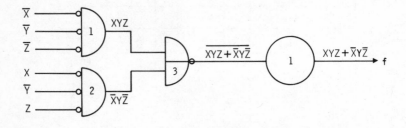

Fig. 10-18A. The logic block diagram that generates the function $XYZ + \overline{X}Y\overline{Z}$.

The electronic circuit that we shall use as our three-input NOR gate is quite similar to the circuit of the two-diode OR gate followed by a transistor inverter. As a matter of fact, the only difference is that we will use another diode in the OR circuit. The voltages that appear at the various inputs, and outputs are listed in Table 10-21. Observe that the voltage tabulation for the output function, e_{of}, is the same as that tabulation in Table 10-19. This, of course, must be true since both circuits generate equivalent functions. The symbolic representation of these voltages is listed in Table 10-22. Notice that, again, the designation number of the function is 0010 0001.

TABLE 10-21. SIGNIFICANT CIRCUIT VOLTAGES

$X = e_1$	-V	0	-V	0	-V	0	-V	0
$Y = e_2$	-V	-V	0	0	-V	-V	0	0
$Z = e_3$	-V	-V	-V	-V	0	0	0	0
$\overline{X} = \overline{e}_1$	0	-V	0	-V	0	-V	0	-V
$\overline{Y} = \overline{e}_2$	0	0	-V	-V	0	0	-V	-V
$\overline{Z} = \overline{e}_3$	0	0	0	0	-V	-V	-V	-V
$XYZ = e_{on1}$	-V	-V	-V	-V	-V	-V	-V	0
$\overline{X}Y\overline{Z} = e_{on2}$	-V	-V	0	-V	-V	-V	-V	-V
$XYZ + \overline{X}Y\overline{Z} = e_{on3}$	0	0	-V	0	0	0	0	-V
$XYZ + \overline{X}Y\overline{Z} = e_{of}$	-V	-V	0	-V	-V	-V	-V	0

TABLE 10-22. LOGIC INTERPRETATION OF THE VOLTAGES

$X = e_1$	0	1	0	1	0	1	0	1
$Y = e_2$	0	0	1	1	0	0	1	1
$Z = e_3$	0	0	0	0	1	1	1	1
$\overline{X} = \overline{e}_1$	1	0	1	0	1	0	1	0
$\overline{Y} = \overline{e}_2$	1	1	0	0	1	1	0	0
$\overline{Z} = \overline{e}_3$	1	1	1	1	0	0	0	0
$XYZ = e_{on1}$	0	0	0	0	0	0	0	1
$\overline{X}Y\overline{Z} = e_{on2}$	0	0	1	0	0	0	0	0
$XYZ + \overline{X}Y\overline{Z} = e_{on3}$	1	1	0	1	1	1	1	0
$XYZ + \overline{X}Y\overline{Z} = e_{of}$	0	0	1	0	0	0	0	1

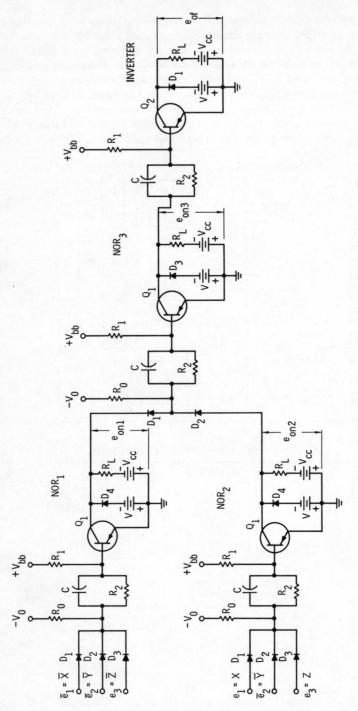

Fig. 10-18B. The schematic of the circuit for the logic block diagram in Fig. 10-18A.

The schematic for the logic block diagram of Fig. 10-18A is shown in Fig. 10-18B. In this circuit, NOR gates 1 and 2 have three diodes each in their inputs. This is expected since we are using three-input NOR logic. Because NOR gate 3 has only two inputs, only two diodes are shown. The

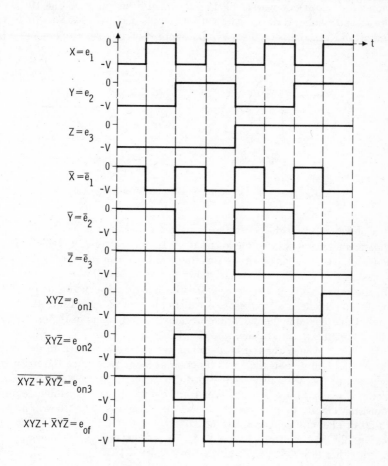

Fig. 10-18C. The waveforms of the circuit voltages.

output of NOR gate 3 is fed to an inverter which has as its output, the function $XYZ + \overline{X}Y\overline{Z}$. The voltage waveforms of the inputs and outputs for Fig. 10-18B are shown in Fig. 10-18C. The waveform corresponding to the Boolean function is the same as that in Fig. 10-17C.

10-3.   Transistor NAND Logic

Before we attempt to develop transistor NAND logic, let us define the NAND operation. As the name implies, the NAND operation is nothing more than the negation of the AND operation. If the AND function is symbolized as XY, the NAND function is then symbolized as $\overline{XY}$, which is the negation of the AND statement. By De Morgan's theorem, $\overline{XY}$ is equal to $\overline{X} + \overline{Y}$. Therefore, we can use two logic symbols to represent the NAND function. The first symbol is the AND gate with a negation shown at its output (see Fig. 10-19A). The second symbol is the OR gate with its inputs negated (see Fig. 10-19B). Understand that both of these symbols represent the same operation. The

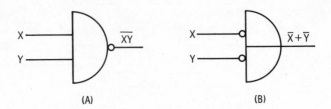

(A)   (B)

Fig. 10-19. The two logic symbols for the NAND function.

idea of representing the NAND function by two symbols is just to make the implementation of NAND functions easier. If, for example, a Boolean function contained a negation of an AND statement, we can implement it readily by using the NAND symbol that shows the negation of the AND function. On the other hand, if we were to see the individual negation of OR statements in a Boolean statement, we can implement this by using the NAND symbol that contains the individual negation of the inputs to the OR symbol. This is a matter of convenience and simplification.

Having explained the NAND operation, we can now proceed to develop a circuit that will give us the NAND function at its output. Since the NAND is a negation of the AND, all we have to do to generate the NAND is to have a diode AND circuit to perform the AND operation, and a common-emitter transistor circuit to perform the negation. This circuit is shown in Fig. 10-20A. The AND gate consists of D_1, D_2, R_a, and V_a. This circuit was thoroughly explained in Chapter 9. If we assume that the voltages e_1 and e_2 are either 0 or $+V$ volts, and that $+V$ volts is less than the $+V_a$ supply voltage, then the output of the AND gate will be $+V$ volts only when e_1 and e_2 are both $+V$ volts. This is illustrated in Table 10-23. In this table, the four possible combinations of e_1 and e_2 are shown, plus the output voltage of the AND gate for each of these combinations of input voltages. The output of the AND gate is symbolized as e_{oa}. The output of the common-emitter inverter is symbolized as e_{on}.

Let us see why the output of the common-emitter circuit is the negation of the input voltage, e_{oa}. For the first combination, e_1 and e_2 are both 0 volts; both diodes, D_1 and D_2, conduct, and e_{oa} is 0 volts. This voltage is fed into the base of the inverter. When the input voltage to the base of the inverter is 0 volts, the transistor will not conduct because of the small

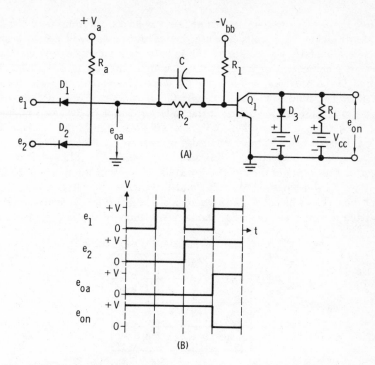

Fig. 10-20. (A) A NAND gate that uses an AND gate and an inverter, and (B) the waveforms of the circuit voltages.

negative voltage it now has between its base and emitter. This negative voltage is due to the $-V_{bb}$ supply and R_1. In the collector circuit, there is a voltage, V, in series with diode D_3. The purpose of this circuit is to clamp the output voltage to $+V$ volts when the transistor is cut off. Since V_{cc} is larger than V, when the transistor is cut off, the voltage applied to the anode of D_3 will be positive with respect to its cathode. This causes D_3 to conduct, and the output voltage, e_{on}, is $+V$ volts. Thus, when the transistor is not conducting, the output voltage is clamped to $+V$ volts. Notice that for this case, 0 volts is fed into the transistor, and $+V$ volts is obtained at its output. This clearly shows the inversion action of the transistor circuit.

TABLE 10-23. SIGNIFICANT CIRCUIT VOLTAGES

e_1	0	+V	0	+V
e_2	0	0	+V	+V
e_{oa}	0	0	0	+V
e_{on}	+V	+V	+V	0

For the next two combinations of input voltages, the output of the AND gate will again be 0 volts because one of the diodes will act as a short circuit. Therefore, the output of the inverter will again be $+V$ volts. For the last combination of input voltages, both e_1 and e_2 are $+V$ volts. The output of the AND gate will also be $+V$ volts. This voltage is present at the input of the transistor, and it causes Q_1 to conduct. Since we are using an n-p-n transistor, the voltage at the collector end of R_L will become negative with respect to its other end. This will cause the output voltage, e_{on}, to be almost 0 volts. For all practical purposes, we shall consider e_{on} to be 0 volts. Again, we can see the inversion action: When $+V$ volts is fed into the inverter, the output of the inverter is 0 volts. This is illustrated in Fig. 10-20B.

If we let 1 represent $+V$ volts, and 0 represent 0 volts, we can represent the voltages in Table 10-23 symbolically as listed in Table 10-24. Notice that the designation number of the output voltage of the AND gate is 0001,

TABLE 10-24.   LOGIC INTERPRETATION OF THE VOLTAGES

e_1	0	1	0	1
e_2	0	0	1	1
e_{oa}	0	0	0	1
e_{on}	1	1	1	0

and that the designation number at the output of the NAND gate (e_{on}) is 1110. This is what we expect because the NAND function is the negation of the AND function.

Figure 10-21 shows the various outputs of the two NAND symbols for the

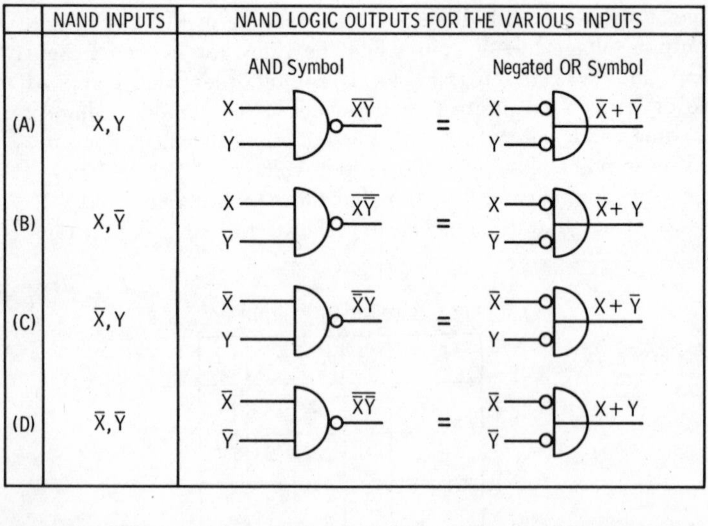

	NAND INPUTS	NAND LOGIC OUTPUTS FOR THE VARIOUS INPUTS	
		AND Symbol	Negated OR Symbol
(A)	X, Y	$X, Y \rightarrow \overline{XY}$	$= \quad X, Y \rightarrow \overline{X} + \overline{Y}$
(B)	$X, \overline{Y}$	$X, \overline{Y} \rightarrow \overline{X\overline{Y}}$	$= \quad X, \overline{Y} \rightarrow \overline{X} + Y$
(C)	$\overline{X}, Y$	$\overline{X}, Y \rightarrow \overline{\overline{X}Y}$	$= \quad \overline{X}, Y \rightarrow X + \overline{Y}$
(D)	$\overline{X}, \overline{Y}$	$\overline{X}, \overline{Y} \rightarrow \overline{\overline{X}\,\overline{Y}}$	$= \quad \overline{X}, \overline{Y} \rightarrow X + Y$

Fig. 10-21. NAND logic outputs for the two NAND symbols, and the four possible input conditions.

corresponding inputs. In Fig. 10-21A, the inputs are X and Y. For the NAND symbol that shows the inversion of an AND, the output is $\overline{XY}$. For the NAND symbol that shows the individual negation of the OR inputs, the output is $\overline{X} + \overline{Y}$. In Fig. 10-21B, the inputs to the NAND symbols are X and $\overline{Y}$, and the outputs are either $\overline{X\overline{Y}}$, or $\overline{X} + Y$. In Fig. 10-21C, the inputs are $\overline{X}$ and Y, and the outputs are either $\overline{\overline{X}Y}$ or $X + \overline{Y}$. Finally, in Fig. 10-21D, the inputs are $\overline{X}$ and $\overline{Y}$, and the outputs are either $\overline{\overline{X}\,\overline{Y}}$, or $X + Y$. Figure 10-21D clearly shows us how we can implement an OR function using NAND logic.

To implement an AND function using NAND logic only, we must negate the output of the NAND as illustrated in Fig. 10-22A. The voltages represented by X, Y, $\overline{XY}$, and XY are listed in Table 10-25. The symbolic repre-

TABLE 10-25. SIGNIFICANT CIRCUIT VOLTAGES

$e_1 = X$	0	+V	0	+V
$e_2 = Y$	0	0	+V	+V
$e_{on} = \overline{XY}$	+V	+V	+V	0
$e_{of} = XY$	0	0	0	+V

sentation of these voltages are listed in Table 10-26. Figure 10-22B shows the schematic. This schematic is simply a NAND gate followed by an inverter. The waveforms that exist at the inputs and outputs of the circuit are shown in Fig. 10-22C. We have now shown how to implement an AND function using NAND logic.

TABLE 10-26. LOGIC INTERPRETATION OF THE VOLTAGES

$e_1 = X$	0	1	0	1
$e_2 = Y$	0	0	1	1
$e_{on} = \overline{XY}$	1	1	1	0
$e_{of} = XY$	0	0	0	1

Let us now implement the following function using NAND logic: $f = XY + \overline{X}\overline{Y}$. Since this function is an OR statement, we can use the individually negated input OR as the output NAND symbol. From Fig. 10-21D we see that to obtain an OR function, we must feed the individually negated terms of the output function into the NAND logic symbol. In other words, to obtain $XY + \overline{X}\overline{Y}$ from the NAND element, we must feed in $\overline{XY}$ and $\overline{\overline{X}\overline{Y}}$. These inputs will, in turn, be the outputs of two other NAND elements. To obtain $\overline{XY}$ from an NAND element, we must feed X and Y into it. To get $\overline{\overline{X}\overline{Y}}$ from the NAND cir-

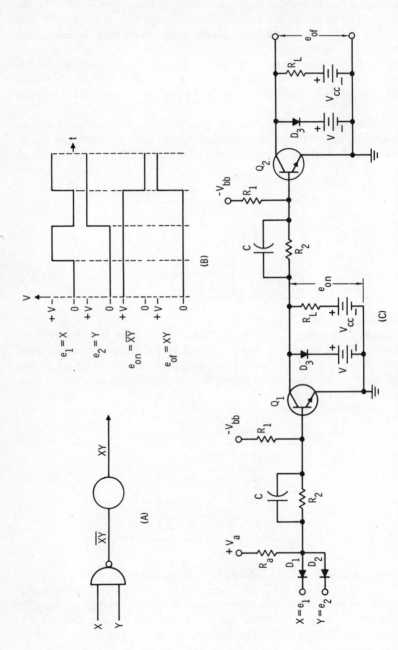

Fig. 10-22. (A) A logic block diagram that generates the function XY, (B) the schematic of the circuit for the logic block diagram, and (C) the waveforms of the circuit voltages.

cuit, we must feed $\overline{X}$ and $\overline{Y}$ into it. The NAND logic block diagram for this function is shown in Fig. 10-23A. The NAND symbol 1 has X and Y as its inputs; its output is, therefore, $\overline{XY}$. The NAND symbol 2 has as its inputs $\overline{X}$ and $\overline{Y}$, and its output is $\overline{\overline{X}\overline{Y}}$. The outputs of these two NAND logic symbols are fed into the NAND logic symbol 3. Since the inputs are $\overline{XY}$ and $\overline{\overline{X}\overline{Y}}$, and since the NAND output will be an individual negation of the ORing of the two inputs, the output of NAND gate 3 will be the function $XY + \overline{X}\overline{Y}$.

The various input and output voltages for the NAND logic symbols are listed in Table 10-27. Notice that the output voltage, e_{on3} is $+V$ volts

TABLE 10-27. SIGNIFICANT CIRCUIT VOLTAGES

$e_1 = X$	0	+V	0	+V
$e_2 = Y$	0	0	+V	+V
$\overline{e_1} = \overline{X}$	+V	0	+V	0
$\overline{e_2} = \overline{Y}$	+V	+V	0	0
$e_{on1} = \overline{XY}$	+V	+V	+V	0
$e_{on2} = \overline{\overline{X}\overline{Y}}$	0	+V	+V	+V
$e_{on3} = XY + \overline{X}\overline{Y}$	+V	0	0	+V

when both e_1 and e_2 are both $+V$ volts. This can be best explained with the aid of the symbolic representation of the voltages listed in Table 10-28. In this table, the function exists (is 1) when both X and Y are 0, and when they are both 1. When X and Y are zero, this is $\overline{X}\overline{Y}$. When X and Y are both 1, this is XY. Thus, we see that the output voltage should be $+V$ volts in the first and fourth columns of Table 10-27.

The schematic of the circuit that will generate this function is shown

TABLE 10-28. LOGIC INTERPRETATION OF THE VOLTAGES

$e_1 = X$	0	1	0	1
$e_2 = Y$	0	0	1	1
$\overline{e_1} = \overline{X}$	1	0	1	0
$\overline{e_2} = \overline{Y}$	1	1	0	0
$e_{on1} = \overline{XY}$	1	1	1	0
$e_{on2} = \overline{\overline{X}\overline{Y}}$	0	1	1	1
$e_{on3} = XY + \overline{X}\overline{Y}$	1	0	0	1

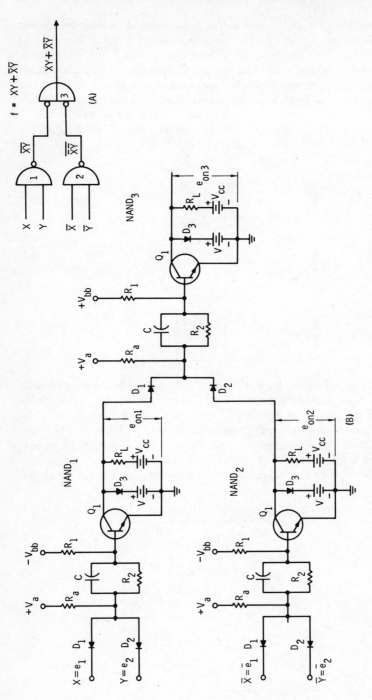

Fig. 10-23. (A) The logic block diagram that generates the function $XY + \bar{X}\bar{Y}$, and (B) the schematic of the circuit for the logic block diagram.

in Fig. 10-23B. This circuit consists of three NAND gates. It is suggested that you trace this circuit for the four combinations of input voltages, and ascertain that the output voltage for each combination will follow the tabulation of Table 10-27.

The waveforms for the various inputs and output voltages in the circuit are shown in Fig. 10-23C. These waveforms are taken from the voltage tabulation of Table 10-27.

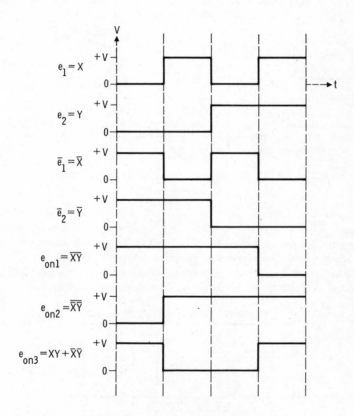

Fig. 10-23C. The waveforms of the circuit voltage.

Figure 10-24A shows one possible solution for a half adder using NAND logic. Recall that the sum of a half adder is the exclusive OR function, $\overline{X}Y + X\overline{Y}$, and that the carry is XY. To put the exclusive OR function in the form shown as the output of the NAND logic symbol 3 in the figure, the following Boolean manipulation is performed:

Step 1: $f = \overline{X}Y + X\overline{Y} = \overline{\overline{\overline{X}Y + X\overline{Y}}}$ (Double Negation)

Step 2: $\overline{\overline{\overline{X}Y + X\overline{Y}}} = \overline{\overline{X}Y} \cdot \overline{X\overline{Y}}$ (De Morgan's Theorem)

Step 3: $\overline{\overline{XY} \cdot \overline{\overline{X}\overline{Y}}} = \overline{(X + \overline{Y})(\overline{X} + Y)}$ (De Morgan's Theorem)

Step 4: $\overline{(X + \overline{Y})(\overline{X} + Y)} = \overline{X\overline{Y} + \overline{X}Y}$ (Law of Distribution)

Step 5: $\overline{XY + \overline{X}Y} = \overline{X\overline{Y}} \cdot \overline{\overline{X}Y}$ (De Morgan's Theorem)

NAND gate 1 has $\overline{XY}$ as its output. This output is fed into two circuits. One of these circuits is the inverter labeled 1. Since the output of an inverter is the negation of its input, the output is XY, which you should recognize as the carry of the half adder. The output of NAND gate 1 is also fed into

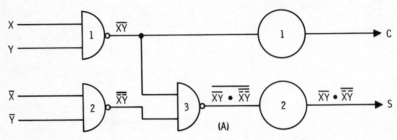

Fig. 10-24A. A logic block diagram of a half adder using NAND logic.

NAND gate 3. The second input to NAND gate 3 is the output of NAND gate 2 which is $\overline{\overline{X}\overline{Y}}$. NAND gate 3 has $\overline{\overline{XY} \cdot \overline{\overline{X}\overline{Y}}}$ as its output. Since the output of NAND gate 3 is the inverse of the sum function of the half adder, an inverter is needed to give the correct sum function. This is inverter 2.

The corresponding input and output voltages for the NAND logic half adder are listed in Table 10-29, and the symbolic representation of these voltages

TABLE 10-29.   SIGNIFICANT CIRCUIT VOLTAGES

$e_1 = X$	0	+V	0	+V
$e_2 = Y$	0	0	+V	+V
$\overline{e}_1 = \overline{X}$	+V	0	+V	0
$\overline{e}_2 = \overline{Y}$	+V	+V	0	0
$e_{on1} = \overline{XY}$	+V	+V	+V	0
$e_{on2} = \overline{\overline{X}\overline{Y}}$	0	+V	+V	+V
$e_{on3} = \overline{\overline{XY}\ \overline{\overline{X}\overline{Y}}}$	+V	0	0	+V
$e_{os} = \overline{XY}\ \overline{\overline{X}\overline{Y}}$	0	+V	+V	0
$e_{oc} = XY$	0	0	0	+V

appears in Table 10-30. Notice that the sum output has the designation number 0110, which is, of course, as it should be for the exclusive OR. Also notice that the carry output has the designation number 0001. This is correct for an AND statement.

TABLE 10-30. LOGIC INTERPRETATION OF THE VOLTAGES

$e_1 = X$	0	1	0	1
$e_2 = Y$	0	0	1	1
$\bar{e}_1 = \bar{X}$	1	0	1	0
$\bar{e}_2 = \bar{Y}$	1	1	0	0
$e_{on1} = \overline{XY}$	1	1	1	0
$e_{on2} = \overline{\bar{X}\bar{Y}}$	0	1	1	1
$e_{on3} = \overline{\overline{XY} \ \overline{\bar{X}\bar{Y}}}$	1	0	0	1
$e_{os} = \overline{XY} \ \overline{\bar{X}\bar{Y}}$	0	1	1	0
$e_{oc} = XY$	0	0	0	1

The schematic and the voltage waveforms for the half adder are shown in Fig. 10-24B and C, respectively. Study this schematic along with the voltage tabulation in Table 10-29, and ascertain that this circuit will give the correct output voltages and waveforms for the different input combinations.

Let us now implement the following three-variable Boolean function using two-input NAND logic: $f = XYZ + X\bar{Y}\bar{Z}$. The first step in implementing this function is to transform the function using the following steps:

Step 1: $f = XYZ + X\bar{Y}\bar{Z}$ (Law of Distribution)

$\quad\quad\quad = X(YZ + \bar{Y}\bar{Z})$

Step 2: $X(YZ + \bar{Y}\bar{Z})$ (Double Negation)

$\quad\quad\quad = \overline{\overline{X(YZ + \bar{Y}\bar{Z})}}$

Step 3: $\overline{\overline{X(YZ + \bar{Y}\bar{Z})}}$ (De Morgan's Theorem)

$\quad\quad\quad = \overline{\bar{X} + \overline{(YZ + \bar{Y}\bar{Z})}}$

Step 4: $\overline{\bar{X} + \overline{(YZ + \bar{Y}\bar{Z})}}$ (De Morgan's Theorem)

$\quad\quad\quad = \overline{\bar{X} + (\overline{YZ})(\overline{\bar{Y}\bar{Z}})}$

Step 5: $\overline{\bar{X} + (\overline{YZ})(\overline{\bar{Y}\bar{Z}})}$ (De Morgan's Theorem)

$\quad\quad\quad = \overline{\bar{X} + (\bar{Y} + \bar{Z})(Y + Z)}$

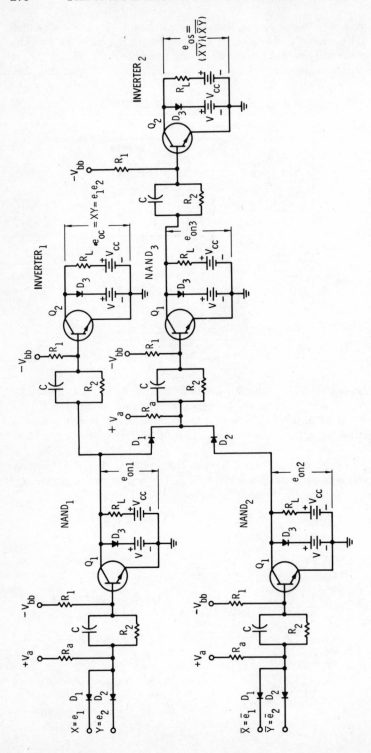

Fig. 10-24B. The schematic of the circuit for the logic block diagram of Fig. 10-24A.

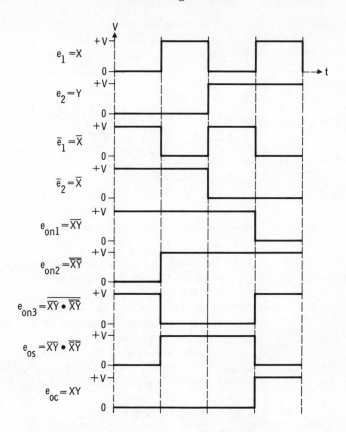

Fig. 10-24C. The waveforms of the circuit voltages.

Step 6: $$\overline{X + (\overline{Y} + \overline{Z})(Y + Z)} \qquad \text{(De Morgan's Theorem)}$$
$$= X\overline{(\overline{Y} + \overline{Z})(Y + Z)}$$

Step 7: $$f = X\,(\,\overline{Y} + \overline{Z})(Y + Z)$$

In *Step 7*, we finally have the function in a form that can be implemented using NAND logic. The term $(\overline{Y} + \overline{Z})$ can be implemented using the NAND element. The same is true of $Y + Z$. These two functions can then be used as inputs to a NAND element whose output would be $(\overline{Y} + \overline{Z})(Y + Z)$. This output, along with X, is fed into the input of another NAND element whose output will be the negation of the function we desire. Therefore, this output must be fed into an inverter from which the function is obtained.

Figure 10-25A shows the NAND logic diagram for the generation of this function. Notice that NAND gates 1 and 2 are in the form of the individually negated OR symbol. This is done to make the generation of the function easier. The outputs of these two NAND gates are fed into the NAND symbol

3. The output of NAND 3 and X are fed to NAND 4. Finally, this output is fed into an inverter from which the function is obtained.

The voltages assigned to the inputs and outputs of Fig. 10-25A are listed

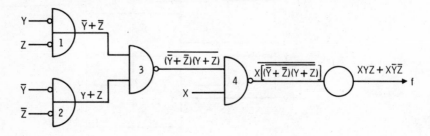

Fig. 10-25A. The logic block diagram that generates the function $XYZ + X\overline{Y}\overline{Z}$.

in Table 10-31. The voltages have been assigned assuming that we are using the previously discussed NAND circuit. The symbolic representation of these voltages is tabulated in Table 10-32. Notice that the designation number of the function is 0100 0001. This can be easily verified: The designation number of XYZ is 0000 0001, and the designation number of $X\overline{Y}\overline{Z}$ is 0100 0000. The logic addition of the two designation numbers is 0100 0001, which is the designation number we obtained for the function.

The schematic for the function under discussion is shown in Fig. 10-25B. Trace this circuit, and make sure you understand the operation of each

TABLE 10-31. SIGNIFICANT CIRCUIT VOLTAGES

$e_1 = X$	0	+V	0	+V	0	+V	0	+V
$e_2 = Y$	0	0	+V	+V	0	0	+V	+V
$e_3 = Z$	0	0	0	0	+V	+V	+V	+V
$\overline{e}_1 = \overline{X}$	+V	0	+V	0	+V	0	+V	0
$\overline{e}_2 = \overline{Y}$	+V	+V	0	0	+V	+V	0	0
$\overline{e}_3 = \overline{Z}$	+V	+V	+V	+V	0	0	0	0
$e_{on1} = \overline{Y} + \overline{Z}$	+V	+V	+V	+V	+V	+V	0	0
$e_{on2} = Y + Z$	0	0	+V	+V	+V	+V	+V	+V
$e_{on3} = \overline{(\overline{Y} + \overline{Z})(Y + Z)}$	+V	+V	0	0	0	0	+V	+V
$e_{on4} = \overline{X(\overline{X} + \overline{Z})(Y + Z)}$	+V	0	+V	+V	+V	+V	+V	0
$e_{of} = XYZ + X\overline{Y}\overline{Z}$	0	+V	0	0	0	0	0	+V

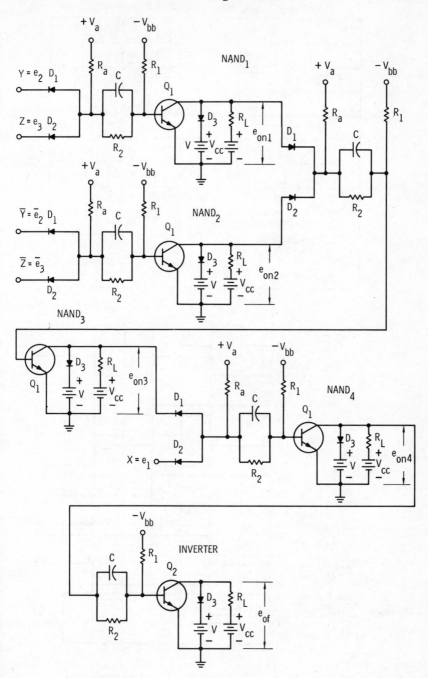

Fig. 10-25B. The schematic of the circuit for the logic block diagram of Fig. 10-25A.

TABLE 10-32. LOGIC INTERPRETATION OF THE VOLTAGES

$e_1 = X$	0	1	0	1	0	1	0	1
$e_2 = Y$	0	0	1	1	0	0	1	1
$e_3 = Z$	0	0	0	0	1	1	1	1
$\bar{e}_1 = \bar{X}$	1	0	1	0	1	0	1	0
$\bar{e}_2 = \bar{Y}$	1	1	0	0	1	1	0	0
$\bar{e}_3 = \bar{Z}$	1	1	1	1	0	0	0	0
$e_{on1} = \bar{Y}+\bar{Z}$	1	1	1	1	1	1	0	0
$e_{on2} = Y+Z$	0	0	1	1	1	1	1	1
$e_{on3} = (\bar{Y}+\bar{Z})(Y+Z)$	1	1	0	0	0	0	1	1
$e_{on4} = X(\bar{X}+\bar{Z})(Y+Z)$	1	0	1	1	1	1	1	0
$e_{of} = XYZ+X\bar{Y}\bar{Z}$	0	1	0	0	0	0	0	1

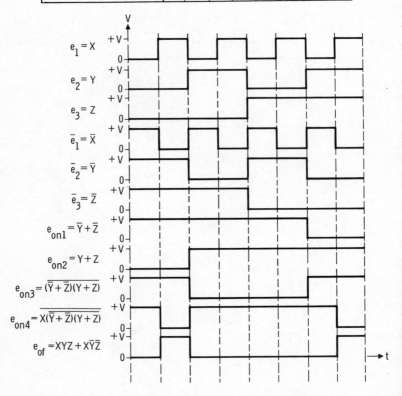

Fig. 10-25C. The waveforms of the circuit voltages.

gate. After you have done this, assign voltages to the variables, X, Y, and Z, and see if the circuit generates the function. The waveforms at the various inputs and outputs are shown in Fig. 10-25C.

If, instead of using a two-input NAND, we were to use a three-input NAND, the implementation of the function $XYZ + \overline{X}\overline{Y}\overline{Z}$ would be different and simpler. This development is shown in Fig. 10-26A. Notice that the inputs to NAND gate 1 are X, Y, and Z, and that the output of this gate is $\overline{XYZ}$. The inputs to NAND gate 2 are X, $\overline{Y}$, and $\overline{Z}$, and the output of this gate is $\overline{X\overline{Y}\overline{Z}}$. The outputs of NAND gates 1 and 2 are used as inputs for NAND gate 3. The symbol that is used for NAND gate 3 is the one that yields the individual negation of the ORing of the inputs as its output. Since the inputs are $\overline{XYZ}$

TABLE 10-33. SIGNIFICANT CIRCUIT VOLTAGES

$X = e_1$	0	+V	0	+V	0	+V	0	+V
$Y = e_2$	0	0	+V	+V	0	0	+V	+V
$Z = e_3$	0	0	0	0	+V	+V	+V	+V
$\overline{X} = \overline{e}_1$	+V	0	+V	0	+V	0	+V	0
$\overline{Y} = \overline{e}_2$	+V	+V	0	0	+V	+V	0	0
$\overline{Z} = \overline{e}_3$	+V	+V	+V	+V	0	0	0	0
$e_{on1} = \overline{XYZ}$	+V	+V	+V	+V	+V	+V	+V	0
$e_{on2} = \overline{X\overline{Y}\overline{Z}}$	+V	0	+V	+V	+V	+V	+V	+V
$e_{on3} = f$	0	+V	0	0	0	0	0	+V

TABLE 10-34. LOGIC INTERPRETATION OF THE VOLTAGES

$X = e_1$	0	1	0	1	0	1	0	1
$Y = e_2$	0	0	1	1	0	0	1	1
$Z = e_3$	0	0	0	0	1	1	1	1
$\overline{X} = \overline{e}_1$	1	0	1	0	1	0	1	0
$\overline{Y} = \overline{e}_2$	1	1	0	0	1	1	0	0
$\overline{Z} = \overline{e}_3$	1	1	1	1	0	0	0	0
$e_{on1} = \overline{XYZ}$	1	1	1	1	1	1	1	0
$e_{on2} = \overline{X\overline{Y}\overline{Z}}$	1	0	1	1	1	1	1	1
$e_{on3} = f$	0	1	0	0	0	0	0	1

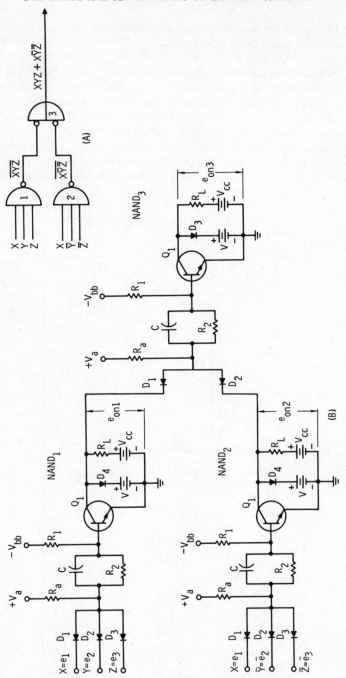

Fig. 10-26. (A) The logic block diagram that generates the function $XYZ + X\bar{Y}\bar{Z}$, and (B) the schematic of the logic block diagram.

and $\overline{X\overline{Y}Z}$, the output of this NAND gate will be the function that we are implementing.

The various voltages assigned to the inputs and outputs of Fig. 10-26A are tabulated in Table 10-33. Notice that, once again, the voltage tabulation for the function, e_{on3}, is the same as that tabulated in Table 10-29. This should be the case because both circuits perform equivalent operations. The symbolic representation of the voltages tabulated in Table 10-33 are tabulated in Table 10-34. Observe that the designation number for the function is, once again, 0100 0001. This is the same as the designation number of Table 10-32.

The schematic for Fig. 10-26A is shown in Fig. 10-26B. Notice that NAND gates 1 and 2 have three inputs, and NAND gate 3 has only two inputs. This is necessary as you can see from the NAND logic block diagram in Fig. 10-26A. In Fig. 10-26C, the waveforms for the various inputs and outputs of the circuit in Fig. 10-26A are shown.

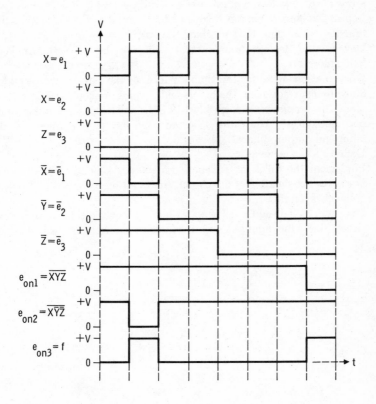

Fig. 10-26C. The waveforms of the circuit voltages.

10-4. Problems

1. Why is an inverter an important circuit in digital computers? Can you think of any other kind of an inverter besides a transistor?

2. State the logic for an inverter.

3. Draw the schematic for a p-n-p inverter. Draw the schematic for an n-p-n inverter.

4. Define a NOR element. How did it get its name? What is the designation number of the NOR function? Prove that this designation number is correct.

5. What polarities of voltages are assigned to a p-n-p NOR gate. Why?

6. What polarities of voltages are assigned to an n-p-n NOR gate. Why?

7. Draw the schematic of the diode input NOR gate.

8. Draw the schematic of the Kirchhoff's adder input NOR gate.

9. Implement the NOR logic block for the following function: $f = \overline{XY} + XY$. Assign voltages to X and Y. For these assigned voltages, make a voltage truth table. Draw the schematic of the NOR logic block. Draw the waveforms at the inputs and outputs of each NOR gate.

10. Repeat **Problem 9** for the following function: $f = X + \overline{X}Y$. Can this function be simplified? If so, show the simplified circuit.

11. Develop the Boolean function that will give the simplest NOR logic half adder.

12. Draw the schematic for the simplest form of the NOR logic half adder. Show the waveforms for the inputs and outputs of each circuit.

13. Show the simplest NOR logic block for the following designation number: 1001 0110. Draw the schematic for this circuit. Show all the input and output voltages.

14. Define a NAND element.

15. Implement the following function using NAND logic: $f = WY + XZ$. Draw the schematic for this circuit. Show all of the input and output voltage waveforms.

16. Develop the half adder using NAND logic. Show the schematic for this circuit. Show the input and ouput voltage waveforms for this half adder.

11

Electronic Counters

Electronic counting circuits are commonly used in many varied applications. For example, they are used to measure frequency and time; they may function as frequency dividers and capacitance meters; and they may simply be used as counting devices, indicating the number of times something occurs. For example, bottles on a conveyor belt can be counted by using a photocell in conjunction with an electronic counter. In this application, the bottles interrupt the light shining on the photocell, causing the photocell to deliver signals (pulses) to the counter.

Digital computers rely heavily on counting circuits to perform numerous functions: Since, under the proper conditions, a counting circuit can retain a number indefinitely, it is used to provide storage for information in computer systems.

In practice, electronic counters differ widely in circuit configuration and operation. They may use unique combinations of basic vacuum and gas tube circuits, or they may use specially-constructed vacuum and gas tubes to achieve the counting effect. The particular circuit, or circuit arrangement used depends, of course, on the application, the basic requirements, and economic factors. The type of electronic counter we shall be concerned with in this chapter is one of the most practical and versatile. It uses the flip-flop as its basic circuit, and can be made to count in a variety of systems or patterns by making simple changes in the circuit arrangement.

11-1. Basic Concepts of Flip-Flops

A flip-flop is a circuit that contains two tubes (or transistors) which are coupled in such a way that only one tube (or transistor) can conduct at a time. The basic vacuum-tube flip-flop is shown in Fig. 11-1A. As shown in the figure, there are two outputs in the flip-flop circuit, and they are taken from the plates of the vacuum tubes. When V_1 is conducting, the potential at its plate is very low; hence, the output of V_1 is low. At the same time, V_2 is not conducting, and its plate potential is high; hence, the output from V_2 is high. When the states of conduction of the tubes are changed, V_1 stops conducting, and V_2 begins to conduct. Under these conditions, the output of V_1 is high, and the output of V_2 is low. To change the states of conduction of the tubes in this circuit, an input signal must be applied to the grid of one of the tubes. When the circuit is thus triggered by an input pulse, whichever tube was conducting ceases to conduct, and

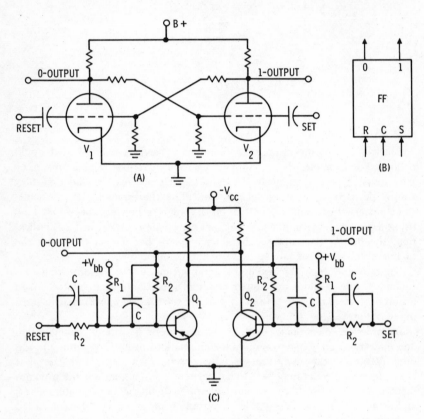

Fig. 11-1. (A) The basic vacuum-tube flip-flop circuit, (B) symbol of a flip-flop, and (C) a transistorized flip-flop circuit.

the tube that was cut off begins to conduct. Each time the circuit is triggered by an input pulse, the state of conduction "flips" from one tube to the other; consequently, the output voltages rise and fall—or "flip" up, and "flop" down. From this description, you can see how the flip-flop derives its name.

The triggering pulses are fed to the grids of the tubes at the terminals designated *set* and *reset* in Fig. 11-1A. These terms shall be explained in the following paragraphs. Either positive or negative pulses may be used to change the states of the tubes. However, flip-flop circuits are generally more sensitive to negative pulses. If positive pulses are used to trigger the flip-flop, they must be of sufficient amplitude to cause the tube that is cut off to begin conducting.

Before attempting to set up a series of flip-flops so that they will count pulses in a predetermined pattern, it is necessary for us to define the logic of flip-flops. The definitions used here have been established by convention, however, they are arbitrary and may be changed.

The symbol used to represent a flip-flop in logic circuits is shown in Fig. 11-1B. Five terminals are represented in the logic block: the output terminals are labeled 0 and 1; and the input terminals are labeled R, C, and S. The 0 terminal contains the output taken from the plate of one of the tubes, and the 1 terminal contains the output taken from the plate of the other tube. These outputs are simply called the 0 output, and the 1 output. By means of the R, or *reset* terminal, pulses are fed to the grid of one tube; through S, or the *set* terminal, pulses are fed to the grid of the other tube. The C, or *complementary*, terminal is connected to the grids of both tubes in such a way that each time a pulse is fed into this terminal, the states of conduction of both tubes change simultaneously. By convention, the following logic is established for the flip-flop.

1. A pulse fed into the *set* terminal causes the flip-flop to be in the 1 state. When the flip-flop is in the 1 state, the 1 output is "hi" (tube is not conducting), and the 0 output terminal is "lo" (tube is conducting). Once the flip-flop is in this defined 1 state, additional set pulses have no effect on the outputs. However, a reset or complementary pulse will change the state of the flip-flop.

2. A pulse fed into the *reset* terminal causes the flip-flop to be in the 0 state. The 1 output is said to be "lo" (tube is conducting), and the 0 output is said to be "hi" (tube is not conducting). Once the flip-flop is in the 0 state, additional reset pulses have no effect on the outputs. However, a set or complementary pulse will change the state of the flip-flop.

3. A pulse fed into the *complementary* terminal will cause the flip-flop to change state. This change may be from the 0 state to the 1 state, or from the 1 state to the 0 state. Each additional complementary pulse affects, or complements the outputs by changing the state of the flip-flop.

A transistorized flip-flop is shown in Fig. 11-1C. The discussion given for tube flip-flops is applicable for transistor circuits. R_1 is the reverse-bias stabilizing resistor.

To understand the development of the counting circuits discussed in the following sections of this chapter, you *must* understand the logic of flip-flops just presented.

11-2. The Basic Binary Counter

As it stands, a single flip-flop is a binary counter capable of counting up to two digits (or one pulse). The pulses to be counted are called clock pulses because they usually occur at regular intervals of time. To prepare the flip-flop for a count, an initial pulse is fed into the reset terminal, putting the flip-flop in the 0 state. Consequently, the 0 output is "hi," and the 1 output is "lo." Since the output taken from the 1 terminal of the flip-flop is "lo," we know that the flip-flop is in the 0 state, and we interpret this to mean that no clock pulses have been transmitted or counted. When the first clock pulse is fed into the complementary terminal of the flip-flop, the state of the flip-flop changes, causing the 0 output to be "lo," and the 1 output to be "hi." Now, the output taken from the 1 terminal is "hi," indicating that the flip-flop is in the 1 state. We can interpret this to mean that 1 clock pulse has been counted. A single flip-flop can count only two digits, 0 and 1, as just described. Additional clock pulses fed into the complementary terminal would only cause a repetition of the count. However, by adding more flip-flops, we can keep a more accurate count of the clock pulses being transmitted. The counter shown in Fig. 11-2 contains three flip-flops, and is capable of counting up to eight digits, or representing the

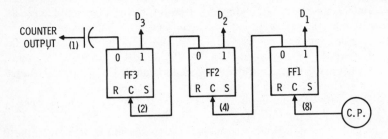

Fig. 11-2. A three-bit binary counter using flip-flops.

binary number 111. The three flip-flops enable the counter to accommodate three binary digits, hence, it is called a three-bit binary counter. A property of the binary counter that is not necessarily a property of other types of counters is that the output at the 1 terminal of each flip-flop represents a binary digit: FF1 represents the first bit, D_1; FF2 represents the second bit, D_2; and FF3 represents the third bit, D_3. When the 1 output is "lo" (the flip-flop is in the 0 state), the binary digit is 0; when the 1 output is "hi" (the flip-flop is in the 1 state), the binary digit is 1. Realizing these conditions, you can understand that the binary number in the counter, after a reset pulse has been fed to each flip-flop, is 000. Realize, however, that a counter is primarily a device that "counts" a certain number of input pulses before it generates an output pulse. As you will see, this three-bit binary counter counts eight input clock pulses before generating an output pulse.

Before we follow the counter through a count, one factor remains to be defined. As shown in Fig. 11-2, the clock pulses are fed into the complementary terminal of FF1 only. The complementary terminals of FF2 and FF3 receive the 0 outputs of the preceding flip-flops as their inputs. If the flip-flops are designed to respond to positive-going pulses only, FF2 and FF3 will change state only when the 0 output of their preceding flip-flop is a positive-going pulse. We know that the 0 output of a flip-flop is "lo" when the flip-flop is in the 1 state, and "hi" when it is in the 0 state. We can say, therefore, that a positive-going pulse is defined when a flip-flop changes from the 1 to the 0 state. True, a negative-going pulse is defined (from the 0 terminal) when the state of the flip-flop changes from 0 to 1; but we have already stated that the flip-flops are designed to respond to positive-going pulses only.

Figure 11-3A shows graphically what happens in the three-bit counter as each clock pulse is transmitted. Toward the right of this diagram is a chart showing the digits represented at the 1 outputs of the flip-flops. When

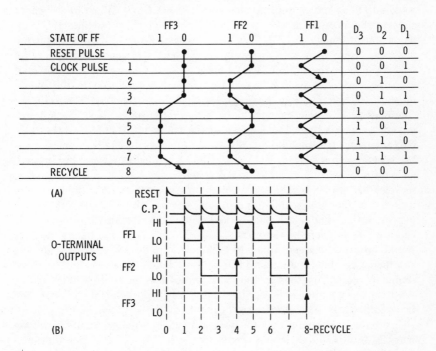

Fig. 11-3. (A) The operation, and (B) waveforms of the three-bit binary counter.

the reset pulse is applied, the three flip-flops are put into the 0 state. As shown in the diagram, FF1 goes from the 0 state to the 1 state when the first clock pulse is transmitted. Since this transition does not constitute a positive-going pulse at the 0 output of FF1, the states of FF2 and FF3 remain unchanged. However, the 1 output of FF1 is now "hi"; and D_1 is 1, as shown in the table. At this point, 1 clock pulse has been counted. Upon the arrival of the second clock pulse, FF1 again changes state. This time, though, it changes from 1 to 0 and delivers a positive-going pulse to the complementary terminals of FF2. Now FF2 changes state from 0 to 1, but does not send a pulse to FF3. FF3, therefore, does not change state. Because of the second clock pulse, the 1 output of FF1 is lo"; and the 1 output of FF2 is "hi." The binary number, 010, has now been counted, corresponding to two clock pulses. Arrowheads are used in the diagram to indicate that the flip-flop has generated a positive-going pulse in changing from the 1 to the 0 state.

When the third clock pulse is transmitted, FF1 again changes state, and its 1 output is "hi." Since it does not generate a pulse, the states of FF2 and FF3 remain the same. However, the binary number represented at the 1 terminals of the flip-flops is now 011, corresponding to three clock pulses. The fourth clock pulse causes FF1 to generate a pulse; this pulse is fed into FF2, and causes it to change state from 1 to 0. When FF2 changes state in this manner, it also generates a pulse which is fed into the complementary terminal of FF3. This pulse causes FF3 to change state for the first time, from 0 to 1. As a result of this chain of reaction, FF3 is the only flip-flop in the 1 state. Its 1 output is "hi"; hence, D_3 is represented as 1. D_2 and D_1 are now 0, and the count has advanced to the binary number 100. So far, four clock pulses have been counted. The counting continues in a similar manner until seven clock pulses have been transmitted, at which time, the number in the counter is 111. Since the 3-bit binary counter is composed of only three flip-flops, the highest binary number it can accommodate is 111. When the eighth clock pulse is transmitted, an output pulse is generated at the 0 terminal of FF3, and the counter recycles to zero; it is then ready to count again. If another flip-flop were included in the circuit, the output pulse generated by FF3 after the transmission of the eighth clock pulse would change the state of FF4 from 0 to 1, causing the flip-flop to represent D_4 as 1. The resulting binary number would be 1000, corresponding to eight clock pulses. But, this is not the case here. The ladder diagram in Fig. 11-3B shows the waveforms at the 0 terminals of the flip-flops as the clock pulses are transmitted. The arrowheads in the diagram indicate the occurrence of positive-going pulses. See how similar this waveform diagram seems to the diagram in Fig. 11-3A.

In addition to saying that the three-bit binary counter counts by 8, we may also say that the counter divides by 8. In Fig. 11-2, notice the numbers, 8, 4, and 2 that are in parentheses near the complementary terminals of the flip-flops. For every eight clock pulses that are fed into FF1, four pulses are fed into FF2, and two pulses are fed into FF3. What happens is that each flip-flop is effectively dividing the number of pulses it receives by two. Before a single pulse appears at the 0 terminal of FF3, it is necessary to have transmitted eight input clock pulses. In view of these observations, we can conclude that the three-bit counter, as a whole, generates one output pulse for eight input pulses; in essence, the circuit divides by eight.

By merely adding more flip-flops to the counter, we can make it perform a straight binary count up to the binary number, 2^n, where n is the number of flip-flops employed. The operation of a counter containing n

flip-flops is basically the same as the oeration of the three-bit counter. You may want to add more flip-flops, and examine the operation of the resulting counter yourself. Regardless of how many flip-flops you add, though, you'll find that none of the resulting counters can count by numbers such as 5, 7, or 10. To accomplish this type of count using flip-flops, it is necessary to employ feedback in the correct manner. Counters using feedback are fittingly called feedback-type counters; these shall be discussed in the next section.

11-3. Feedback-Type Counters

To assist us in our analysis of feedback-type counters, we shall use as an example, a counter that is capable of counting by seven (or, if you wish, dividing by seven). To successfully count by seven, the counter must generate an output pulse for every seven clock pulses transmitted. This is the only unchangeable condition that must prevail. By making slight changes in the three-bit binary counter, and adding a feedback loop, we can produce a circuit that meets this condition, and counts by seven. The first problem we will deal with is how to arrange the feedback loop. We know that eight clock pulses are needed before the binary counter will produce an output, but we want the circuit to have an output for only seven pulses. We can get around this by feeding back to FF1 one pulse generated in the counter during the cycle in addition to the seven externally applied clock pulses. Recall that during one cycle in the binary counter, FF1 generates four pulses, FF2 generates two pulses, and FF3 generates one pulse. Since we need only one pulse, we feed the output of FF3 back to FF1 to compensate for the missing clock pulse. The feedback line may be considered as another input to the complementary terminal of FF1. Since it is not feasible to feed both inputs to the complementary terminal separately, we must somehow combine them without changing the individual input signals in any way. This can be done, as shown in Fig. 11-4 by using an OR gate. There is sufficient delay inherent in the flip-flops to make certain that the feedback pulse

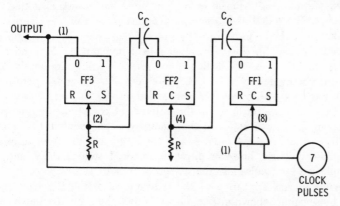

Fig. 11-4. Using feedback to count by seven.

and a clock pulse do not arrive at the OR gate simultaneously. Rather, the feedback pulse arrives at the gate sometime in between two successive clock pulses. If a clock pulse and feedback pulse arrive simultaneously, one count would be lost. By providing feedback in this manner, we have made it possible for the counter to produce an output pulse for every seven clock pulses it receives as an input. But, there is another problem to consider. In the three-bit binary counter, an output pulse was generated upon the transmission of the eighth clock pulse, then the counter recycled to *zero*. When the counter recycled, it returned to the initial reset condition as if a pulse were fed into each reset terminal, putting each flip-flop into the 0 state. Because we feed the output pulse back to FF1 in the count-by-seven counter, we realize that all the flip-flops will not, in this case, be returned to the 0 state. We have to determine, therefore, the states of the flip-flops after they recycle. In doing this, we are also determining the initial reset condition required if the counter is to count by seven. Only then can we correctly reset the flip-flops initially.

To determine the reset condition, let us assume that the counter is operating, and has just counted six clock pulses. Under this reset condition, we know that all the flip-flops will be in the 1 state, and that one more clock pulse will cause the counter to generate an output pulse and recycle. As shown in Fig. 11-5A, we have assumed that all of the flip-flops are in the 1 state. Now, assume that one more clock pulse is fed into the complementary terminal of FF1, and see what happens. FF1 changes state from 1 to 0, and sends a pulse to FF2. FF2 changes state from 1 to 0, and sends a pulse to FF3. FF3 also changes state, delivering an output pulse as if the counter has just counted to seven, and is recycling. But, the output pulse is fed to FF1, and causes it to change state again. This time, FF1 changes from 0 to 1 as shown in the diagram. The flip-flops are now in the states they must be in to begin the count by seven again. We have just established that in the initial reset condition, FF1 is in the 1 state, and FF2 and FF3 are in the 0 state. As the diagram indicates, the count then proceeds normally until the seventh clock pulse has been transmitted. When the count is concluded, the initial reset conditions prevail once more.

Realize that the counter must be prepared to count by a certain predetermined number (in this case, seven) by being put in the proper initial reset conditions. Once it has begun to count, it will continuously recycle, and keep counting until the clock pulses cease to be fed in. However, if we wish to stop the counter in the midst of a count, and have it begin again from zero, we must set up the initial reset conditions by putting each flip-flop in the proper state. In the count-by-seven counter, FF3 and FF2 must be in the 0 state; therefore, a pulse is fed into the reset terminals of these flip-flops. FF1, however, must be in the 1 state initially, and this is accomplished by a pulse into the set terminal of FF1.

The waveforms appearing at the 0 terminals of the flip-flops during a count by seven are shown in Fig. 11-5B. Notice the similarity between these waveforms, and the patterns in the graphical diagram of the states of the flip-flops in Fig. 11-5A. The arrowheads in Fig. 11-5B indicate the occurrence of positive-going pulses. You can also see how the waveforms are affected by the feedback pulse from FF3.

Another difference between this counter, and the three-bit straight binary counter is that the number of pulses that have been counted cannot be determined by observing the states of the flip-flops (or the voltage levels at the 1 terminals) as the count proceeds. There are other means, however, by which an indication of the pulses counted can be obtained. Later in this chapter, we shall discuss lighting systems which provide visual indications of the pulse-by-pulse count.

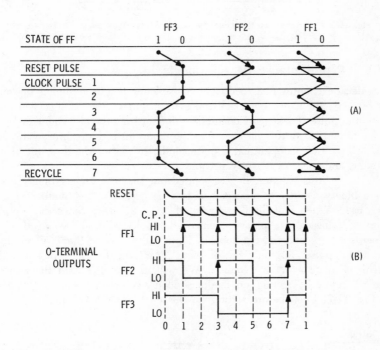

Fig. 11-5. (A) The operation, and (B) waveforms of a count-by-seven counter.

An alternative circuit arrangement that can be used to obtain a count by seven is shown in Fig. 11-6. Since the feedback pulse from FF3 does nothing more than change the state of FF1 from 0 to 1 after the seventh pulse, it can be fed directly to the set terminal of FF1 instead of to the complementary terminal. By feeding the feedback pulse to the set terminal, we can eliminate the OR gate used in the circuit of Fig. 11-4. The same initial reset conditions apply for both circuit arrangements.

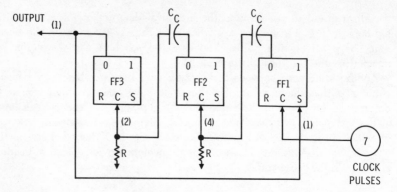

Fig. 11-6. A variation of the count-by-seven counter that does not require an OR gate.

11-4. Representative Decade Counters

A decade counter is a feedback-type counter that is designed to count by ten, i.e., for every ten clock pulses transmitted, the counter generates an output pulse. The decade counter is different from the two counters previously discussed in that it uses four flip-flops instead of three; however, you will see that its operation is quite similar to that of the three-bit binary counter, and the count-by-seven counter.

Earlier in this chapter, it was pointed out that the largest binary number a binary counter could count to is 2^n, where n is the number of flip-flops used. When four flip-flops are used, $2^n = 2^4 = 16$. Since the decade counter is basically a binary counter altered by feedback connections, it is necessary to feed the flip-flops 16 input pulses before they will produce an output pulse. But only ten of these pulses can be clock pulses if the circuit is to be a decade counter. We will, therefore, obtain the remaining six pulses by setting up feedback loops. A decade counter is shown in Fig. 11-7. Even before setting up this circuit, we know that each flip-

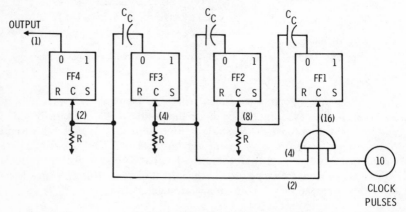

Fig. 11-7. A decade counter.

flop will divide the number of pulses applied to its complementary terminal by two. As shown in the figure, FF1 would have an output of eight pulses for every 16 pulses it receives; FF2 would generate four pulses for each eight pulses it receives; FF3 would have an output of two pulses for every four input pulses; and FF4 would generate an output of one pulse for every two input pulses it receives. If we feed back the outputs of FF2 and FF3 to the complementary terminal of FF1, we will have obtained the remaining six pulses needed to make the counter operate as a decade counter. As before, an OR gate is used to combine the feedback lines, and the clock pulse line. Because of the delay inherent in the flip-flops, the feedback pulses and the clock pulses do not arrive at the gate simultaneously.

Having set up the feedback loops, we must now determine the initial reset conditions of the flip-flops. This is done by assuming that the counter has just counted nine clock pulses (or 15 input pulses to FF1), and all the flip-flops are in the 1 state. The states of the flip-flops are shown graphically in Fig. 11-8A. To make the counter recycle, we feed a pulse into

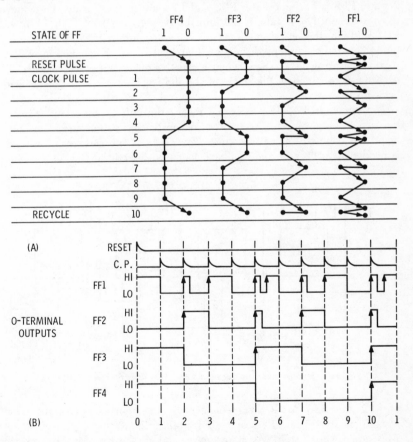

Fig. 11-8. (A) The operation, and (B) waveforms of a decade counter.

298   Principles and Applications of Boolean Algebra

the complementary terminal of FF1. The action that follows is displayed in the diagram. FF1 changes from state 1 to state 0. In doing so, it delivers a pulse to FF2, which also changes state from 1 to 0. When FF2 changes state, it delivers a pulse to FF3 and to FF1 because of the feedback connection. The feedback pulse from FF2 causes FF1 to change state again, from 0 to 1; this time, no pulse is generated by FF1. At the same time, FF3 changes state from 1 to 0, and delivers a pulse to FF4 and to FF1 by way of the second feedback connection. Once more, FF1 changes state from 1 to 0, and generates a pulse. This pulse is fed to FF2, causing it to change state from 0 to 1. (No pulse is generated here.) The pulse delivered to FF4 from FF3 causes FF4 to generate a pulse when it changes state from 1 to 0. This pulse is the output pulse for the last cycle or count, and it is not fed back to FF1. At length, all the flip-flops reach a steady state, and are ready to begin a new count. This steady state is the initial reset condition from which the count must begin if the counter is to count ten clock pulses accurately. As you can see from Fig. 11-8A, FF1 is in the 0 state, FF2 is in the 1 state, FF3 and FF4 are in the 0 state. To achieve this reset condition, a pulse is fed into the reset terminals of FF1, FF3, and FF4, and into the set terminal of FF2. The waveforms that appear at the 0 terminals of the flip-flops during a count by ten are shown in Fig. 11-8B. Again, the arrowheads show when a positive-going pulse is generated by each flip-flop, and how the states of the flip-flops are affected by the feedback pulses.

The circuit in Fig. 11-7 is by no means the only arrangement that can be used to obtain a decade counter. For instance, another circuit arrangement that counts by ten is shown in Fig. 11-9. As you can see, no OR gate is needed here because the feedback loops go directly to the set terminals

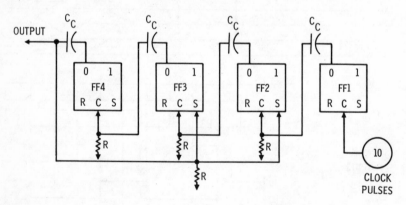

Fig. 11-9. A variation of the decade counter that does not use an OR gate.

of FF2 and FF3. With these connections, the counter begins the count by ten at 0110, i.e., FF4 and FF1 are in the 0 state, and FF2 and FF3 are in the 1 state. As an exercise, and to see for yourself how this circuit operates, construct a diagram such as that in Fig. 11-8A, and observe the states of the flip-flops as they are affected by the feedback connected as shown in Fig. 11-9.

Thus far, we have analyzed the development, and operation of the three-bit binary (count-by-eight) counter, the count-by-seven counter, and the decade (count-by-ten) counter. Having seen how to alter the basic binary circuit by adding feedback lines, and establishing initial reset conditions so that it can perform the desired count, you should be able to develop similar counters that will count by 5, 9, 12, etc.

11-5. Lighting Systems for Electronic Counters

In certain electronic applications, it is desirable to have a visual indication of the number of pulses counted as they are passing through the electronic counter. This is often accomplished by the use of the aforementioned lighting systems. The actual indicator used in lighting systems may be an elaborately arranged device, or a rather simple display panel such as the one in Fig. 11-10. Here, a set of eight neon bulbs are used,

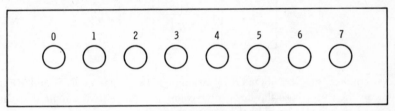

Fig. 11-10. A neon-bulb indicator for a three-bit counter.

and near each bulb is a number (decimal) indicating the number of pulses that have been counted. If bulb 2 lights, two pulses have been counted; if bulb four lights, four pulses have been counted, etc. The circuit used to activate the neon bulbs is a simple, straightforward arrangement which relies on the states of the counter's flip-flops for its operation.

To begin the analysis of lighting systems of the type described, let us first consider the three-bit binary counter. For convenience, this counter has been redrawn in Fig. 11-11, and the flip-flops are designated as A, B,

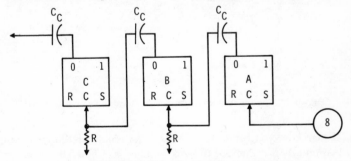

Fig. 11-11. A three-bit binary counter using flip-flops.

and C, instead of 1, 2, and 3. The truth table, Table 11-1, shows the states of the flip-flops as they proceed through a count. Looking at this table, you can see that each incoming clock pulse has some effect on the state of FFA, but not necessarily on the states of FFB and FFC. Since FFA always gives some indication that the count has changed, we use it as the switching flip-flop. Information regarding the exact number of clock pulses that have

TABLE 11-1. THE STATES OF THE FLIP-FLOPS
IN THE BINARY COUNTER

CLOCK PULSE	FLIP-FLOPS		
	C	B	A
0	0	0	0
1	0	0	1
2	0	1	0
3	0	1	1
4	1	0	0
5	1	0	1
6	1	1	0
7	1	1	1

been counted may be obtained by examining the states of FFB and FFC; we can then use these flip-flops for recognition. A resistive circuit that can be used in conjunction with FFA as a switching network is shown in Fig. 11-12. The values of the resistors in this circuit are very high, on the order of 1 or 2 megohms; and the B+ voltage is usually around 300 volts. The

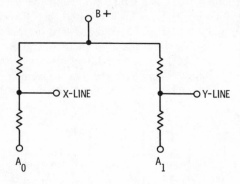

Fig. 11-12. The resistive switching network used in lighting systems.

terminal marked A_0 is connected to the 0 terminals of the switching flip-flop, FFA; and A_1 is connected to the 1 terminal of FFA. The relative potential of the x- and y-lines depends on the state of FFA, or the voltage levels

at its terminals. One side of each neon bulb is connected to either the
x-line or the y-line as you will see.

The recognition circuit for the binary counter lighting system is shown
in Fig. 11-13. Let us see how this circuit operates by studying the states
of the flip-flops in Table 11-1, and by determining the relative potentials
existing in the circuit as each clock pulse arrives.

Pulse 0. Before any pulses have arrived, the binary counter is in the
reset condition; all of the flip-flops are in the 0 state. The switching flip-
flop determines the potentials of the x-line and the y-line. Refer to Fig.
11-12. When FFA is in the 0 state, terminal A_0 is "hi" and terminal A_1
is "lo," consequently, there is more of a voltage drop across the resistors

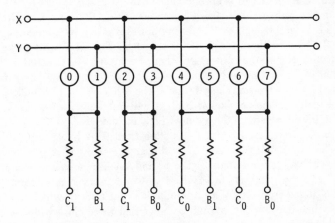

Fig. 11-13. The recognition circuit for the binary counter lighting system.

between B+ and A_1 than there is between B+ and A_0. We can say, therefore, that the potential of the x-line is higher than that of the y-line; or, the
x-line is "hi" and the y-line is "medium." Now look at Table 11-1, and note
that, for pulses 0 and 1, the states of FFB and FFC are uniquely 0. If we
connect one side of bulb 0 and bulb 1 to the 1 terminal of FFB and FFC,
that side of each bulb will be "lo." Now, when no pulse has arrived, the
x-line is "hi." Since the neon bulb will light only when a "hi-lo" potential
is applied, we must connect the other side of bulb 0 to the x-line. In
doing so, we cause bulb 0 to have a "hi-lo" potential across it when no pulse
has arrived, and it will light. Bulb 1 will not light at this time if we connect
its other terminal to the y-line. If this is done, a "medium-lo" potential is
established across bulb 1. Bulb 1 cannot light unless it has a "hi-lo" potential across it.

Pulse 1. When the first clock pulse is transmitted, the state of FFA
changes from 0 to 1, causing terminal A_0 to be "lo," and A_1 to be "hi." This
change in potential at the terminals of FFA switches the potentials of the
x- and y-lines. Now, the x-line is "medium," and the y-line is "hi." When this

is the case, the potential across bulb 0 changes from "hi-lo" to "medium-lo," and bulb 0 goes out. However, the potential across bulb 1 is now "hi-lo" because one end is connected to the y-line, and the other end is connected to terminal B_1. Under these conditions, bulb 1 lights, indicating that one clock pulse has been counted.

Pulses 2 and 3. When the second pulse is transmitted, FFA changes state from 1 to 0, terminal A_0 is "hi," the x-line switches to "hi," terminal A_1 is "lo," and the y-line switches to medium. For clock pulses 2 and 3, the states of FFB and FFC are again unique: FFB is in the 1 state, and FFC is in the 0 state. Because their states are unique for the second and third clock pulses, we can use these flip-flops to obtain recognition of pulses 2 and 3. The idea is to keep one side of bulbs 2 and 3 "lo" by connecting them to the proper terminals of FFB and FFC. Knowing in advance that terminals C_1 and B_0 will be "lo" during pulses 2 and 3, we connect one end of bulbs 2 and 3 to these terminals as shown in Fig. 11-13. To make bulb 2 light during the second pulse, its other end must be connected to the "hi" line that is "hi" during pulse 2 so that a "hi-lo" potential will be established across the bulb. During clock pulse 2, the x-line is "hi"; so bulb 2 is connected to the x-line as shown. Bulb 3 will not light during clock pulse 2 since it is connected to the y-line which is "medium" at this time. When clock pulse 3 arrives, FFA changes state from 0 to 1, causing terminal A_0 to be "lo," and A_1 to be "hi." This change in potential at the terminals of FFA switches the potentials of the x- and y-lines: now, the x-line is "medium," and the y-line is "hi." Bulb 2 goes out because the potential across it has changed from "hi-lo" to "medium-lo." But bulb 3, which is connected to the y-line goes on. Thus, bulb 3 shows that three clock pulses have been counted.

Succeeding Pulses. The connections for pulses 4, 5, 6, and 7 are treated in the same manner as those for pulses 0, 1, 2, and 3 just described. Using

TABLE 11-2.   THE STATES OF THE FLIP-FLOPS
IN THE DECADE COUNTER

CLOCK PULSE	FLIP-FLOPS D	C	B	A
0	0	1	1	0
1	0	1	1	1
2	1	0	0	0
3	1	0	0	1
4	1	0	1	0
5	1	0	1	1
6	1	1	0	0
7	1	1	0	1
8	1	1	1	0
9	1	1	1	1

the fact that the states of FFB and FFC are uniquely the same during pulses 4 and 5, and 6 and 7, we are justified in connecting bulbs 4, 5, 6, and 7 as shown in Fig. 11-13. The reason for each connection is essentially the same as that used for the first four connections; hence, you should be able to follow through with the remainder of the development yourself.

To show one more example of the development of a lighting system, we will consider a system that can be used with a decade counter. The first step is to set up a table showing the states of each flip-flop as the count proceeds, see Table 11-2. For reference, the decade counter has been redrawn in Fig. 11-14A. Notice that the flip-flops are designated as A, B, C,

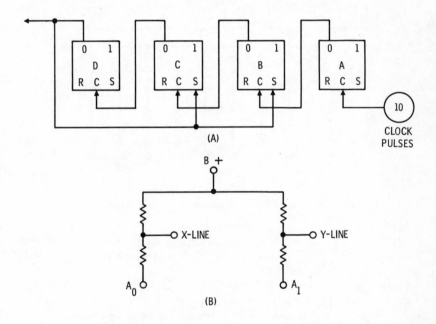

Fig. 11-14. The development of a lighting system for a decade counter.

and D, rather than 1, 2, 3, and 4. This change has been made for easier reference. Again, FFA changes state with every incoming clock pulse, and can be used as the switching flip-flop. The resistive switching network used in conjunction with FFA is shown in Fig. 11-14B. It operates in the same way as the switching network for the straight binary lighting system. The recognition circuitry for the decade counter lighting system is devised with the aid of the truth table, Table 11-2. As you see, the unique combinations of the states of the flip-flops have been blocked in. Knowing that flip-flops B, C, and D remain in the same state for clock pulses 0 and 1, we can connect terminals B_0, C_0, and D_1 through a resistive network to one side of bulbs 0 and 1 as shown in Fig. 11-15A. These terminals are "lo" during clock

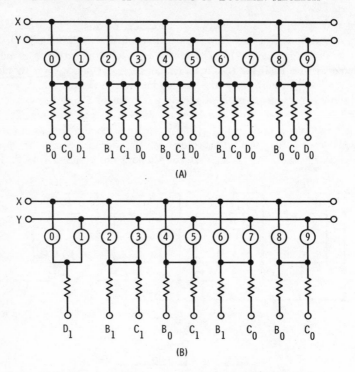

Fig. 11-15. The recognition circuits for a decade counter lighting system.

pulses 0 and 1. The switching takes place when FFA causes the relative potentials of the x- and y-lines to reverse, thereby changing the potentials at the other ends of bulbs 0 and 1.

Further examination of the states of the flip-flops reveals that flip-flops B, C, and D remain in the same states for clock pulses 2 and 3, 4 and 5, 6 and 7, and 8 and 9. Using this information, we develop the remainder of the circuit in Fig. 11-15A. One end of bulbs 2 and 3 are maintained at a "lo" potential by connecting the bulbs, through resistors, to B_1, C_1, and D_0; each of these terminals are at a "lo" potential during clock pulses 2 and 3. Similarly, we use terminals B_0, C_1 and D_0 for bulbs 4 and 5; terminals B_1, C_0, and D_0 are used for bulbs 6 and 7; and terminals B_0, C_0, and D_0 are used for bulbs 8 and 9. Because of the potentials at the flip-flop terminals to which they are connected, the side of only one pair of bulbs is "lo" at any given time. As the clock pulses are counted, the appropriate bulb is selected as follows:

Clock Pulse 0: Terminals B_0, C_0, and D_1 are "lo"; x-line is "hi," and y-line is "medium"; bulb 0 lights.

Clock Pulse 1: X-line is "medium," and y-line is "hi"; bulb 1 lights.

Clock Pulse 2: Terminals B_1, C_1, and D_0 are "lo"; x-line is "hi," and y-line is "medium"; bulb 2 lights.

Clock Pulse 3: X-line is "medium," and y-line is "hi"; bulb 3 lights.

Clock Pulse 4: Terminals B_0, C_1, and D_0 are "lo"; x-line is "hi," and y-line is "medium"; bulb 4 lights.

Clock Pulse 5: X-line is "medium," and y-line is "hi"; bulb 5 lights.

Clock Pulse 6: Terminals B_1, C_0, and D_0 are "lo"; x-line is "hi," and y-line is "medium"; bulb 6 lights.

Clock Pulse 7: X-line is "medium," and y-line is "hi"; bulb 7 lights.

Clock Pulse 8: Terminals B_0, C_0, and D_0 are "lo"; x-line is "hi," and y-line is "medium"; bulb 8 lights.

Clock Pulse 9: X-line is "medium," and y-line is "hi"; bulb 9 lights.

When the tenth clock pulse is counted, the counter generates an output pulse, recycles to zero, and is ready to count again.

The circuit shown in Fig. 11-15A is not the simplest circuit that can perform the operation just described. In fact, it is possible to simplify the circuit considerably by eliminating some resistors as shown in Fig. 11-15B. The justification for the elimination of the resistors may be found by closer examination of Table 11-2. Notice that for both clock pulses 0 and 1, FFD is in the 0 state. Also notice that this does not happen again for any pair of clock pulses. Because the state of FFD is unique for clock pulses 0 and 1, it alone can be used to recognize these pulses without the aid of FFB and FFC. We can, therefore, eliminate the resistors leading to terminals B_0 and C_0, and still retain the correct recognition conditions. During clock pulses 2 and 3, FFB and FFC are both in the 0 state, and this does not happen again for any other pair of clock pulses. We can, therefore, use these two flip-flops to recognize clock pulses 2 and 3, thereby eliminating the resistor leading to D_0. The states of FFB and FFC are unique for each of the other pairs of clock pulses also, whereas FFD remains in the 1 state, and does not actively contribute to the recognition. For this reason, we can eliminate each of the resistors leading to FFD, and still retain the correct recognition conditions for pulses 4 and 5, 6 and 7, and 8 and 9. It is suggested that you check the voltages in the simplified circuit during a count; you will find that the correct bulb lights each time.

11-6. Pulse-Advancing Counters

As the name implies, pulse-advancing counters are systems in which the incoming clock pulses are fed (or advanced) to higher-order flip-flops in addition to the first or lowest-order flip-flop. By advancing the clock pulses under the control of feedback from the higher-order flip-flops, it is possible to change the states of the flip-flops during a count so that the counter operates in code. The particular code in which the decimal counter operates depends on the arrangement of the feedback circuits as you shall now see.

11-7. Decimal Counter for the NBCD Code

The Natural Binary Coded Decimal, or 8-4-2-1 code, is in Table 11-3A. As you may recall from an earlier chapter, the 8-4-2-1 code has the same pattern as a simple binary count. This observation suggests that it may be feasible to make a binary counter operate in the 8-4-2-1 code. But, the similarity between the code and the binary count ends at decimal number 10 because only the decimal numbers from 0 through 9 are represented in the code. If the binary counter is to operate in the 8-4-2-1 code, it must

TABLE 11-3. THE DEVELOPMENT OF THE RECOGNITION
CIRCUIT FOR THE NBCD COUNTER

	CLOCK PULSE	FLIP-FLOPS 8	4	2	1	
(A)	0	0	0	0	·0	
	1	0	0	0	1	
	2	0	0	1	0	
	3	0	0	1	1	
	4	0	1	0	0	
	5	0	1	0	1	
	6	0	1	1	0	
	7	0	1	1	1	
	8	1	0	0	0	
	9	1	0	0	1	
	RECYCLE 10	1	0	1	0 —→	TEMPORARY STATES
		UNIQUE				
(B)	10	1	0	1	0	
		R		R		
		0	0	0	0 —→	DESIRED STATES AFTER TENTH CLOCK PULSE

recycle to zero upon receiving the tenth pulse, and begin again. By the addition of recognition circuits, and the use of pulse-advancing techniques, the basic binary counter can be modified so that it operates faster, and in the 8-4-2-1 code. A modified binary counter is shown in Fig. 11-16. As illustrated, the incoming clock pulses are fed to each flip-flop at the same time through AND gates. This arrangement serves to eliminate the time delay introduced by the flip-flops, and makes the pulse-advancing counter faster than the basic binary counter. However, it then becomes necessary to insert delay devices (indicated as D in the figure) to prevent pulses from preceding flip-flops from triggering the gates prematurely. This delay can be accomplished by using an RC network (see Sect. 7-4). While they do delay the output pulses of the flip-flops sufficiently, these delay devices do not appreciably reduce the maximum operating speed of the counter itself.

Before aproaching the development of the recognition circuits, let us examine more closely the operation of each flip-flop during a count:

Pulse 0. Before any clock pulses have been transmitted, all of the flip-flops are in the 0 state. This is indicated in the table of states, Table 11-3A.

Pulse 1. The first clock pulse is fed to the complementary terminal of FF1, causing it to change from 0 to 1. The pulse is also fed to A_1, but, because the second input to A_1 is not present, the gate generates no output.

In changing from the 0 state to the 1 state, the 1 terminal of FF1 goes from "lo" to "hi," and a pulse is generated. Because of the delay introduced by D_1, this pulse arrives at A_1 just after clock pulse 1 has terminated. However, terminal 1 remains in the "hi" condition until the next clock pulse is transmitted; thus, A_1 is primed with one input voltage, and will generate an output as soon as clock pulse 2 is transmitted. As a result of clock pulse 1, then, the states of the flip-flops are 0001, conforming to the code.

Pulse 2. This clock pulse is fed to A_1, and FF1 simultaneously. A_1 is primed by the "hi" potential existing at the 1 terminal of FF1, and it gen-

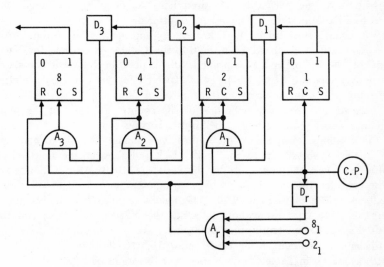

Fig. 11-16. A pulse-advancing counter for the NBCD code.

erates an output when it receives clock pulse 2. This output is fed to the complementary terminal of FF2 and to A_2. FF2 changes states from 0 to 1, and its 1 terminal goes from "lo" to "hi." In doing so, a pulse is generated and fed to A_2 through D_2. Because of the delay, this pulse reaches A_2 just after the output pulse of A_1 has terminated. Although A_2 does not generate an output at this time, it is primed by the "hi" potential existing at the 1 terminal of FF2. A_1 is no longer primed because clock pulse 2 causes FF1 to change state from 1 to 0, and the 1 terminal is "lo." As a result of clock pulse 2, the states of the flip-flops are now 0010, conforming to the code.

Pulse 3. This pulse is fed simultaneously to FF1 and A_1. A_1 is not primed, and does not generate an output. FF2, therefore, remains in the 1 state, and A_2 remains primed. Clock pulse 3 does change the state of FF1 from 0 to 1. Consequently, the 1 terminal of the flip-flop goes from "lo" to "hi." This change in the potential at this terminal constitutes a pulse which is delayed by D_1 and fed to A_1 shortly after clock pulse 3 has terminated. The "hi" condition of terminal 1, however, leaves A_1 primed. The effect of clock pulse 3, therefore, is to put the flip-flops in states 0011; again, this conforms to the 8-4-2-1 code.

Pulse 4. Clock pulse 4 is fed to A_1, and FF1 at the same time. A_1 has been primed by the preceding pulse; thus, when it receives the clock pulse, both of its inputs are present, and it generates an output. Its output is fed to the complementary terminal of FF2, and A_2. A_2 has also been primed, and it, too, generates an output when it receives its second input from A_1. The output of A_2 is delivered to FF4, and to A_3. Since only one input is present at A_3, no output is generated here. Clock pulse 4 changes the state of FF1 from 1 to 0, leaving A_1 unprimed. The output of A_1 causes FF2 to change state from 1 to 0, leaving A_2 unprimed. Finally, the output of A_2 causes FF4 to change from the 0 to the 1 state. As a result, the 1 terminal of FF4 is "hi," and A_3 is primed. At this point in the count, the states of the flip-flops are 0100, which is as expected for the 8-4-2-1 code after the fourth clock pulse has been transmitted.

Succeeding Pulses. The operation of the counter proceeds in the same general manner until the tenth clock pulse. Having gone through the action of the flip-flops for the first four pulses, you should be able to continue the analysis yourself up to the tenth clock pulse. After the tenth clock pulse, however, the states of the flip-flops are 1010. At this point, we must consider the development of a recognition circuit that will direct feedback pulses to FF8 and FF2. The feedback pulses will nullify the 1 states of these flip-flops without affecting the adjacent flip-flops; and the desired states for the tenth pulse, 0000, will have been obtained.

Recognition Circuit. After clock pulse 10, the flip-flops are in states 1010, as shown in Table 11-3B. Notice that the states of FF8 and FF2 are unique, i.e., this is the only occasion for which the states of both these flip-flops are 1 simultaneously. By feeding the output at the 1 terminals of FF8 and FF2 to an AND gate, we can obtain a feedback pulse every time the count reaches 10. If we apply this pulse, which is the output of the AND gate, to the reset terminal of FF8 and FF2, these flip-flops will change state from 1 to 0 before the next clock pulse is transmitted. The AND gate, A_r, used in the recognition circuit is a three-input gate. As shown in Fig. 11-16, its inputs are taken from the 1 terminals of FF8 and FF2, and from D_r. D_r insures that clock pulse 10 will cause the flip-flops of the counter to change state before it reaches A_r. In other words, because of the delay introduced by D_r, clock pulse 10 and the outputs FF8 and FF2 all reach A_r at the same time. A_r, in turn, produces an output which is fed to the reset terminals of FF8 and FF2. Finally, the temporary states, 1010, of the flip-flops change to the desired recycle states, 0000. A glance at Table 11-3A tells you that the counter has been properly modified so that it operates in the 8-4-2-1 code.

11-8. Decimal Counters for Other Codes

By merely changing the recognition circuit properly, we can develop pulse-advancing counters that operate in codes other than the 8-4-2-1 code. Let us first consider a counter that operates in the XS3 code. As shown in Table 11-4A, the XS3 code begins at 0011 rather than at 0000. This means that the pulse advancing counter for this code must begin every count with its flip-flops in the states 0011. Assuming that we can make the counter begin its very first count at 0011, we have to find a recognition circuit

TABLE 11-4. THE DEVELOPMENT OF THE RECOGNITION CIRCUIT FOR THE XS3 COUNTER

	CLOCK PULSE	FLIP-FLOPS				
		A	B	C	D	
	0	0	0	1	1	
	1	0	1	0	0	
	2	0	1	0	1	
	3	0	1	1	0	
	4	0	1	1	1	
(A)	5	1	0	0	0	
	6	1	0	0	1	
	7	1	0	1	0	
	8	1	0	1	1	
	9	1	1	0	0	
	RECYCLE 10	1	1	0	1 →	TEMPORARY STATES
		UNIQUE				
(B)	10	1	1	0	1	
		R	R	S		
		0	0	1	1 →	DESIRED STATES AFTER TENTH CLOCK PULSE

that will make the counter recycle to 0011 instead of to the next binary number, which, as shown in Table 11-4A, would be 1101. After the tenth pulse, the temporary states of the flip-flops are 1101. As indicated in Table 11-4B, we can obtain the desired states, 0011, by resetting FFA and FFB, and setting FFC. The table also indicates that the temporary states of flip-flops A, B, and D are unique; we can, therefore, use them to obtain recognition. The exact arrangement of the recognition circuit is shown in Fig. 11-17. As you can see, the clock pulses fed to A_r, are delayed. Also, the inputs A_1, B_1, and D_1 are fed back from the 1 terminals of flip-flops A, B, and D. Clock pulses are continually being fed to A_r; but it is not until the tenth clock pulse that the other three inputs are present at the gate. In this way, feedback is made to control the clock pulses being fed to the set and reset terminals of the flip-flops. When all four inputs are present at A_r, a pulse is generated, and fed to the desired flip-flops. This has the same effect on the flip-flops as the transmission of six more clock pulses. The counter literally skips over the next six binary numbers (remember that the count began at 0011), and recycles to 0011. It is then ready to count again in the XS3 code.

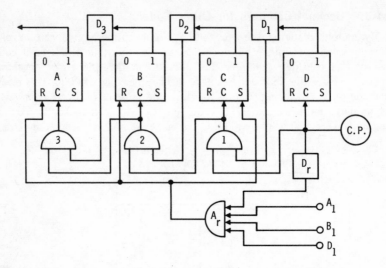

Fig. 11-17. A pulse-advancing counter that operates in the XS3 code.

The development of a recognition circuit for operation in the $2'$-4-2-1 code is slightly different from that for the two preceding counters. You can see why by referring to Table 11-5. In the $2'$-4-2-1 code, a series of binary numbers between decimal 7 and decimal 8 are nonexistent, i.e., the code goes from 0111 to 1110, eliminating the intermediate binary numbers. Although this is a departure from what we have seen in the preceding

TABLE 11-5. THE DEVELOPMENT OF THE RECOGNITION CIRCUIT
FOR THE $2'$-4-2-1 COUNTER

	CLOCK PULSE	\multicolumn{4}{c}{FLIP-FLOPS}	
		$2'$	4	2	1	
(A)	0	0	0	0	0	
	1	0	0	0	1	
	2	0	0	1	0	
	3	0	0	1	1	
	4	0	1	0	0	
	5	0	1	0	1	
	6	0	1	1	0	
	7	0	1	1	1	TEMPORARY STATES EXIST BETWEEN SEVENTH AND EIGHTH CLOCK PULSES
	8	1	1	1	0	
	9	1	1	1	1	
	RECYCLE 10	0	0	0	0	
(B)	7	0	1	1	1	UNIQUE
	8	1	0	0	0	TEMPORARY
			S	S		
		1	1	1	0	DESIRED STATES AFTER EIGHTH CLOCK PULSE

two codes, it is no more difficult to develop the recognition circuit. Using the same decimal counter that was used for the other two codes, we know that clock pulse 8 would cause the flip-flops to be in the states 1000. These are shown as temporary states in Table 11-5B. For the eighth pulse, we want the flip-flops to be in the states 1110; and we can effect this change by applying a pulse to the set terminals of FF4 and FF2 immediately after the temporary states have been established by clock pulse 8. Notice in the table that the states of FF2′ and FF4 are unique during clock pulse 8. We can use their outputs to prime A_r so that it will generate a pulse upon receiving the delayed clock pulse 8. The circuit is shown in Fig. 11-18. Because FF4 is in the 0 state after clock pulse 8, we must use the "hi" output from its 0 terminal; FF2′ is in the 1 state, and its "hi" output

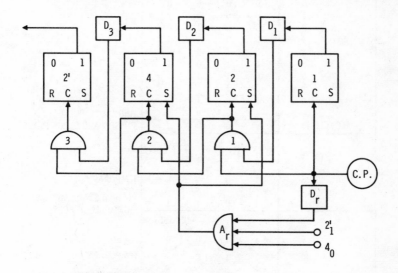

Fig. 11-18. A pulse-advancing counter for the 2′-4-2-1 code.

is at the 1 terminal. The effect of feeding a pulse to the set terminals of FF4 and FF2 is to make the counter skip six binary numbers between decimal 7 and and decimal 8. In doing this, the desired states, 1110, of the flip-flops are obtained for the eighth clock pulse, and the count then proceeds normally.

The last counter we shall consider operates in the 5-4-2-1 code, shown in Table 11-6A. The recognition circuit required for the 5-4-2-1 code pulse-advancing counter is more complicated than those required for the previous three counters because the code does not contain the binary numbers between decimal 7 and decimal 8, and between decimal 9 and decimal 10. However, the procedure for developing the recognition circuit is the same as that used before. The steps in developing the first part of the recognition circuit are shown in Table 11-6B. The count proceeds normally through clock pulse

7. Upon the transmission of the eighth clock pulse, the states of the flip-flops are 1000. These are considered as temporary states, and must be changed to 1011 if the counter is to conform to the code. To obtain the desired states, we can send a pulse into the set terminals of FF2 and FF1 as indicated in Table 11-6B. This would change the flip-flops from 1000 to 1011. Since the states of flip-flops 5, 4, and 2 are unique after the

TABLE 11-6.   THE DEVELOPMENT OF THE RECOGNITION
CIRCUIT FOR THE 5-4-2-1 COUNTER

	CLOCK PULSE	FLIP-FLOPS 5	4	2	1	
(A)	0	0	0	0	0	
	1	0	0	0	1	
	2	0	0	1	0	
	3	0	0	1	1	
	4	0	1	0	0	
	5	0	1	0	1	
	6	0	1	1	0	
	7	0	1	1	1	(1)
	8	1	0	1	1	(2)
	9	1	1	0	0	
	RECYCLE 10	0	0	0	0	
(B)	(1) 7	0	1	1	1	UNIQUE
	8	1	0	0	0	TEMPORARY
		1	0	S 1	S 1	DESIRED STATES AFTER EIGHTH CLOCK PULSE
(C)	(2) 9	1	1	0	0	UNIQUE
	10	1	1	0	1	TEMPORARY
		R 0	R 0	0	R 0	DESIRED STATES AFTER TENTH CLOCK PULSE

TEMPORARY STATES EXIST BETWEEN: (1) CLOCK PULSE 7 AND CLOCK PULSE 8; (2) CLOCK PULSE 9 AND CLOCK PULSE 10

eighth clock pulse, we shall use the outputs of these flip-flops to prime the AND gate, A_{r1}, so that it will deliver a pulse when it receives the delayed clock pulse 8. The circuit arrangement is shown in Fig. 11-19. Notice that it is necessary to use the 1 terminal of FF5, and the 0 terminals of FF4 and FF2. Each of these terminals is "hi" after the eighth clock pulse; so they fully prime A_{r1} which has an output only when the four inputs are present simultaneously. The effect of this part of the recognition circuit is to make the flip-flops show states 1011 for the eighth clock pulse. The count then continues normally to 1100 for the ninth clock pulse. Upon receiving clock pulse 10, the counter would normally progress to 1101; hence, we need the second part of the recognition circuit to make the counter recycle to 0000, thus conforming to the 5-4-2-1 code. As shown in Table 11-6C, we can make the flip-flops change from 1101 to 0000 by sending a pulse to the reset terminals of flip-flops 5, 4, and 1, changing their states from 1 to 0. As shown in the figure, the temporary states of FF5, FF4, and FF1 are unique. We can, therefore, use the outputs of these flip-flops to prime A_{r2}. Since each is in the 1 state, their terminals are "hi"; the feedback inputs to A_{r2} are, therefore, 5_1, 4_1, and 1_1. When the tenth clock pulse is transmitted, the states of the flip-flops are temporarily 1101. The outputs from the 1 terminals of flip-flops 5, 4, and 1 prime A_{r2}. When clock pulse 10, which has been delayed by D_{r2}, arrives at A_{r2}, an output pulse is generated, and fed to the

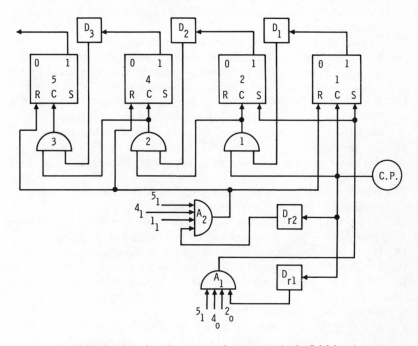

Fig. 11-19. A pulse-advancing counter that operates in the 5-4-2-1 code.

reset terminals of flip-flops 5, 4, and 1. The reset pulse causes each of these flip-flops to change from the 1 state to the 0 state. Consequently, the desired states, 0000, of the flip-flops are obtained. The counter has recycled as required for the 5-4-2-1 code, and the count begins again.

11-9. Problems

1. What conditions exist at the output terminals of a flip-flop when it is in the 1 state? When it is in the 0 state? How is the state of a flip-flop changed?

2. Explain how the complementary terminal is connected in the flip-flop circuit. What is the function of this terminal?

3. How many binary digits can be represented by a counting circuit that contains eight flip-flops? What is the largest binary number that can be counted by a counter containing five flip-flops? Containing seven flip-flops?

4. Why is a counter also considered to be a divider?

5. When does a flip-flop generate a positive-going pulse? A negative-going pulse?

6. Can a three-bit counter be made to count by numbers higher than eight by the use of feedback? Why?

7. In Fig. 11-4, what would happen if a clock pulse and a feedback pulse arrived at the OR gate simultaneously? Why doesn't this happen in the circuit?

8. Explain what is meant by *initial reset condition*.

9. How many flip-flops does a decade counter use? How many input pulses are required for the decade counter to generate an output pulse? Of this number, how many are clock pulses, and how many are feedback pulses?

10. Assume that the states of the flip-flops in the decade counter of Fig. 11-7 are in the states 0111. How would these states change if a pulse were fed to the set terminal of FF3? Into the reset terminal of FF2?

11. Devise an electronic counter that can count by nine. Draw diagrams that show the operation of this counter, and the waveforms at the 0 terminals of its flip-flops.

12. Why are lighting systems used? How would you construct a lighting system for a four-bit binary counter?

13. Why is the lowest-order flip-flop used as a switching flip-flop in lighting systems? Can any other flip-flop be employed just as easily?

14. How are the flip-flops used for recognition in lighting systems selected?

15. Develop a lighting system that can be used for a count-by-nine counter.

16. What is the primary difference between an ordinary feedback counter, and a pulse-advancing counter? Which type of counter would you use for counting in code? Why?

17. In Fig. 11-17, why must the clock pulses be delayed by D_r? How much of a delay is introduced by D_1, D_2, and D_3? Why are these delay devices used?

18. Devise a pulse-advancing counter that can count in the 6-3-1-1 code. Show how the recognition circuit for this counter is developed. (The 6-3-1-1 code was given in Table 1-10.)

Appendix

A-1. Derivation of the Voltage Proportionality Law

In Fig. A-1, $I = E/R_T = E/(R_1 + R_2 + R_3)$. The voltage drop across R_1 can be found by multiplying the current by the resistance R_1. Thus, $V_{R1} = IR_1$. Substituting for I its equivalent, $E/(R_1 + R_2 + R_3)$, in the voltage drop

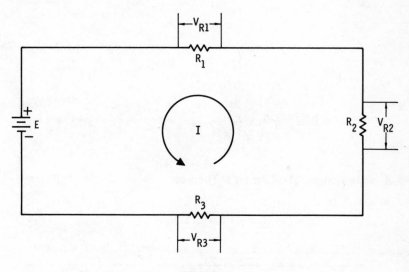

Fig. A-1.

equation, gives the voltage proportionality law as a result. Thus,

$$V_{R1} = ER_1/(R_1 + R_2 + R_3)$$

Performing the same derivation for the other two resistors yields:

$$V_{R2} = ER_2/(R_1 + R_2 + R_3)$$

and

$$V_{R3} = ER_3/(R_1 + R_2 + R_3)$$

315

A-2. Derivation of the Current Inverse Proportionality Law

In Fig. A-2, $I_T = I_1 + I_2$. Therefore, $I_2 = I_T - I_1$. Since the voltage drops are equal, $I_1R_1 = I_2R_2$. However, $I_2 = I_T - I_1$. Therefore,

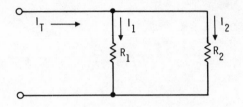

Fig. A-2.

$$I_1R_1 = R_2\,(I_T - I_1) \;=\; I_TR_2 - I_1R_2$$
$$I_1R_1 + I_1R_2 = I_TR_2$$
$$I_1\,(R_1 + R_2) = I_TR_2$$
$$I_1 = I_TR_2/(R_1 + R_2)$$

Also:

$$I_1 = I_T - I_2$$
$$I_1R_1 = I_2R_2$$
$$R_1\,(I_T - I_2) = R_2I_2$$
$$I_2R_2 + I_2R_1 = I_TR_1$$
$$I_2\,(R_1 + R_2) = I_TR_1$$
$$I_2 = I_TR_1/(R_1 + R_2)$$

A-3. Derivation of Millman's Theorem

In Fig. A-3:

$$I_1 = (E_1 - E_0)/R_1$$

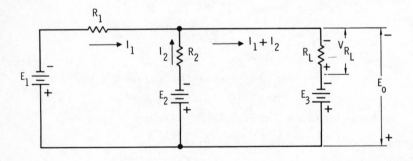

Fig. A-3.

$$I_2 = (E_2 - E_0)/R_2$$
$$I_1 + I_2 = (E_0 - E_3)/R_L$$

Therefore,

$$(E_1 - E_0)/R_1 + (E_2 - E_0)/R_2 = (E_0 - E_3)/R_L$$

Multiplying each term by $R_1R_2R_L$, we obtain:

$$R_2R_LE_1 - R_2R_LE_0 + R_1R_LE_2 - R_1R_LE_0 = R_1R_2E_0 - R_1R_2E_3$$

Transposing terms and factoring:

$$E_0(R_1R_2 + R_2R_L + R_1R_L) = R_1R_2E_3 + R_2R_LE_1 + R_1R_LE_2$$

Dividing both sides of the equation by $R_1R_2 + R_2R_L + R_1R_L$,

$$E_0 = \frac{E_1R_2R_L + E_2R_1R_L + E_3R_1R_2}{R_1R_2 + R_2R_L + R_1R_L}$$

Dividing the numerator and denominator by $R_1R_2R_L$:

$$E_0 = \frac{E_1/R_1 + E_2/R_2 + E_3/R_L}{1/R_1 + 1/R_2 + 1/R_L}$$

When E_3 is zero, E_3/R_L is zero, E_0 becomes V_{RL}, and the equation reduces to:

$$V_{RL} = \frac{E_1/R_1 + E_2/R_2}{1/R_1 + 1/R_2 + 1/R_L}$$

A-4. Derivation of the Voltage Drops Across Capacitors

Since Fig. A-4 shows a series circuit, the charge, q, flowing through the capacitors must be the same. Therefore,

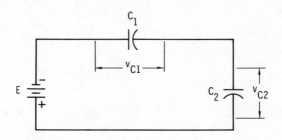

Fig. A-4.

$$q = v_{C1}C_1$$
$$q = v_{C2}C_2$$

Taking a ratio of these two equations we obtain:

$$1 = v_{C1}(C_1)/v_{C2}(C_2)$$

Therefore,

$$v_{C1}/v_{C2} = C_2/C_1$$

But, $v_{C1} = E - v_{C2}$. Substituting this value of v_{C1} in the previous equation we obtain:

$$(E - v_{C2})/v_{C2} = C_2/C_1$$

Manipulating this last equation algebraically, we obtain the desired equation. Thus,

$$E - v_{C2} = v_{C2}\ (C_2/C_1)$$
$$E = v_{C2} + v_{C2}\ (C_2/C_1)$$
$$v_{C2}\ (C_1 + C_2) = EC_1.$$

Therefore,

$$v_{C2} = EC_1/(C_1 + C_2)$$

To solve for v_{C1}, substitute for v_{C2}, $E - v_{C1}$ in the equation: $v_{C1}/v_{C2} = C_2/C_1$. Thus,

$$v_{C1}/(E - v_{C1}) = C_2/C_1$$
$$v_{C1} = E\ (C_2/C_1) - v_{C1}\ (C_2/C_1)$$
$$v_{C1}\ (C_1 + C_2)/C_1 = E\ (C_2/C_1)$$

Therefore,

$$v_{C1} = EC_2/(C_1 + C_2)$$

Bibliography

1. Bartee, Thomas C., *Digital Computer Fundamentals*, New York: McGraw-Hill Book Co., 1960, pp. 342.
2. Benrey, Ronald M., *Understanding Digital Computers*, New York: John F. Rider Publisher, Inc., 1964.
3. Boole, G., *Collected Logical Works*, Vol. I, LaSalle, Illinois: Open Court Publishing Co., 1952, pp. 500.
4. Caldwell, Samuel H., *Switching Circuits and Logical Design*, New York: John Wiley and Sons, Inc., 1958, pp. 686.
5. ERA, *High Speed Digital Computers*, New York: McGraw-Hill Book Co., 1950, pp. 451.
6. Fitchen, Franklin C., *Transistor Circuit Analysis and Design*, Princeton: D. Van Nostrand Co., Inc., 1962, pp. 350.
7. Flores, Ivan, *Computer Logic*, Englewood Cliffs, N. J.: Prentice-Hall, 1960, pp. 458.
8. Hurley, Richard B., *Transistor Logic Circuits*, New York: John Wiley and Sons, Inc., 1961, pp. 355.
9. Irwin, Wayne C., *Digital Computer Principles*, Princeton: D. Van Nostrand Co., Inc., 1960, pp. 321.
10. Ledley, R. C., *Digital Computer and Control Engineering*, New York: McGraw-Hill Book Co., 1960, pp. 835.
11. Maley, Gerald A., and Earle, John, *The Logic Design of Transistor Digital Computers*, Englewood Cliffs: Prentice-Hall, 1963, pp. 317.
12. Millman, Jacob, *Vacuum Tube and Semiconductor Electronics*, New York: McGraw-Hill Book Co., 1958, pp. 632.
13. Murphy, John S., *Basics of Digital Computer Programming*, New York: John F. Rider Publisher, Inc., 1964.
14. Pressman, Abraham, *Design of Transistorized Circuits for Digital Computers*, New York: John F. Rider Publisher, Inc., 1959, pp. 316.
15. Richards, Richard K., *Arithmetic Operations in Digital Computers*, Princeton: D. Van Nostrand Co., Inc., 1958, pp. 397.
16. Whitesitt, J., *Boolean Algebra and Its Application*, Reading, Mass.: Addison-Wesley Publishing Co., Inc., 1961, pp. 182.

Index

A

Absorption, law of, 66
Adders:
  binary coded decimal (BCDA), 228-232
  full, 223-228
  half, 220-223
  quarter, 220
Addition, 22-26
  binary, 25
  decimal, 22-24
  octal, 25
All element, 51, 70
Alpha (α), 182
AND:
  function, 51
    developed using NOR logic and transistor circuits, 249-251
    implemented using NAND logic, 271
  gate:
    circuit analysis, 206-211
    logic block for, 54
    in matrix circuits, 233
    with three inputs, 210
  statement (function):
    designation number development, 102
    truth table representation, 89, 90, 91
Arabic system, 2
Association, law of, 65-66
Atoms, 170

B

Base, 2
  current, 178
  of transistor, 177
Beta (h_{fe}), 185
Binary:
  addition, 25
    with logic circuits, 219
  coded decimal adder (BCDA), 228-232
  counter:
    count by 8, 291
    divide by 8, 292
    number of flip flops in, 293
  number system:
    addition in, 25
    bits, 7
    counting in, 8
    division in, 46

    multiplication in, 40
    numbers, general representation of, 8-9
    radix of, 7
    subtraction in, 29-31, 35, 36
  point, 8
Biquinary code, 18-19
Bits, 7
Boolean:
  algebra:
    addition, 51, 52
    constants, 51
    definitions, 50-51
    identities, 68
    laws of combination, 64-67
    logic blocks in, 52-63
    logical relationships in, 51
    methods of combination, 51
    multiplication, 51, 52
    negation, 51
    postulates, 52
    simplifying Boolean statements with, 123-128
    symbolic representation in, 50
    universe, 51
    variables, 50
  function; *see also* Boolean statements:
    simplification of, 116-128: by Boolean algebra, 123-128; by designation numbers, 129-137; by Veitch diagram, 116-123
    writing Boolean functions from designation numbers, 104
  statements; *see also* Boolean function:
    AND, 52
    exclusive OR, 52
    logic blocks for generating, 52-63
    mixed AND and OR, 53
    OR, 52

C

Capacitor:
  basic concepts of, 157
  charge, 157
  current equation for, 157
  in parallel, equations for, 159
  in series, equation for, 158, 317-318
Characteristic curves:
  input:
    common-base circuit, 182
    common-emitter circuit, 188, 189